Assembling Ericksonian Therapy:

THE COLLECTED PAPERS OF
STEPHEN LANKTON
VOLUME I: 1985–2002

Assembling Ericksonian Therapy:

THE COLLECTED PAPERS OF
STEPHEN LANKTON
VOLUME I: 1985–2002

Zeig, Tucker, & Theisen, Inc.
Phoenix, Arizona

Library of Congress Cataloging-in-Publication Data
Assembling Ericksonian therapy
p. cm.
ISBN 1-932462-10-4 (alk. paper)
1. Psychotherapy. 2. Psychotherapy. 3. Hypnotism — Therapeutic
use. 4. Erickson, Milton H.
RC480.A836 2003
616.89 '14—dc22   2003067230

© Copyright 2004
Zeig, Tucker, & Theisen, Inc.

Published by
Zeig, Tucker, & Theisen, Inc.
3614 North 24th Street
Phoenix, AZ 85014

Manufactured in the United States of America

10 9 8 7 6 5 4 3 2 1

Contents

ANXIETY AND TRAUMA

Foreword

Each of us embodies a unique world of understanding that is in continuous growth and development. How fortunate we are if we find a mentor who can recognize and respond appropriately to facilitate the expansion of our unique perspective. Steve Lankton is just such a mentor for many people from all walks of life who share the evolving humanistic ethos that inspires the pages of this book. In this first volume of papers, Lankton lays the groundwork for a systematic approach to Ericksonian Therapy for helping people to find their own paths to "Freedom of Thought and Joy of Living."

For a new generation of therapists who never had an opportunity to meet Milton H. Erickson, M.D., the founder of the American Society of Clinical Hypnosis, Lankton provides a well-focused overview of Erickson's life, from his personal struggles with rehabilitation from childhood and adult polio that helped shape his professional development to the still-evolving matrix of his radical transformation of the landscape of psychotherapy. Lankton recounts how other pioneers, such as Gregory Bateson, Margaret Mead, and Jay Haley, interacted with Erickson to generate the communication theory approach to psychotherapy and its practical applications to the new concepts of Brief Therapy, Strategic Therapy, and Family Therapy. The main line of the history and evolution of psychotherapy in our time is presented with simplicity and clarity, which enables the reader to truly understand where we have been, where we are now, and where we may be headed.

In the first section, Lankton introduces the meaning and methods of Ericksonian Hypnosis and Therapy by emphasizing that therapists today are involved in something much more than a collection of techniques and technology for fixing people. Further, he outlines a fundamental States of Consciousness Model of Ericksonian Hypnotherapy that goes far beyond the traditional view that hypnosis is merely a form of suggestion for programming people. The focus is on ways of knowing, learning, and transformation — the deep epistemology of psychotherapy — that involves people in the synthesis and creative reassociation of their personal experience of the world rather than simply responding to their therapist's direct suggestions. This core of Ericksonian epistemology presaged the revolutionary research of current neuroscience that documents how every meaningful recall and replay of memory can facilitate the creative resynthesis of mind and memory in the actual molecular structure of the brain.

How to "Just Do Good Therapy" for the practical facilitation of his lofty goal of building a better brain to live a better life is the essence of much of Lankton's writing, teaching, and presenting workshop demonstrations around the world. This volume of his papers provides a single source for some of his most requested ideas and stimulating approaches to "The Use of Therapeutic Metaphor" and the practical details of "How You Can Decide Which Metaphors Are Right for a Particular Client." The bare bones of his use of simple metaphor, Multiple Embedded Metaphors, Goal-Directed Metaphors, the Scramble Technique, and Indirect Suggestions and Binds are presented with the insight and good humor that make his workshops memorable and transforming experiences.

The final section of this volume deals with some of the most significant breakthroughs in our current approaches to anxiety and trauma. Trauma recovery interventions have been a consistent theme in much of Lankton's carefully crafted work. He covers the various posttraumatic syndromes and how to "assemble" Ericksonian approaches to therapeutic hypnosis to motivate clients with a history of early family violence. His introduction to "The Complex Association/Dissociation Approach" for the decisive resolution of the "coping limitations" resulting from moderate to severe trauma is a model of clarity for working with the intracacies of the therapist's daily work. His case examples and transcripts from his training workshops put the nuts and bolts of applied psychotherapy within the reach of beginning and intermediate students so they may assemble their own healing craft — each in his or her own way. With all that is contained in the first volume of Steve Lankton's collected papers, we can assume that there will be many more creative opportunities ahead.

Ernest Lawrence Rossi

Introduction

This volume includes previously published chapters that span a period of 17 years. My goal has been to provide, in a single volume, many of the requested techniques, protocols, and frameworks of my approach. The sections feature Ericksonian Hypnosis and Therapy, Brief Therapy, Metaphor, and Anxiety and Trauma, and within each the material is designed to increase the power of therapy, not just within the parameters of an Ericksonian approach, but of any psychotherapy.

ERICKSONIAN HYPNOSIS AND THERAPY

"Ericksonian Therapy" opens this first section and it provides a brief, yet comprehensive overview of the approach. The chapter covers the history, current status, theory, and methodology behind the approach, as well as a case example to move the discussion from idea to action. The summary is directed to both those who know something of Erickson's work and those who are new to it.

In "Milton Erickson's Contribution to Therapy: Epistemology — Not Technology," a cogent framework is presented that highlights aspects of the emerging epistemology of change and compares with the more established epistemology of "labeling." One of my clients recently referred to the latter epistemology as the "model for depression," which seems like an apt description in contrast to the dynamics of the emerging model best represented by Milton Erickson.

"Jay Haley's Impact on the Rise of Ericksonian Therapy" illustrates the use of alterations of communication in a dual induction, and the fact that Haley (et al.) was quite correct in stating that an environment using double-bind communication will lead to "pathology." My framework provides a unique understanding of the psychosomatic and physiological problems that can result from interpersonal communication so typified.

"A State of Consciousness Model of Ericksonian Hypnotherapy" is an update of the States of Consciousness (SoC) model originally offered by Charles Tart. Tart's model had not taken into account the current understanding of hypnotic induction, especially that practiced by Dr. Erickson. By placing Erickson's work within a SoC model, therapists and theorists can unite hypnosis and family therapy.

I present my model of a multilevel interactive dynamic of family experience in the chapter "Ericksonian Systems Approach." A matrix is proposed that demonstrates the relationship between stress on families due to the demands of developmental stages and problem-solving skills available in the system. Whereas some schools of therapy intervene at one or another level, Erickson's systemic approach requires intervention at each level.

BRIEF THERAPY

"Ericksonian Strategic Therapy" defined the active role for therapists in terms that can be directly traced to Erickson's work. The chapter discusses the tenets of the strategic therapy based upon its reliance on a nonpathological model, indirection, utilization, action, future-orientation, and enchantment. Valid criticisms of the approach are also discussed. In "Using Hypnosis in Brief Therapy," the induction of hypnosis is covered as is an explication of my indirect suggestion and therapeutic binds. I then show how these can be effective in the treatment of anxiety and for performance enhancement. Here we find another highly requested technique, "Self-Image Thinking," a tool developed in 1979, but which is usually taught in my workshops and is not often found in print.

In "Just Do Good Therapy," it is suggested that therapists do work in accordance with several ways of thinking about oneself, one's clients, and how the client thinks about therapy. Good therapy follows such "rules" rather than the theory or guidelines of any particular school.

"The Occurrence and Use of Trance Phenomena in Nonhypnotic Therapies" clarifies several aspects of how communication process and content affect clients at the level of stimulus input and information processing. This is a rare summary of my previous contributions to the early development of NLP. I give a couple of case examples to show how trance phenomena result from such communication, and one case in particular reveals a spectacular moment of emotional breakthrough for a client severely limited by a previously forgotten childhood trauma.

METAPHOR

In 1983, I coined the term "multiple embedded metaphors" (MEM) to explain entire sections of Dr. Erickson's works. In my only writing that deals solely with this topic, "Multiple Embedded Metaphor and Diagnosis," the framework is elucidated.

Prior to developing the structure of MEM, I relied on isomorphic metaphors in therapy. Later I developed goal-directed metaphor structures and protocols. These two differing approaches are explained in "The Use of Therapeutic Metaphor in Social Work" and "How Can You Decide Which Metaphors Are Right for a Particular Client?"

ANXIETY AND TRAUMA

An effective, but seldomly seen technique for reducing anxiety attacks in Brief Therapy is "The Scramble Technique," which I developed in the mid-1970s. This rare article illustrates my use of the technique in a case a decade later in a Boston training group.

When specific traumatic events have precipitated a client's anxiety, more complex interventions are necessary to resolve the critical aspects that are preventing further growth and joy. I have promoted three levels of different interventions for three degrees of traumatic severity, which are illustrated in an extensive case transcript in the final two chapters: "Goal-Directed Interventions for Decisive Resolution of Coping Limitations, Resulting from Moderate and Severe Trauma" and "Using Hypnosis to Motivate Clients with a History of Early Family Violence." These chapters present a wide, but still not comprehensive view of Ericksonian Therapy. As a body, they are convergent and rarely repetitive. It is my hope that they provide a range of explanations and models that will help readers assemble the puzzle of Ericksonian Therapy.

Stephen Lankton

Ericksonian Hypnosis and Therapy

1

Ericksonian Therapy[1]

Milton Erickson was a handicapped person who suffered all kinds of disabilities, including dyslexia, tone deafness, and polio but who ended up as one of the most knowledgeable people in the field of psychology and psychiatry. Along the line, he became interested in hypnosis, for which he is best known. Central to understanding his theory is the concept of the unconscious, which can be considered as like an iceberg, the larger part the individual, with consciousness the smaller part. Consequently, in Ericksonian therapy, the therapist attempts to communicate directly to the unconscious via hypnosis. Communications to the unconscious differ from communications to the conscious mind, stressing experiences rather than logic, with the therapist attempting to "go under" the person's limiting rationality.

Erickson did not limit himself to hypnosis but used a variety of techniques, and his followers also did not limit themselves to this procedure. For example, some research has shown that indirect suggestions are more successful than direct suggestions. Lankton suggests that the Ericksonian approach is somewhat like aikido in that one uses the energy of the client to essentially direct the individual in his search for the desired outcome. This unique system has already affected other psychotherapies.

---

[1] Lankton, S. (2001). Ericksonian therapy. In R. Corsini (Ed.), *Handbook of innovative psychotherapy* (2nd ed., pp. 194–205). New York: Wiley. Reprinted with permission.

DEFINITION

Ericksonian therapy is based on the innovative work of the late Dr. Milton H. Erickson. It is often characterized from two different perspectives, the most common of which involves defining it by its reliance on distinctive interventions such as hypnosis, indirect suggestion, therapeutic stories, double binds, homework assignments, paradoxical prescription, and so forth. These definitions may also indicate that Ericksonian therapy encompasses a spectrum of approaches including strategic therapy, brief therapy, and general psychotherapy, often with an emphasis on the use of hypnosis.

The other perspective on Ericksonian therapy emphasizes an approach that focuses on how clients dynamically use themselves, limit their resources, and create the problems they present for treatment. Therapists do not observe clients to discover a diagnosis and treat it by "doing something to" the client. Instead, therapists must approach therapy as a context in which they participate with clients to cocreate the meanings they reach. The interventions listed are, in this light, merely descriptions of the relationships with clients that help them come to use their experiential resources in the context in which they are needed.

HISTORY

The history of Ericksonian therapy, of course, begins with the life of Milton Erickson, M.D. (1901–1980). He was born in Nevada, lived in a small farmhouse, and attended a one-room schoolhouse. He had learning disabilities similar to dyslexia and was tone deaf, but that was only the beginning of the enormous physical challenges he would face. He contracted polio in 1919 and overheard doctors explain to his parents that their boy would be dead the next day. He was angry that a mother should be told such a thing based on opinion. That afternoon, he instructed family members to arrange the furniture in a particular way that allowed him to see out the west window, proclaiming, "I was damned if I would die without seeing one more sunset" (Rossi, Ryan, & Sharp, 1983, p. 10). He, of course, did not die and devoted his life to proving one could overcome imposed limiting expectations.

With great determination and effort, Erickson spent many introspective hours working to regain sensitivity in those muscles not completely destroyed by polio. Within a year he had control of his upper torso and sensation in his legs. He embarked, solo, on a 1200-mile canoe trip on the Mississippi River and was able to walk again on his return. He maintained that dealing with his various challenges made him more observant of others. For example, because he was tone deaf he learned to tell the quality of a pianist by the range of touch he or she employed. He also learned to attend to inflections in the voice and explained that left him less distracted by the content of what people say. Many patterns of behavior are reflected in the way a person says something rather than in what he says (Haley, 1967).

After the canoe trip, he entered the University of Wisconsin and studied premedicine. He became interested in psychology, psychopathology, and criminology and studied hypnosis with Clark Hull, obtaining a master's degree in psychology while completing his medical degree. He completed his psychiatric residency in Colorado and then joined the psychiatric staff at Worcester State Hospital in Massachusetts (1930–1933), eventually becoming chief psychiatrist. In 1933 he accepted a position at Eloise State Hospital and Infirmary in Michigan (1933–1945) and taught at Wayne State University.

Erickson did intense research on hypnotic phenomena, such as color blindness, analgesia, time distortion, and age regression. During the 1930s, he was interested in Freud's notion of the unconscious and its influence on behavior. Early research focused on tracing a client's symptomatic presentation or neurosis to its origin in the past. Later in his professional development, however, Erickson shifted his focus from historical causes of symptoms to the present functioning and interactions of clients. Eclecticism and pragmatism were always priorities.

In the mid-1940s, Erickson began to receive worldwide recognition for his work in hypnosis and was regarded as the world's leading practitioner of medical hypnosis. He wrote entries on hypnosis for *Americana, Colliers* (1952–1962), and *Britannica* (1945–1973) encyclopedias for as many as 20 years. His dedication to exploring the use of hypnosis in therapy was reflected in his publishing over 100 papers on this subject. He founded, in 1957, the American Society for Clinical Hypnosis and edited its journal for the next 10 years, but his influence extended beyond hypnosis. Margaret Mead became interested in his work while she was married to Gregory Bateson, and their friendship led to early collaboration that had far-reaching influence on the development of communication theory, brief therapy, and family therapy.

In 1952, Bateson's research project on communication elected to investigate Erickson's work since he, more than any other therapist known to the team, was concerned with the pragmatics of how people change (Haley, 1985a). The team included John Weakland, Jay Haley, Don Jackson, William Fry, and later, Virginia Satir.

The lasting influence can be seen in such works as "Toward a Theory of Schizophrenia" (Jackson, 1968a) and subsequently, citations of Erickson by Bateson (1972), Haley (1963, 1967), Jackson (1968a, 1968b), and Satir (1964) as they developed models of Brief and Family Therapy. Under the later direction of Watzlawick, Weakland, and Richard Fisch, the Mental Research Institute (MRI) continued to attempt to develop communication models for techniques that originated in Erickson's work. These influences gave rise to systems models, brief therapy, strategic therapy, and family therapy.

CURRENT STATUS

Erickson's career spanned more than 50 years, as he worked up until his death in March 1980. His developed ideas were embraced by earnest students who studied with him and collected his works, translated his actions into a set of heuristics, and continued educational, training, and supervision efforts for professionals worldwide.

The Milton H. Erickson Foundation, in Phoenix, Arizona, was founded in 1979 and coordinates institutes, education, and training. It was at the foundation's first international congress that the term "Ericksonian Psychotherapy" was first used, with Erickson's knowledge. Unfortunately, he died before this congress, but the invited faculty of over 123 professionals demonstrated a vast expertise in therapy following various aspects of Erickson's work.

Currently, over 70 institutes within dozens of countries teach or offer some form of Ericksonian Psychotherapy. However, there is no tight control over the actual practice or conduct often done under the rubric of Ericksonian Therapy. Some therapists seem to rely upon one or another of his techniques to the exclusion of others and, in many cases, it is likely that much of the underlying subtlety of Erickson's work is overlooked in striving for the dedication and hard work necessary to master the approach.

THEORY

Traditional therapy is based on the assumption of an objective reality that is independent of our efforts to observe it. The posture toward reality is separation from it and study by reduction. But while the simple act of reducing and labeling seems innocent enough, it does not credit the observer with the action of inventing the label that is applied. Furthermore, this description

4

often pathologizes the individual and typically excludes his or her current life context.

The therapeutic stance of separateness and the pathology orientation results in an adversarial position that the language of therapy reflects with metaphors of resistance, conflict, defense, hidden motive, suppression, power, and attack. When placed in an adversarial position, either purposefully or inadvertently, labeled individuals will easily demonstrate more behaviors that will reinforce a therapist's conviction about the independent existence of an internal patholo-gy. It was this very trend that Erickson wished to avoid throughout his career (Erickson, 1985).

There was clearly a progression from his early work with hypnosis when Erickson, like others in that time, used repetition, references to sleep, auth-oritative stance, and direct suggestion. Later in his life, however, he observed that indirection allowed him to show respect for clients by not directly chal-lenging them to do what their conscious mind, for whatever reason, would not do. This was in contrast to earlier writing that referred to neurosis, resis-tance, conflict, and hypnoanalysis to reveal latent content in the unconscious. He considered anxiety as due to the breakdown of defense mechanisms and the threat of previously suppressed material emerging. But over time, he de-parted from this vocabulary almost entirely and described anxiety as the result of a breakdown of relations between people and understood all problems to be the result of an inability to have desired resources in the context in which they were needed.

Erickson's approach was oriented to interactions that helped people change and aimed to be scrupulously unique with each client. Each question, silence, discussion, metaphor, or paradoxical directive was delivered with an ongoing sensitivity to the special needs of the listener. Interventions were seemingly reinvented for each individual and each goal. In this regard, the approach was extremely unconventional and was often misunderstood since it could not be explained according to a structural theory of personality. Erickson resisted even attempting to set forth an explicit theory of personality and warned that rigid adherence to theory often becomes a Procrustean bed that cuts the legs off clients in order to make them fit.

There were many stories, however, that described a theory of learning. For instance, a portion of one story concerned how his son explained events of a date at a malt shop and roller-skating rink. The son's explanation of the super-ficial behavior was contrasted with Erickson's own interpretation about the same events. Erickson stated, "I knew what he'd really been doing. He'd been looking in her eyes, having mucous membrane stimulation, touching her, and having rhythmical physical activity."

This theory of human development assumes people are in a continuous cycle of learning experiences with ever-increasing complexity. Success in learning simple sets of experiences provides a foundation for subsequent learning of greater complexity. Socialization experiences retrieve, encourage, and stabilize experiences. A person's awareness of this socialization experience is merely the tip of an iceberg, while the remainder is stored below the surface, as unconscious. Throughout life, we are learning as we are being socialized and simultaneously displaying and using previous learning. When the demands of our developmental tasks and current environment do not teach us how to perform, we rely upon previously learned patterns. These patterns of perception, cognition, emotion, behavior, and self-monitoring determine our success.

Fluctuations in family stability are most often precipitated by changes brought on when particular developmental stages require novel experiences or alterations in the usual types of transactions. For instance, the birth of a baby signals a change to the child-raising stage of development, and hundreds of new experiences, transactions, and behaviors must be learned: looking at the child and smiling, postponing gratification for the sake of the child's needs, learning to ask for help with the child, being able to experience joy in the child's growth, acquiring a vast array of caretaking skills, and so forth. If these experiences are readily available as resources due to previous learnings, the disorganization within the family system is relatively short and the transition to the new organization easy. Conversely, to the extent that the resources are not available, the disorganization becomes more debilitating and resolutions more difficult. When problem-solving behaviors are greatly out of synchronization with contextual demands, people may seek therapy for various symptoms.

Central to the theory of learning is the unconscious and its relationship to consciousness. The unconscious is the complex set of associations outside awareness at any moment. These include a broad range of experiences and processes, some of which become conscious at times, although most do not ever become conscious. These unconscious patterns regulate, control, and guide moment-to-moment conduct. They are resources that can be used in therapy to cocreate different perceptions, experiences, and behaviors. In Ericksonian Therapy, the unconscious is considered a repository of resources and skills that can be employed for positive therapeutic change. Unconscious process and content need not be made conscious in order to be utilized.

Problems are the natural result of attempts to solve developmental demands in ways that do not fully work for the people involved. Intervention, then, should help clients actively participate in changing the way they live. As people find more effective ways of achieving goals and experiences they wish to have, previously learned patterns of behavior will drop away. In other words, clients will make the best choice possible for themselves at any given moment with the learnings they have.

Therapy is based on observable behavior and related to the present and future circumstances of the client. While people have memories, perceptions, and feelings regarding their past, preoccupation with the past to the exclusion of present and future will unnecessarily prolong and complicate the process of therapy. The hallmark of an Ericksonian approach is an emphasis on current interpersonal relationships and their influence on the development and resolution of problems. Individuals may have developed a symptomatic behavior in the distant past, but the Ericksonian view focuses on how the problem is maintained in the present. Efforts are concentrated on increasing new arrangements of learning that can be applied to solving problems in the client's present life.

METHODOLOGY

Several tenets that guide methodology in Ericksonian Therapy can be crystallized from the preceding discussion of theory. These tenets affect the practice of therapy as they summarize the way in which problems and people are viewed.

1.   Problems are thought to be the result of disordered interpersonal relations in that clients fail to use resources from earlier learning in the current context. Consequently, diagnosis is an activity that frames the presenting problem in terms of the developmental and interpersonal climate experienced by the individual and his or her family. Therapy is directed toward making a creative rearrangement in those relationships so that developmental growth is maximized.

2.   The therapist is active and ultimately responsible for initiating therapeutic movement. This is done by introducing material into the therapy session, helping to punctuate experience and focus awareness, and by the use of extramural assignments. That is, therapy does not always wait until clients spontaneously bring up material but often sets the pace and challenges clients to grow and change.

3. Change comes from experience and not from insight. Mental mechanisms and personality characteristics need not be analyzed for the client. They can be utilized as processes for facilitating therapeutic goals. Indirect methods (metaphor, indirect suggestion, and ambiguous function assignment) are used to retrieve needed resources (attitudes, abilities, feelings, etc.) that can be directed to creating new adjustments to current life demands.

4. A major goal is getting clients active and moving in perceptions, cognition, emotions, and small and large behavior.

5. Utilization is employing clients' perceptions and resources for movement and change. It occurs in two areas. One is the here-and-now use of material presented by the client. If a client demonstrates relaxation, tension, talkativeness, silence, questioning, passivity, movement, stillness, fear, confidence, and so forth, it is to be accepted and used to further the therapeutic movement. So-called resistance is not seen or labeled as such, but rather is accepted and in some manner used to facilitate a context for change. The second area refers to using whatever talents, interests, and potential abilities a client brings as a vehicle to gain further experience and learning. Therapists make an effort to speak the clients' experiential languages and join them at their model of the world.

6. Indirection refers to the use of controlled ambiguity. It encourages clients to make their own relevant meaning instead of being told what to do. The ambiguity in suggestions and stories gives rise to pleasant mental excitement and enhances communication. It is not limited to the hypnosis context.

7. Therapy is future oriented. Since the client has come to therapy due to an inability to meet developmental demands in his or her current life, therapy is focused on pinpointing and developing resources to meet these present demands. Recognizing the mechanisms by which a client can maintain needed resources in the current context is seen as much more important than analyzing how a shortcoming came to exist in the past.

These seven tenets guide the use of particular methods throughout Ericksonian Therapy, which begins as the assessment stage unfolds. For instance, imagine that a young man enters the office exuding inadequacy. An Ericksonian therapist recognizes that a logical set of behaviors and emotions is lacking in this client's behavior in the present context. But in speaking to the man in order to understand his presenting complaint, it is perfectly reasonable for the therapist to make comments that presuppose increased feelings of pride, confidence, and assertive behavior. Therapists observe how clients respond to such presupposition and minimal suggestions as part of the ongoing assessment that ascertains flexibility in experience and available resources. Therapy is not simply a two-part process consisting of an initial assessment followed by continued treatment; rather, it continues throughout communication and contact with clients.

Assessment does, however, include an intake interview that addresses four areas. First, the presenting problems as well as preliminary goals are determined. Next, family organization is assessed, including a conceptualization of the current stage of development (and related demands) as well as the likely demands of the next logical stage of development the family will be entering. An understanding is developed of the family's way of explaining typical time structuring, involvement with career and social networks, and each person's involvement with the symptom. Particular interest concerns how engaging in the symptom represents an adaptive response or "best choice" (Lankton & Lankton, 1983) to the interpersonal and developmental demands currently being encountered. Third, the initial assessment involves gathering background information about the problem itself: how each person responds to the problem, what is being accomplished by having the problem, what might be accomplished if the problem were not present, how the problem started, and previous treatment received for it. The fourth area determines cogent information about the family of origin of the client, even if it might initially seem unrelated to the specific presenting problem.

Goal setting usually includes the specific gains stated by the client as well as other subtle prerequisites, such as changes in perception, cognition, emotion, behavior, social role, family structure, and self-image that support the larger goal. Treatment is almost entirely centered on helping clients find and use experiential resources in the context in which they need them. Various interventions are employed to retrieve and reassociate experience, including those techniques identified with the Ericksonian approach, such as positive framing, utilization, paradoxical prescriptions, skill-building homework, indirect suggestion, therapeutic metaphors, ambiguous function assignments, dissociated visual rehearsal, reciprocal inhibition, and hypnosis. This does not preclude the use of more common activities, such as interpretation, confrontation, specifying, clarification, crystallization, and empathy.

9

Empathy, for Ericksonian therapists, means putting one foot in the client's world and leaving one in the therapist's own. Therapists need to literally speak the same vocabulary and speech patterns spoken by clients. This means therapists must be able to vary their behavior and perform a wide range of verbal and nonverbal styles. This means stretching oneself to mumble with almost inarticulate mumblers, matching the exasperated nonverbals provided by tentative clients, speaking rapidly, crudely, or eloquently, depending on what is offered. Communication messages are packaged to be understood correctly by the receiver.

Positive framing is an attitude expressed in two ways. First, therapists attend to the ideas expressed by clients to scan for and monitor goals, attitudes, and desires that have been expressed in any form other than positive. Then, therapists sincerely restate those goals, attitudes, or desires in a positive and realistic manner acceptable to the client. Reframing such as this may apply to the interpretation of a common daily event or to a large portion of a client's life experience. Reframing is a transaction. It is not enough that a therapist has a terrific idea — the idea must be communicated successfully to the client for reframing to occur.

Utilization is defined as recognizing and using the energy brought by clients to move their actions or thoughts in the direction of the therapeutic goal. In conventional therapy, certain behavior is considered to be resistant. However, in Ericksonian Therapy, all behavior is seen as problem-solving attempts. For instance, a person who continually disagrees with the therapist might realistically be seen as someone who has solved most of his problems by correcting others and thinking for himself. While this may not be appropriate social conduct and may even be detrimental to the treatment goals, it must nonetheless be recognized as a statement that he is trying to solve the problem in the way best known to him. The utilization technique is used correctly with such a person when the therapist asks him to "continue to try to solve the problem by discarding the things I say and doing a great deal of thinking for yourself." The potential adversary becomes a teammate when his behavior is framed as an attempt to solve the problem.

Paradoxical prescription is a request for clients to continue doing something they have been doing while making a minor alteration in some aspect of it. For example, spouses may be asked to refrain from having sexual relations but to keep a notebook and record in it, each day, compliments they would be reluctant to say to their spouse at this time. When this sort of intervention is used, clients are refusing to have sexual relations due to the therapist's demand and not to their own anger toward each other. At the same time, an important behavior is being built to further marital intimacy. By writing in the notebook but not showing it to the spouse, each person is rehearsing skills needed to create positive communication in the marriage. Furthermore, there is mystery introduced in the marriage regarding the other spouse's positive comments. In effect, each spouse may begin to think, "I wonder what nice thing my partner is thinking about me." Thus, paradoxical intervention can skillfully help clients reach their goal of marriage fulfillment. It helps them find a way to give up the power plays and develop positive expectations without losing face and without winning or losing a game of "who's to blame?"

Skill-building homework assignments are intended to create a context outside the office in which clients can obtain bits and pieces of experience. Each assignment intends to evoke a small subset of experience such that, taken as a whole, the experiences approximate a complex socialization event. For example, an individual who is uncomfortable dating and has sought therapy for related issues might be given the following homework assignments without being told the reason. He may be asked to see the midnight showing of a popular movie. Another assignment might ask him to go to a restaurant and order two desserts and eat them. A third assignment might ask him to purchase new pants and a shirt. Still a fourth assignment might ask him to engage an attractive bank teller in a long conversation. In each of these four assignments, however, his attention would be diverted away from how they might be subsets of the dating goal. If the client were to think his success in dating depended on success in any of these assignments, his anxiety might be all that he learned while doing them. If, instead, he participates in skill-building assignments for reasons other than dating, his learned limitations will not prevent him from acquiring the experiences he needs.

Therapeutic suggestion refers to a large category of verbal and nonverbal communication. While all communication contains aspects of suggestion, few people realize how to consciously and effectively formulate those suggestions at the process level of communication. The goal of suggestion is to help the client search for and retrieve experiences. This refers to experiences that are needed for ongoing understanding of therapy, as well as to experiences that pertain to the contracted treatment goals. The former category of experiences includes such things as listening with comfort, being specific, and taking risks. The latter category may include experiences that result from homework assignments, paradoxical interventions, visual rehearsal, and so forth. One of the intentions of Ericksonian Therapy is to use suggestions in such a way that

11

clients do not feel obligated to respond to them. Clients respond to suggestions that are relevant to them. The more ambiguous a suggestion is, the greater the latitude and range of options available to the client. Indirect suggestions thus should not evoke resistance.

Therapeutic metaphors are stories with a specific structure. Unlike parables or fables, the goal usually is not to drive home some point, but rather to elicit experiences. This is accomplished in much the same way as viewers of a movie retrieve experiences. Watching the movie, a person will identify with particular characters and assign internal objects to stand for those characters in the movie. As those characters change relationships with one another, the internal objects used to represent them alter their relationships to one another as well. This results in certain predictable emotional experiences and attitudinal shifts. Clients listening to therapeutic metaphors can also be sensitized to certain behaviors. These changes provide a sort of window of opportunity for the client to reconsider available resources. They operate as an effective tool to evoke, retrieve, and associate relatively novel experiences into the context in which they are needed.

Ambiguous function assignments are a special category of homework designed to help a client suspend his rational limitations and understandings. While participating in this assignment, a client will attempt to understand the rather odd behavior that has been assigned. Attempts to understand will require that the client resurrect understandings and meanings that were evoked during the therapy session. In other words, this type of assignment helps the client search more deeply within himself between therapy sessions. A typical ambiguous function assignment consists of specific behaviors pertaining to a specific object chosen by the therapist. These behaviors are assigned to be carried out at specific times in a specific location. However, the actual point or meaning behind these behaviors and this object are not explained. Instead, the client is asked to discern for himself what the meaning might be. Ideally, the therapist has absolutely no idea as to what sort of meaning might be derived. All the therapist needs to know is that the behavior is ethical, legal, doable, and not terribly unpleasant for the client.

Dissociated visual rehearsal refers to techniques that can be performed with or without the use of hypnosis but in each case have at least three features in common. The first of these features is that the client assumes a state of comfort and creativity. This state may be the result of previous empathy, suggestion, positive framing, or assignment. The second feature requires that the client disconnect current experiences from visual memories. Finally, the client needs to conduct an elaborate visual rehearsal of the past or anticipation of the future. In doing this, previous associations to the memories or anticipations are altered. The technique, when applied to mild or moderate traumatic memories, helps the client discover additional available positive resources in the context of the previously unpleasant memory. When applied to an anticipation, the technique helps clients prefigure their perceptions and add a longer anticipation of all the positive experiences they are feeling at the time of the therapy session. In one sense, this visual rehearsal is a self-generated metaphor that allows clients a context in which to associate desired resources to a situation in which they are needed. Future experiences of the same type are expected to become associated with the state of comfort and creativity that was established during the intervention. Even if some of the previous threatening experiences are evoked during future experiences of the same type, they will be "rechunked" or diluted since the client's participation in this activity has created an awareness for and experience of positive associations in the face of the trauma.

Reciprocal inhibition is the name given to the class of interventions that create change by interfering with the mind's ability to experience a previously unpleasant set of associations. The dissociated visual rehearsal discussed above is one example of reciprocal inhibition. Other means of facilitating reciprocal inhibition include working with a sequentially incongruent client in such a way as to evoke both major incongruities at the same time for the same event. Still other means involve urging a client to retrieve an avoided memory, pain, or symptom upon request in the office (out of context). For instance, a therapist might ask a client with "shooting pains" in his hands to "take a few moments and create them here in the office so I can better understand." If the client obliges, the pains are not happening to the client as a victim but rather are happening at the client's initiative. This is often the first step toward realizing responsibility for change and freeing oneself from the victim role.

Hypnosis is simply a modality for communication, despite considerable misunderstanding to the contrary. It is a state of heightened internal awareness with a limited range of perceptual focus. During prolonged episodes of such internal absorption of attention, various phenomena are likely to be experienced. Trained subjects are better at producing these trance phenomena, but most people can experience a degree of each of them even in their first session. These experiences can be heightened and associated just as other experiential resources can. The experiences of dissociation, body distortion, amnesia, and time distortion, for instance, can be strategically applied to pain control.

It is possible to focus and direct very subtle experiences in order to change perception and attitudes for problems as acute as pain. However, Ericksonian therapists often help a client to use such focus to enhance a visual rehearsal, or to embellish desired experiences, such as tenderness, confidence, joy, pride, or even sadness or anger. The use of hypnosis in therapy requires special training, and often special licensing. This is not due to any inherent danger with hypnosis, but rather to the possible misuse of the tool by untrained therapists.

It is often believed that Erickson used hypnosis with all of his clients. Neither Erickson himself, nor the range of Ericksonian therapists who practice today, do this. Many Ericksonian therapists never use hypnosis and prefer to work primarily with homework assignments. Others prefer to work with only assignments and metaphor, while others prefer to rely on paradoxical interventions and suggestion. Erickson preferred that therapists employ a wide range of interventions and not be committed to any small subset of his techniques. Moreover, Erickson would urge therapists to invent new techniques for each client and not rely on any formula at all. He would insist only that the principles mentioned previously be followed within the theoretical frame he modeled.

The course of treatment often fluctuates greatly with each client. Some cases occur as single-session "cures," while most others are resolved within a few weeks or months. Rarely, a case continues for as much as a year or sometimes two. This situation is most often the result of the particular needs of the client and the existence of severely inhibiting childhood experiences.

APPLICATIONS

Contributions from Erickson's work have been reported in nearly all forms of therapy appropriate to outpatient populations. These include any imaginable concern for anxiety-related symptoms, sexual functions, pain control, habit control, childbirth, autism, phobias, asthma, and marital and family therapy. Some limited venues have reported work with inpatient populations, including patients showing psychotic symptoms and character disorders. A few treatment regimens have also reported the use of Ericksonian Therapy with substance abusers, counseling for gays, adolescents, and hospital venue work with cancer victims and grief patients. Many of these reports can be seen in the *Ericksonian Monographs*. These and other emerging and growing areas, including corporate consulting, can be found in the professional programs shared by invited faculty at the International Congresses of the Milton Erickson Foundation, Inc., in Phoenix, Arizona.

As the popularity of Ericksonian Therapy has risen, so have criticisms, due to a lack of published research. Despite the uniqueness of each intervention, specified protocols or intervention patterns do exist and are becoming more widely known. These may provide the basis for effectiveness studies. Some of the research finds limitations because the underlying clinical epistemology does not lend itself to procedures conforming to requirements of laboratory measurement. A few typical studies are cited below.

Alman and Carney (1980) reported that indirect suggestions were more successful in producing posthypnotic behavior than were direct suggestions. McConkey (1984) concluded that "indirection may not be the clinically important notion as much as the creation of a motivational context where the overall suggestion is acceptable such as making the ideas congruent with the other aims and hopes of a patient" (p. 312). Stone and Lundy (1985) investigated effectiveness in eliciting body movements following suggestions and reported indirect suggestions to be more effective than direct suggestions in eliciting the target behaviors.

Mosher and Matthews (1985), investigating a claim made by Lankton and Lankton (1983), found support for the structural effect of embedding metaphors on amnesia, but also reported that indirect suggestion did not enhance the effect of amnesia. They indicated that as a result of stories told to six clients, five reported thinking about the meaning of the therapeutic stories during the intervening week and how they might act differently with regard to the presenting issue. Each of these five clients reported a positive change in the presenting problem. The sixth client reported almost total amnesia for each of the metaphor sessions.

Nugent (1989a) attempted to show a causal connection between Erickson's notion of "unconscious thinking without conscious awareness." In a series of seven independent case studies each client reported a clear, sustained positive change with respect to the presenting problem. While individual case study has certain methodological limitations, Nugent's (1989a) use of seven independent cases with a carefully followed treatment protocol makes his conclusion of causality more convincing. In a related study, Nugent (1989b) used a multiple baseline design to investigate the impact of an Ericksonian hypnotic intervention and found that target behaviors changed as a result of treatment intervention. Each of the Nugent studies has methodological weaknesses, as does the Matthews and Langdell (1989) study, but these still represent examples of current attempts to systematically investigate the clinical validity of Ericksonian interventions.

Despite these and other studies, it can be seen that in doing research it is easier to discuss Erickson's *techniques* than to discuss the subtle and perhaps more important contributions of his overall approach. With an overemphasis on technique, novice therapists have frequently been guilty of applying interventions without an adequate sense of how such techniques develop out of a natural interaction with clients. Effective application of Ericksonian techniques relies heavily on principles of utilization and cooperation in the clinical context.

CASE EXAMPLE

Frank, a 23-year-old single, white male, visited my office with a complaint of blood phobia. He had been a medical student but suspended his studies due to the development of his fear. He stood up in the waiting room as I approached him, and when I reached out to shake his hand, I noticed that he held my hand limply and hesitantly. In my office he explained that he had a prolonged previous medical history. He related the following facts.

As a child of 14 he had developed lactose intolerance. He experienced an array of symptoms and saw many doctors before, at 16, he was diagnosed and his problem corrected. In the process of seeking many medical tests he decided that he might like to be a physician when he grew up. He never wavered from that dream again.

However, a most unpleasant incident occurred at age 16 when he was in a weakened state from vomiting and not sleeping well for days. On this occasion he recalls passing out briefly (he thinks due to low blood sugar) as he watched a vacuum needle draw a quantity of blood from his arm. At that point he developed a phobia. It was intense for a year; by the time he was 18 the phobia had been nearly forgotten. Even after undergraduate school his medical studies seemed to go well. In dissection labs, he had almost no memory of his past trauma.

Unfortunately, this comfort did not last. Eight months before seeing me, his reaction to a dissection lab was so frighteningly intense that he nearly passed out and had to run from the room. He even fainted at a movie when a surprising scene of blood appeared on one occasion. As a result of these events he sought therapy with another approach, Eye Movement Desensitization and Reprocessing (EMDR), to trauma resolution. After several treatments with that approach, his therapist declared that he was not making expected progress and recommended that Frank see me.

Inquiring about the constellation of symptoms, I discovered that he does not have any thoughts about death or irrational fears. He simply anticipates fainting if he sees blood. I was interested in what might have triggered the anxiety attacks associated with blood now, after he had been free of the disruption for several years. As I inquired about his life experiences, I also asked about his life at 16 when the phobic reaction began. While I was interested in contrasting and comparing these periods, he believed they had nothing in common as far as the phobia of blood was concerned. It became clear, in fact, that he wished to find no other etiology at work.

However, as he answered my questions, it became most apparent that he had developed another unique set of experiences that might also have bearing on his present complaint. The onset of his first episode, his notable lack of aggression, even passivity, when he shook my hand, and his worried manner all gave rise to another line of inquiry. Eventually, Frank related that both of his parents were troublesome for him. His father had been quite passive as his mother was critical, aggressive, and controlling. It was her criticism that made him feel most hesitant, and he had developed a posture of being friendly and responsive to others rather than standing up to her or taking a dominant position of any kind. He avoided taking charge, expressing disagreement, competing, and so on.

In his recent life, the reemergence of his problem coincided with a week of efforts to begin dating a young woman whom he met at school. He stated that this was no more than a coincidence and that the dissection lab had simply been scheduled to happen that week. It struck me as developmentally similar, at least in the use of experiential resources, to what one does as a 16-year-old: interest in girls, planning for independence, moving away from reliance upon a mother, becoming sexually active, and so on. All of these issues were not exclusively confined to his life at 16 and his life at 23. He had in fact headed off to college, moved away from home, and taken an apartment off campus prior to this. Such behavior had certainly involved breaking reliance on his father and his mother and involved plans of moving toward independence. And yet something about this set of developmental demands was parallel and his behavioral and experiential responses employed the same phobic behavior as part of his problem-solving regimen.

During the discussion he confirmed the family dynamics and his hesitance to become aggressive. A final additional concern for Frank was that his girlfriend had just broken up with him by means of a phone call. She did not wish to see him again or discuss the matter. He said she gave him no indication of the reason and he was only aware of her vague sense of distance lately. He reported being so upset by this that it "almost" took precedence over his concern about the blood phobia. Of course he needed to correct the phobia and return to medical school. We mapped out a rough treatment plan that would involve heightening his sense of confidence and assertiveness and using these experiences to inhibit and replace his conditioned response to seeing large volumes of blood. He scheduled two more sessions to follow his first visit.

Session 2 began with Frank's reminding me that his problem was an example of phobic conditioning (and suggesting that it therefore had nothing to do with anxiety about his mother, his assertiveness, or any such emotional factors). I agreed that his awareness and understanding began at that time and quickly asked if I could help him get oriented to the session by relating one or two case stories that might be helpful to him as he unraveled this mystery and gained the resources he sought. He agreed and I explained to him that I would like to do something I had never done before. Usually, I ask clients to basically attend to me without distraction during such a story, as I want their reaction to help them form some creative experiences for approaching the solution to their problem afresh. However, in his case, as he was already distracted by a number of things, I asked him to purposely distract himself from me as I talked. Specifically, I asked him to doodle and sketch on my large notepad whatever ideas, images, foolishness, points, memories, or entertainment might come to his mind as I spoke. I reminded him that this was just a sort of creative warm-up for the crux of our agreed-on direction and that after 10 minutes or less, I would want to move on. He reiterated my instructions and emphasized that he really didn't draw well. I agreed that he understood my request and added that it would be fine to doodle or even jot down some words if he liked — although I favored his doing the novel act of drawing.

I handed him the pad and markers and began telling him of a case involving a man who sought therapy for hypertension and who insisted that his physical symptom had only a medical cause. I reminded Frank to ignore my speaking as much as he could and let it just be background noise, warming up his creativity by drawing what came to mind. The story continued for about eight minutes and detailed the therapy of the man with hypertension. In the story, the man's father had recently died of a heart attack and the man actually carried a blood pressure monitor with him and measured his hypertension throughout the day in hope of confirming that he was not like his father in this way. He would run and perform relaxation exercises to reduce the readings on his monitor. However, whenever he would be before his students or with his wife, his blood pressure would rise again. He was unable to find that he was unlike his father in this way despite his efforts to improve himself.

As I spoke, Frank colored random doodles on the pad and split his attention between listening to the story and the art before him. He began drawing thick black lines between blotches of colors. Red was noticeably absent from the image.

In the story the protagonist came to discover that his almost obsessional concerns were an attempt to hide his emotional vulnerability. He subsequently used therapy to imagine returning to his father's deathbed, wept with sadness that he could not or did not express his own needs in the past, and expressed anger that he was provided with such a model for how to be a man. Finally, he declared that he had needs he would no longer ignore and would essentially acknowledge them and act as his own father to see that they were met. In this act he firmly and aggressively asserted that he was not like his father and would learn more than his father could teach him — he would not remain limited just because his father could not teach him.

I had made the story as vivid and accurate as I could in the short time that it took to relate a very emotional session that had actually taken place with the protagonist. At that point Frank was not drawing but was sitting and staring off into space. He volunteered that he could identify with the man in the story in many ways. He asked if I thought something like that might be good for him as well.

In direct response to that interest, I asked him to do a two-part exercise for the remainder of the session. It consisted of the paradoxical directive to allow his phobia to continue for the next couple of weeks so his interest in learning from it could guide him better. He agreed, especially since working directly to destructure it had so far failed. I asked him to visually rehearse a scene with certain characteristics and tell me what he got out of it and what it meant. The fantasy involved recalling several moments when he demonstrated his strengths, confidence, pride, determination, and firmness. As his body and self-report reflected success in his amassing these feelings, I had him change the fantasy to become an image near the time of his traumatic past incident. I asked him to continue to stay confident but witness how he and his parents were getting along prior to the time of the trauma. In this waking-state concentration, Frank slowly shared what he remembered of his father's exasperation with Frank's eating and vomiting complaints, his parents' quarreling, and his mother's oppressive control of his life during the hours leading up to and

19

including taking him to the hospital. He was asked to keep an image of his younger self in the fantasy and simultaneously be aware that he was a more confident older self, as it were, watching from my office sofa. I asked him not to conclude or change any of his reactions at this point, just to remember and learn anything that seemed important.

As the session closed I asked Frank to do an assignment outside the office. I asked him to perform this activity three times before I saw him again; he could decide when those times would be. Since he was living at home, I wanted him to borrow his father's hammer and leave the house with it at sundown. I asked him to go to the pier or boardwalk on Pensacola Beach and use the hammer to pound down any and all nails that he saw protruding in any way above the wood. He was not to speak to anyone and could just act like this was his job if he needed to. In any case, he was to do this for at least an hour for three nights. If he pounded all the protruding nails in these two locations he could proceed to the wooden walkovers that bridged the sand dunes and connected the beach road to the shoreline. When he returned for the next session, I would want him to tell me what he thought the learning from such an assignment had been.

We began the third session with his rendition of the homework assignment. He said that while it was odd to say so, he had experienced it to be strangely freeing to be in public banging, making noise, hammering, and pounding. In fact, he did it four times instead of the assigned three. Frank said he had never done this sort of thing before, as he always felt or had been inhibited from doing anything like that. Asked what the learning of the assignment was, Frank concluded that maybe the point had been to show that he had more capabilities inside him than he expected. Still, he wasn't sure how this would cure his phobia.

Hearing that he had hammered for an extra night, I asked him to close his eyes and recall the freeing experience that he sought and found on that evening. Once again we used the time to dissociate from and visually rehearse the events leading up to and including the phobia. Additionally, I asked that Frank also visually rehearse the newest onset of the phobia eight months ago and, while he was at it, the moment leading up to meeting his girlfriend and beginning to date her. Finally, I asked him to visually rehearse the recent breakup with her.

Upon completing the dissociated review, Frank reported that he felt stronger about almost all of these matters. He was still unsure why his girlfriend had broken up with him, but thinking about it did not seem as demoralizing as it had. Asked if he were ready to have the same feeling about seeing quantities of blood or if he wanted to wait until he understood his former girlfriend, he replied that he was ready to get over the phobia. I asked him to set yet another appointment for the next week and used the remaining 10 minutes of session to elaborate about tools. I explained a number of characteristics about tools that my father had passed along to me. I put special emphasis on those tools that I had once thought were useless but which I later appreciated a great deal, such as the wood plane that I did not use as a child but which I had found irreplaceable for fixing closets and doors once I became a homeowner. I also elaborated on my appreciation for the pliers that used to belong to my mother and my favorite hammer that had been my father's, then mine, and which I passed along to my son. I explained what makes a hammer a "good" hammer.

Since he had found value in his father's hammer, I asked him to bring it in for the next session and let me examine it. I also asked him to write a short essay about the value of some of his father's tools so I could ostensibly evaluate his ability to express himself in writing. Finally, I asked that he approach his father, tell him in any way he could that he found the hammer to be valuable to him, and request that his father make a gift of it to him.

When he came back with his father's hammer, I examined it carefully and declared it a wonderful hammer. I asked if he had requested it as a gift yet, and he said he had not. I insisted that he do so, and in fact, do so immediately before therapy continued. Handing him the telephone, I urged him to call his father at work, tell him something had come up and he needed to know if he could have the hammer as his own and that he would explain later if necessary. At first he was embarrassed and reluctant. However, realizing that he had never really asked for anything so spontaneously, and remembering how excited he had become using it, and too, realizing the therapy session was about building such resources, he saw no harm in it. He called his father. His father was friendly and a little confused by the inquiry but had only minor hesitation and then agreed, saying that if the hammer meant that much to Frank, he could certainly have it.

He said that while getting the hammer made sense at the time, having it now seemed a little silly. I asked him to be seated with it, close his eyes and revivify the memories of pounding with it during the previous week. He signaled me when he had the experience, and I asked that he imagine and come to believe as much as he could in fantasy, that he was still on the boardwalk on Pensacola Beach pounding nails. I counted backward from 20 to 1 and, in general terms, suggested that he could create an increasingly deeper self-induced trance hearing my voice and keeping the dual awareness of pounding the nails. After completing the deepening, suggestions were used to offer him the possibility of imagining that he was smashing vacuum needles filled with blood and other previously feared stimuli, including movie scenes, dissection lab carcasses, and objects in his memories of the original trauma. He reported being strong, not violent and angry, as he did this to all but the memories in the trauma. Toward these memories he reported being defiant and "sort of angry." He didn't want them to control him anymore.

I asked him to put the hammer down but keep the feelings and, in fantasy, to coach the younger Frank in the visual rehearsals. I suggested that he could pass along this feeling to Frank just as his father passed along the hammer to him. He could give the younger self the tools to express his desires that his mother stop controlling him. Finally, in due course, Frank was urged to switch to the visual fantasy with his former girlfriend and imagine doing the same in dialogue with her.

This was his last session with me. He left that session reporting that he would be curious about his reaction to blood now and would initially test it by renting a movie and call me with the outcome. That weekend Frank rented *Blade*, as it was reported to have a great deal of gratuitous violence and blood content. He said the scenes did not create a problem for him, that the movie was rather enjoyable, and I might enjoy watching it as well. He said it wasn't as bad as people made it out to be — he had seen a lot worse at the hospital. Three weeks passed after the last session and Frank moved back to the university in Alabama and restarted medical school with the new semester. After a couple of months he called to report he was a bit apprehensive at first but had not had any difficulty up to that time with duties at the hospital that used to frighten him. He jokingly said that he just had to keep "hammering on" to complete school. He said, however, that, more interestingly, he thinks the major gain from therapy turned out to be that he was more tolerant of himself and that he could make mistakes and have less anxiety.

SUMMARY

In summary, an Ericksonian approach to therapy is perhaps like the execution of a martial art known as aikido. Aikido is almost diametrically opposite karate and tae kwan do. In aikido practitioners are to do very little *to* an attacker but instead use the energy and behavior *of* the attacker to neutralize the attack.

Ironically, there are a number of skills the aikido practitioner must learn in order to do nothing to the attacker. Among these skills are understanding the dynamic energy brought by the other person and assessing where the other person is headed, and how the person is using himself to get there. Someone using aikido may, in a relaxed and rapid fashion, place himself in the path of the opponent — not so as to offer direct resistance, but so as to deflect the vector of the attack and redirect the attacker's center. Doing so changes the outcome. Little, if anything, is added to the attacker that he didn't already have. In the end it appears that the person using aikido did nearly nothing.

In Ericksonian Therapy, the therapist does not "do" anything to the client but instead accepts the energy given by the client. Assessing the direction and resources held by the client, the Ericksonian therapist may place ideas and tasks in his path — not to block or resist, but to alter the forward momentum. In the end the client changes himself with his resources and his momentum. The therapist does not want to take any credit for the gains made by the client. The therapist is only a catalyst for the outcome. Ericksonian therapy creates a context for change whether that is in the session, outside the session, or in concentrated internal absorption of self-hypnosis.

References

Alman, B., & Carney, R. (1980). Consequences of direct and indirect suggestion on success of posthypnotic behaviour. *American Journal of Clinical Hypnosis, 23*, 112–118.

Bateson, G. (1972). *Steps to an ecology of mind.* New York: Ballantine Books, division of Random House.

Erickson, M. (1985). *The seminars, workshops, and lectures of Milton H. Erickson: Vol. 2. Life reframing in hypnosis.* E. L. Rossi, M. O. Ryan, & F. A. Sharp (Eds.). New York: Irvington.

Fisch, R. (1990). The broader interpretation of Milton H. Erickson's Work. In S. Lankton (Ed.), *The Ericksonian monographs: No. 7. The issue of broader implications of Ericksonian Therapy* (pp. 1–5). New York: Brunner/Mazel.

Haley, J. (1963). *Strategies of psychotherapy.* New York: Grune & Stratton.

Haley, J. (Ed.). (1967). *Advanced techniques of hypnosis and therapy: Selected papers of Milton H. Erickson, M.D.* New York: Grune & Stratton.

Haley, J. (1973). *Uncommon therapy: The psychiatric techniques of Milton H. Erickson, M.D.* New York: Norton.

Haley, J. (1985a). *Conversations with Milton H. Erickson, M.D.: Changing individuals.* New York: Norton.

Jackson, D. (Ed.). (1968a). *Communication, family, and marriage: 1.* Palo Alto: Science and Behavior Books.

Jackson, D. (Ed.). (1968b). *Therapy, communication, and change: 2.* Palo Alto: Science and Behavior Books.

Keeney, B. (1983). *The aesthetics of change.* New York: Guilford.

Lankton, S., & Lankton, C. (1983). *The answer within: A clinical framework of Ericksonian hypnotherapy.* New York: Brunner/Mazel.

Matthews, W. J., & Langdell, S. (1989). What do clients think about the metaphors they receive? *American Journal of Clinical Hypnosis, 31*(1) 242–251.

Maturana, H., & Varela, F. (1987). *The tree of knowledge.* Boston: New Science Library, Shambhala.

McConkey, K. (1984). The impact of indirect suggestion. *The International Journal of Clinical and Experimental Hypnosis, 32*, 307–314.

Mosher, D., & Matthews, W. (1985). Multiple embedded metaphor and structured amnesia. Paper presented at the American Psychological Association meeting, San Diego, CA.

Nugent, W. (1989a). Evidence concerning the causal effect of an Ericksonian hypnotic intervention. *Ericksonian Monographs, 5*, 35–55.

Nugent, W. (1989b). A multiple baseline investigation of an Ericksonian hypnotic approach. *Ericksonian Monographs, 5*, 69–85.

Rossi, E., Ryan, M., & Sharp, F. (Eds.). (1983). *Healing in hypnosis by Milton H. Erickson.* New York: Irvington.

Satir, V. (1964). *Conjoint family therapy.* Palo Alto: Science and Behavior Books.

Stone, J. A., and Lundy, R. M. (1985). Behavioural compliance with direct and indirect body movement suggestions. *Journal of Abnormal Psychology, 3*, 256–263.

2

Milton Erickson's Contribution to Therapy: Epistemology — Not Technology[1]

INTRODUCTION

I am writing about Erickson's contribution to therapy in terms of epistemology and ontology and therefore run the risk of having the article mistaken for one on philosophy. As a family therapist and hypnotherapist, I am not qualified or prepared to do justice to the field of philosophy — either traditional or post-modern. But I do feel comfortable speaking about epistemology (I will use the single term to refer to both the epistemology and ontology à la Bateson, 1972), which refers here to the general approach taken and presuppositions made about people and problems.

Years ago, I heard Dr. Dan Goleman, editor of *Psychology Today*, state that Dr. Erickson had made a contribution to psychology equal to that of Freud's. Where Freud had made his contribution in terms of theory, Erickson had made his impact in terms of intervention. Indeed, some professionals feel that Erickson's most significant contribution was the advancement of hypnosis, whereas others feel it was his use of language whether indirect suggestion, metaphor, anecdotes, confusion, or therapeutic binds. Still others would argue that his contribution was the development of such concepts as utilization, indirection, and speaking the client's language, among others.

---

[1] Lankton, S. (1997). Milton Erickson's contribution to therapy: Epistemology — not technology. At *http://lanktkon.com/epist-bg.htm*, July 1995.

I suppose that arguing the merits of one of these aspects of intervention over another is a matter of personal and professional judgment. But I would like to express what I believe to be a linchpin of all of these interventions — his approach to people and problems; or, if you like, his epistemological and ontological position.

Before I begin writing about this, I should perhaps warn you, or at least remind you, that thought and experience are not linear even if (sometimes) writing is. The act of *communicating* thoughts can also be nonlinear. Therefore, writing about thought and communication is likely to result in a sort of paradox based on the necessary task of having to express nonlinear thoughts and experience in linear terms.

To make things worse, I have chosen a topic that concerns the thoughts and perceptions of Dr. Erickson. Since he neither is present to defend himself from what I am about to say, nor do his written works *directly* deal with the issues I am presenting, it might be concluded that I am about to speak about something I don't know anything about, and cannot communicate even if I do! Well, with such a challenge before me, I better get right to it.

BACKGROUND

I would like to begin with some ancient history, as I feel this will put the current ideas in powerful relief. I want to elucidate the concepts that can be seen in the following chart. The left column of the chart refers to a development in Western thought spanning centuries and ending within the last few decades. Although such an overview will oversimplify the lifeworks of many famous persons, it will suffice to make one point clear regarding the birth of psychology and the epistemology from which it is being weaned.

From ancient times, we have been given to believe that an independent Truth exists. Let's begin with fourth century B.C. Plato for convenience. His contribution of "a priori deductive idealism" informed us that there exists an a priori Truth of the universe that must in some manner become known by us. *On the Heavens* in 340 B.C. was written by his student Aristotle and introduced us to "induction" and empirical observation, but more important perhaps, Aristotle is known for the early syllogisms of logic by means of which a person with very little sensory investigation might reason his or her way to the Truth. For example, for spiritual reasons, he argued that Earth was the center of the universe. Within just 140 years, an elaboration of this idea was accomplished by Ptolemy and the Ptolemic model of the universe became widely accepted. It is astounding that this idea built on the premise of a knowable Truth went unquestioned for almost 2,000 years. It cuts deeply into the souls of our most mundane routines even today. Just as it blinded those who looked into the skies, it still blinds many of us as we look into the lives of our clients and patients.

COMPARISON CHART

Traditional	**Emergent/Ericksonian**
Truth exists and can be "known"	*Co-creation* of what is considered true
Observing carefully will reveal the truth	*Participation* is all that is possible — observation is participation
Adversarial position is taken by nature	*Cooperative* position is taken by nature
Observers are *separate* from the observed	Observers are *in the system* they observe
Reduction of larger parts will get closer to the truth	*Punctuation of experience* is basically arbitrary
Labeling of parts is a banal event	*Pattern identification* is limited by the labeler's experience and choices
Problem-oriented — identifies causes	*Goal-oriented* — solves the task
Pathology "uncovering" — disease can be uncovered	*Health-discovering* helps build desired resources
Past-oriented — causes lie in past	*Future-oriented* — purpose lies in the present and immediate future
Individuals operate *independently of environment*	Individuals and environments form an ecosystem
Causes are *inside* of the individual	Problems are reciprocally and cyclically between and with parts of the system
Experts "give" treatment	Change agents help *create a context* for problem solving

Traditional epistemology is also based on a separateness from nature and an adversarial posture toward nature. We might trace this too to Plato, but the principle of mind–body dualism, found in Plato was greatly magnified by the

Latin church father Saint Augustine (354–430) when he wrote with authority the *City of God*. Already blinded in their world view, people had come to seek the truth by rising above the adversarial human body, which seemed to tether them to the lesser world of the senses. It is easy to understand how this atmosphere spawned an entire race that could deny their senses for 14 centuries until the Copernican revolution was triggered. Centuries of presuppositions were built on the notion that human beings were separate from nature and able to seek an independent Truth.

Nicholas Copernicus circulated his model of the universe anonymously in 1514 A.D., but it was nearly 100 years before the heretical idea that Earth was not the center of the universe took root in 1609. And this came only after the invention of the telescope when Galileo, using the Kepler telescope, discovered the moons in orbit around Jupiter and this provided evidence at last that all of the heavens did not orbit the Earth. Finally, people began to have some tangible evidence, which in turn allowed them the courage to reason from more careful observations. In a way, this stroke of brilliance known as the Enlightenment proved to be a mixed blessing for psychology, which was due primarily to the slightly misguided notion that we could observe linear-causality in the universe without affecting it — but I'm getting ahead of my story. I want to build the drama and impact of the growing traditional epistemology so I can better emphasize the climate in which we now reach for an alternative.

The Age of Reason was born, and with it the enormous scientific and intellectual advancement of the 17th century. However, it further alienated us from a sense of cooperation and participation in nature. For instance, in 1620, the empiricist Francis Bacon wrote *Novum Organum* and put forth the idea that we must *torture* nature and make her give up her secrets. This, by the way, was the same year that the first ships carrying slaves landed on our colonial shores. By now, you may be asking why am I telling you all of this in a paper on psychotherapy? The answer is that we should look at the deep impact of our "evolution" and what gave rise to psychology: In this age of Enlightenment, the Truth exists in nature independent of the observer, who is separate from, and at times extremely adversarial toward, it, even to the point of torturing it. We came to expect it as fact that we were impartial observers, and if nature, or even some race of people, did not seem to conform to our conception, we could torture them and make them give up their secrets. This vision has far-reaching ramifications for our culture and one of them is that it is easy to see how we could come to label people as resistive, or pathological, or something else, and treat them with suspicion even in this post-modern age of therapy.

Referring to my chart, we see that I have now illustrated what I mean by saying that traditional epistemology embodies the concepts of "truth," "observing," "separate," and "adversarial." The next two items are "reduction" and "labeling." I see these as part of the traditional epistemology rising from the incredible ideas that emerged within the next 150 years. To visit then briefly, in 1676, Ole Roemer determined the speed of light fairly closely for his time. This sort of knowledge was an advancement of profound dimension. It must have seemed that there was nothing we could not reduce, label, and measure. To add further reinforcement, in 1687, Descartes' student Newton developed the laws of motion, calculus, and the principle of gravity, space, and time.

These accomplishments were so impressive that I am tempted to deviate from my central thesis to discuss them further but I will keep to the point that this world view was powerfully seductive and it was quickly developing a forceful momentum as all sorts of knowledge were advanced. I'll add just a few: Within less than 200 years, Clerk Maxwell had developed the wave theory. Twenty years later, Michelson and Morley performed their famous experiments with light that were later reexamined by Einstein. My point is that the changes brought by observation and reductionism were so remarkable that they provided use with enormously convincing details about the nature of things. The tools of mathematics and observation had taken us from the heavens all the way to the inside of the atom, all the while teaching us to reduce and label, to observe and feel separate from, and to seek the Truth as if we did not influence that which we sought. This movement told us that we could observe the Truth in nature and it must be that this methodology, this epistemology was correct and should be followed. Most important to my thesis is that this was 1887, just nine years before Freud's work on hysteria. In 1896 Sigmund Freud entered the scene and launched the ship of psychology. Naturally, he would be hugely influenced by the science of his day and the belief in natural law and universal order. After all, it was on these waters that his ship was to sail. Naturally, he would develop an approach that searched for problems with linear causes, rooted in the past. By reduction he would look inside the individual and consider himself capable of finding a truth through observation. The scientist/psychiatrist was an expert who would gather the facts and provide the passive patient with a treatment leading to a "cure," just as a physician would provide surgery or medication. Of course, therapists would reduce and label reified parts of individuals as they looked for the cunningly hidden causes within. When the subject did not respond to the expert, he or she was deemed "resistant," or worse.

29

Let's flip the channel for a moment. Contrary to this growing force there was a rising problem in the epistemology. Hume, and later Kant, in 1871, had mentioned aspects of it. In the natural sciences, several experiments were leading thinkers to the conclusion that we imposed order on the universe by our attempts to merely observe it. One could see this in the "wave-particle" theory (11 years before Kant), in the Michelson/Morley problem with light, in the conceptualization of the quantum principle in 1920 by Max Plank, and, of course, in the "Indeterminacy Principle" of Heisenberg in 1926, better known as the "uncertainty principle." But given the scientific achievements, I suppose, none of this made much sense at the time. In fact Freud had aggressively dismissed Kant's ideas (Freud, 1966, p. 538). Yet, particle physics and quantum math arose, helping theorists to come to grips with the anomalies of this epistemology (Hawking, 1988) and begin to understand a participatory universe. These understandings were vague to those outside of the advanced science labs and so psychology continued to travel in the direction in which it had been launched. Unfortunately, some things have not changed.

So, let's turn our attention to more recent times. As physics and mathematics began to develop a different epistemology, the same began to happen in social science. Perhaps the most articulate and capable of the thinkers grappling with this was Gregory Bateson. After his work on self-governing mechanisms and cybernetics, he turned to the human systems and created a study team known as the "communication project."

In 1952, Bateson's research project on communication elected to investigate Erickson's work since he, more than any other therapist known to the team, was concerned with how people change (Haley, 1985a) rather than how they were sick. Erickson's pragmatic contributions were appreciated by the esthetically oriented Bateson (Keeney, 1983), as well as by other members of the research project: John Weakland, Jay Haley, Don Jackson, and William Fry. In the important 1956 paper, "Toward a Theory of Schizophrenia" (Jackson, 1968a), Bateson, Jackson, Haley, and Weakland discussed examples of Erickson's work. Subsequently, members of the clinically oriented Mental Research Institute continued to cite Erickson for several years (Bateson, 1972; Haley, 1963, 1967; Jackson, 1968a, 1968b; Satir, 1964) as they developed family therapy. Under the later direction of Watzlawick, Weakland, and Fisch, MRI continued to provide robust models for ideas and techniques drawn from Erickson's work throughout the 1970s, especially as they related to change in human systems and brief strategic therapy. Much of Erickson's work was simultaneously attended to by hypnotherapists, as he was the founder, in 1957, of the American Society of Clinical Hypnosis and editor of its journal for 10 years.

As the Bateson team attempted to articulate a transactional approach to therapy, Haley published a remarkable work elucidating many examples of Erickson's "strategic therapy" with both individuals and couples (1963). It seems clear in retrospect that Erickson's work contained some of the sparks of inspiration for an emerging approach and an emerging language in therapy.

Bateson frequently attempted to clarify the difference between the traditional and emerging approaches as: "The difference between the Newtonian world and the world of communication is simply this: that the Newtonian world ascribes reality to objects and achieves its simplicity by excluding the context . . . In contrast, the theorist of communication insists upon examining the metarelationships while achieving its simplicity by excluding all objects" (Bateson, 1972, p. 250). He saw that, with little exception, the entire profession of therapy had been influenced by the belief, common to psychoanalysis, that we could know the truth of a separate reality and that acts of observation did not alter this external reality. Psychology's posture toward reality was separation from it — studying it by reduction. The simple act of reducing and labeling seems innocent enough on one level, but it does not credit the "observer" with the action of inventing the label that is applied, and then punctuating the stream of experience and ordering the events. Consequently, Bateson felt that traditional therapy, in its attempts to search for problems rooted in the past, developed a rich language to describe the intrapsychic domain of single individuals. This description often pathologizes the individual and typically excludes or diminishes his or her present life context.

The therapeutic stance of "separateness," pathology orientation, and search for problems occasionally results in an adversarial position. The developed language of therapy reflects this adversarial position with the metaphors of resistance, conflict, defense, hidden motive, suppression, power, and so on. Szasz (1961) and Laing (1967, 1972) have spoken eloquently about the individual and social injuries that are the by-product of attempting to help within such a framework. Placed in an adversarial position, purposefully or inadvertently, labeled individuals will easily demonstrate more behavior to reinforce a therapist's conviction about the independent existence of an internal pathology. It was this very trend that Erickson wished to avoid throughout his career (Erickson, 1985) and that seemed to attract Bateson and his team.

In an attempt to clarify the unique differences between the traditional and emerging views, I listed the features of this Ericksonian approach in the right-

31

hand column of the chart. I hope my language is more palatable than Bateson's, and yet respectful of his conception of the distinctions. Instead of believing in an observable truth, might we not better say that we co-create the truth with our participation? I can't think of a more obvious way to understand Erickson's use of reframing and retrieving experiential potentials. To summarize a well-known case: When the newlyweds came for counsel due to the lack of sexual intercourse, it was not that the husband did not have love for his bride (which might have seemed true to the observer), and it was not formulated that the man had erotic desires for his mother and experienced internal conflicts owing to his fear of retribution from his father. Rather, Erickson offered the view that he was attempting to express his unique and profound desire for his bride in a way he had not previously been able to do and he needed to develop some special manner by which to manifest his superlative expression. In this simple case, we see Erickson's contribution clearly: his way of viewing the situation not as that of an expert seeing the truth linked to the past in a causal and linear manner, but as an active participant, helping to create a context for change, discovering health as it unfolds, and orienting them toward the current and future goal by retrieving resources.

INDICATIONS OF THE NEW EPISTEMOLOGY

I want to briefly discuss four aspects of therapy as they can reflect the difference between the traditional and emergent epistemologies. I will then demonstrate Erickson's position regarding these issues. These four issues are the purpose and use of suggestion, metaphor as indirect intervention, the meaning of a symptom, and what constitutes a cure.

Some of the distinctive features of therapy and interventions associated with Erickson's work are important not for their "uncommon-ness," but for their function as a vehicle to bind the therapist and client in the process of co-creating a context for change. We might look at indirection and its use as one example. The traditional epistemology favors the use of direct suggestion. Direct suggestion could be used by the expert to tell the observed subject just what he or she should do to improve from the identified problem. Indirect suggestion, on the other hand, is offered so that a client will take that which is of subjective value and apply it to the process of retrieving and associating experiences needed to reach the current goals. Indirect suggestion assumes an active and participating client with a certain innate wisdom. The therapist learns from the response of the client when to elaborate the presented ambiguity in even more helpful ways.

THE USES OF SUGGESTION

Item	Traditional	Emergent
Use of suggestion	Direct, authoritarian	Indirect, permissive
Indirection, metaphor	If done by client, it is an indication of primary process, a sign of client regression	Resource retrieval, allowing client to create a unique response, an experiential context that helps build a bridge for learning
Meaning of symptom	Internal conflict, not well defended	A communication about developmental needs
Cure	Due to insight, ego strengthening, internal conflict resolution	Development of a new relational pattern and creative response to environment

The conception of a problem or symptom as a sign or a communication is another facet of the emerging epistemology. The existence, and continuance, of the symptom can be many things: feedback that the client cannot associate to the needed resources, a probe by the client to stimulate the environment, a communication, and so on. These ways of seeing the symptomology are part of the interaction, goal-oriented, future-oriented view. Contrast this to the view that a symptom is a sign of an internal conflict. Of course, people are indeed conflicted when they are not solving problems in an adaptive and creative manner. The decisive distinguishing feature between the old and new epistemologies may lie in the conception of priority as it pertains to the idea of a symptom. Is this strip of experiences we call a symptom caused by the conflict within, or is the symptom a sign of the person's attempts to solve a relational problem? It seems reasonable to me to suggest that if we say a symptom is the former, we are of the old tradition; if we say the latter is more accurate, we operate from the emergent perspective.

33

The final area of "cure" can also be seen to reflect the differences in approach. The traditional view of cure, as I have understood it in my education, is related to the resolution of an internal conflict, building of ego strength in the individual, the removal of resistance, the removal of symptoms, and, finally, the capacity for work and love. The emphasis in this scenario is on an individual in a vacuum, someone who has somehow "worked through" events from the past about which he or she was conflicted, lacked ego strength, and from which he or she developed parataxic distortions. Such a cure often involved insight and sometimes involved corrective emotional experiences. It is a concept of cure based on a past-orientation. A future-oriented perspective evaluates a cure on the basis of the loss of the symptom, the development of adaptive relationships with those persons in the current social environment, and the acquisition of new skills for handling developmental demands.

ERICKSON'S CHANGING VIEWS

I suspect that many students of Erickson's work have encountered the difficulty of sorting out the "real" Erickson. Some may have read articles that claimed that Erickson was very directive. Some contend that he was very authoritarian, and others say he was permissive. One can either check the sources of these comments and sift through them for signs of professional jealousies and alliance, first-hand accounts versus second-hand knowledge, or perhaps just decide not to generalize and conclude that Erickson displayed a wide range of conduct that subsumed both positions. But, like most of us, Erickson's views changed and developed over time. One would assume a different awareness seeing his work in 1945 than one would from his work in 1975. In order to demonstrate how his view of clients and problems reflected this emerging epistemology, I want to chronicle this change in those four previously mentioned areas — purpose and use of suggestion, use of metaphor as indirection, meaning of symptom, and the cure.

Direct Suggestions and Redundant Suggestions

We see in Erickson's early explanations of hypnosis a sign that he moved from the position of an authoritarian expert who "did" something to a client, to a position of co-creator of a context for change wherein he "offered stimuli" to the subject who has to put ideas together for himself or herself. In a

1945 published transcript, we find him using the redundant repetition of "sleep," as in the sentence, "Now I want you to *go deeper and deeper asleep*" (p. 54) and in the statement, "*I can put* you in any level of trance" (p. 64) [italics mine] (Erickson, with Haley, & Weakland, 1967).

By 1976, we find Erickson making a full reverse on this method of redundant suggestion and writing that he believed *indirect* suggestion to be a "significant factor" in his work (Erickson, Rossi, & Rossi, 1976, p. 452). More interesting still is the growth we see by the end of his life in work published after his death in 1980. Here he has come to take the position not of authoritative expert who makes someone go into trance, but of someone who will "offer" ideas and suggestions (pp. 1–2). Contrary to his earlier conduct, he stated, "I don't like this matter of telling a patient *I want you to get tired and sleepy*" (p. 4) [italics mine] (Erickson, & Rossi, 1981). This position represents a clear departure from the traditional to the emerging epistemology!

Metaphor as Indirect Intervention

There can be little doubt that Dr. Erickson was comfortable with the role of ambiguity in therapy. In 1944, he used a complex story to help stimulate a client's neurotic mechanisms (Erickson, 1967). So we see from very early work that he, nevertheless, felt that therapy was a matter of offering ambiguity for the client to develop his or her own unique response. Still, in 1954, Erickson was delivering what he called "fabricated case histories" to help a client be relieved of fleeting symptomatology (Erickson, 1980, p. 152). And, of course, by the year 1973, we see several examples of case stories used for illustrating points in therapy and normal communication (Haley, 1973). Finally, in a 1979 publication, we actually see section headings on "metaphor" as intervention (Erickson, & Rossi, 1979). It would be most accurate to say that Erickson's use of ambiguity, permissiveness, and indirection in therapy was present at the beginning of his work and was used with increasing frequency over time.

The Meaning of Symptoms

Regarding the meaning that Dr. Erickson attributed to symptoms, we find a pattern of change from the traditional, analytic view in his early career to that of the systemic and interpersonal view by his death. His medical degree was obtained in 1928, and he then went to Colorado General Hospital for his internship and was there until 1938 or 1939. But as late as 1954, he wrote,

"The development of neurotic symptoms constitutes behavior of a defensive, protective character" (Erickson, 1980, p. 149). This strikes me as reflecting a traditional analytic view with concepts such as "defense and attack."

However, by 1966 an emergent epistemology could be glimpsed in his description: "Mental disease is the breaking down of communication between people" (Erickson, 1980, p. 75). And by 1979, he had arrived at the fully formed idea state: "Symptoms are forms of communication" and "cues of developmental problems that are in the process of becoming conscious" (Erickson, & Rossi, 1979, p. 143). This view is much more in keeping with the ideas he repeatedly expressed verbally. He said many times that he did not have a theory of personality and that he invented a new theory with each unique client.

Cure Seen as Reassociation of Experience, Not Direct Suggestion

One of the most revealing areas of comparisons is in the question of what constitutes cure. On this issue, we see that there was essentially no change between his view in 1948 and that at the end of his life. In 1948, he recognized that cure was not the result of suggestion, but rather developed from reassociation of experience (Erickson, 1980, vol. 4, p. 38). (In this piece, we also can see that Erickson did not wish to use direct suggestion in treatment but preferred to use indirect suggestion for treatment, and in the earlier 1954 quotation, he still used direct suggestion for induction.) We see essentially the same quote in Erickson's writing at the end of his career (Erickson, 1979; Erickson, & Rossi, 1980, p. 464; and Erickson, & Rossi, 1981).

The point that we might draw from this is that while his use of suggestion and redundancy changed over the course of his career from the traditional to more permissive, his use of permissive ambiguity, or what constituted a symptom, and what facilitated a cure was consistent from his earliest works. We also see that reliance on this emergent epistemology increased in frequency over time. Clearly, in these important and revealing ways, Erickson's work evolved from a modification of the traditional approach to a full representation of the emergent epistemology, increasing in degree of usage from 1944 to the end of his career.

THE EPISTEMOLOGY OF USE

Are we thinking about therapy to analyze it or to use it? Perhaps the answer to this should determine our guiding principle. Restricted as we are by an inability to speak a language of phenomenology, discourse regarding the on-going process of therapy easily digresses into an explanation formed from traditional epistemology. The solution to this dilemma is the development and acceptance of a more adequate language ... but then, as I said at the start, speech is linear. Perhaps living in a participatory epistemology and speaking in a linear and causal epistemology is the horse we must ride. And, too, perhaps the tension between our ability to conceptualize and participate in creating our own future and that of our clients in therapy must continue. Indeed, I rather wonder if that tension is not a motivating force in the evolution of mind. In the end, we must only be partially satisfied with writing about the change process and not let this limitation distract us from attempts to further research and refine the participatory process of the emerging epistemology, which we actually find ourselves working toward in therapy. But I do not believe that Erickson's greatest contribution was in his remarkable interventions. In fact, his interventions can be used by therapists bound to the traditional epistemology and they will "work," so to speak — but generally they will be no more useful, exciting, or dramatic than conventional interventions. Furthermore, they do not rise naturally out of the traditional framework and so will be challenging to employ. However, they seem to almost flow from the posture created with the emerging epistemology and create a total package for powerful change even in a brief number of sessions. In the end then, it's not Erickson's interventions that are his greatest contribution but rather it is his epistemology that has made the most profound impact.

References

Bateson, G. (1972). *Steps to an ecology of mind.* New York: Ballantine.

Bateson, G. (1979). *Mind and nature.* New York: Dutton.

Erickson, M. (1948). Hypnotic psychotherapy. In E. L. Rossi (Ed.). (1980), *The collected papers of Milton H. Erickson on hypnosis: Vol. 4. Innovative hypnotherapy* (pp. 35–51). New York: Irvington.

Erickson, M. (1954). Special techniques of brief hypnotherapy. In E. L. Rossi (Ed.). (1980), *The collected papers of Milton H. Erickson on hypnosis: Vol. 4. Innovative hypnotherapy* (pp. 149–171). New York: Irvington.

Erickson, M. (1966). Hypnosis: Its renascence as a treatment modality. In E. L. Rossi

(Ed.). (1980), *The collected papers of Milton H. Erickson on hypnosis: Vol. 4. Innovative hypnotherapy* (pp. 52–75). New York: Irvington.

Erickson, M. (1967). With Haley, J. & Weakland, J. A transcript of a trance induction with commentary. In J. Haley (Ed.), *Advanced techniques of hypnosis and therapy: Selected papers of Milton H. Erickson, M.D.*

Erickson, M. (1967). The method employed to formulate a complex story for the induction of the experimental neurosis. In J. Haley (Ed.). (1963), *Advanced techniques of hypnosis and therapy: Selected papers of Milton H. Erickson, M.D.* (pp. 312–325).

Erickson, M., & Rossi, E. (1979). *Hypnotherapy: An exploratory casebook.* New York: Irvington.

Erickson, M., & Rossi, E. L. (1980). The indirect forms of suggestion. In E. L. Rossi, (Ed.), *The collected papers of Milton H. Erickson on hypnosis: Vol. 1. The nature of hypnosis and suggestion* (pp. 452–477). New York: Irvington.

Erickson, M., & Rossi, E. (1981). *Experiencing hypnosis: Therapeutic approaches to altered state.* New York: Irvington.

Erickson, M. H., Rossi, E. L., & Rossi, S. I. (1976). *Hypnotic realities: The induction of clinical hypnosis and forms of indirect suggest.* New York: Irvington.

Freud, S. (1938). *The basic writings of Sigmund Freud.* New York: Random House.

Freud, S. (1966). *The complete introductory lectures on psychoanalysis.* James Strachey (trans.). New York: Norton.

Haley, J. (1963). *Strategies of psychotherapy.* New York: Grune & Stratton.

Haley, J. (1973). *Uncommon therapy: The psychiatric techniques of Milton H. Erickson, M.D.* New York: Norton.

Haley, J. (1985a). *Conversations with Milton H. Erickson, M.D.: Changing individuals.* New York: Norton.

Hawking, S. (1988). *A brief history of time: From the big bang to the black holes.* New York: Bantam Books.

Jackson, D. (Ed.). (1968a). *Communication, family, and marriage: 1.* Palo Alto: Science and Behavior Books.

Jackson, D. (Ed.). (1968b). *Therapy, communication, and change: 2.* Palo Alto: Science and Behavior Books.

Keeney, B. (1983). *The aesthetics of change.* New York: Guilford.

Laing, R. D. (1967). *The politics of experience.* New York: Ballantine.

Laing, R. D. (1972). *The politics of the family.* New York: Ballantine.

Lankton, S., & Lankton, C. (1983). *The answer within: A clinical framework of Ericksonian hypnotherapy.* New York: Brunner/Mazel.

Satir, V. (1964). *Conjoint family therapy.* Palo Alto: Science and Behavior Books.

Szasz, T. (1961). *The myth of metal illness, foundations of a theory of personal conduct.* New York: Hoeber-Harper.

3

Jay Haley's Impact on
the Rise of Ericksonian Therapy[1]

Jay Haley demystified the role of communication in both socialization and change, making it a valid area of study in psychology, increasing the visibility of Milton Erickson's creative work in therapy, and providing the means for understanding the connection between transactions and experience.

MARRIAGE OF TRANSACTION AND EXPERIENCE

In the history of psychotherapy a trend or direction emerges that shows an increased ability to articulate observations, interventions, and outcomes. If you look for the place in the history of therapy where it became obvious to people that we could systematically study transactions, the impact they have on people, and tactics for change, you find it started with Don Jackson, Gregory Bateson, Jay Haley, John Weakland, and William Fry. Their collaboration at MRI ushered in a different era that also laid a groundwork that made it possible for us to know what we know about Milton Erickson.

---

[1] Lankton, S. (2001). Jay Haley's impact on the rise of Ericksonian therapy. In J. Zeig (Ed.), *Changing directives: The strategic therapy of Jay Haley* (pp. 59–83). Phoenix: The Milton Erickson Foundation Press. Reprinted with permission.

INTERACTIONAL VIEW OF HYPNOSIS

Jay Haley was among the first to understand and promote the interactional explanation of hypnosis. Hypnosis and reports of hypnosis are subjective. Primarily, we decide if someone is in a trance by what they tell us. Subjectivity is hard to research, unless taken as a communication from a subject. As a serious student of communication, Jay Haley did just that with two questions about hypnosis: Does the hypnotized subject communicate differently? And what sequences of communication between the hypnotist and the subject produce the behavior typical of trance? Those questions were profoundly different from any others being asked in psychology at that time. The answers demystified hypnosis and also introduced a wide range of ideas for socialization in families, individual biochemistry, and somatic illness, as I will show here.

Generally, waking-state communication is characterized by congruent, although often ambiguous, communication. Trance communication, however, is marked by distinct incongruity. Haley offered an empirical scheme to begin examining the incongruity of that communication (Haley, 1973a). In any communication there will be a sender, a receiver, a message, and a context in which it is taking place. This can be described as having four parts:

A) I
B) am communicating this
C) to you
D) in this situation.

In a hypnotic trance the subject must communicate in such a way as to deny, or at least fail to affirm, one or more of these elements. Incongruity of "A" is that the subject must do what the hypnotist suggests, while denying that "he" is not responding to the suggestion. That's paradoxical and incongruent. If the hypnotist says, "Let your hand lift," and the subject reports "my hand is lifting," it is his hand and not "he" doing the response. The subject is the one sitting in the chair listening but reports incongruently as if he has nothing to do with the event. And the hypnotist is, in fact, instructing him that he has nothing to do with it! Another example of this incongruity is communicated in the statement: "And when your *eyes* close, *you'll* have great difficulty in opening them." In that instance, the eyes are closing but the subject is not closing his eyes. Thus, the first incongruity in typical trance behavior is found as a denial of the "I" — 'it's just happening.'

Next, "B," the subject may deny that there is *communication* arising from him. If all of his communication is congruently reporting a denial in a communication, we would say that the subject has amnesia. He may say that his arm did not lift or that he has nothing at all to communicate. Typical of trance behavior, he is denying part "B," the message in the communication. Parts "C" and "D" 'to you in this situation,' are denied in typical trance behavior commonly considered dissociation or regression. In effect the subject is saying "Really, nothing is being communicated *to you*, the hypnotist, in this situation, because I am not here with you." That is typical of what we often consider "deeper" trance communication such as age regression. This is an empirical way of looking at communication in trance or waking state that no one, until Haley, had looked at from that perspective.

DOUBLE BINDS

Trance inductions and trance behaviors are rich in denials and multilevel incongruence of communication. Bateson, Jackson, Haley, and Weakland introduced the double-bind theory of schizophrenia in 1956, making the point that parents could ostensibly communicate "I love you" while simultaneously discrediting that comment on another level. In families, the child cannot "leave the field." Haley defined the double bind as a communication in which one person communicates a message and at the same time qualifies or contradicts that message with an incongruent message in a situation where the other person must respond to these contradictory messages, cannot leave the field, and cannot comment on the contradiction (Bateson, Jackson, Haley, & Weakland, 1974). The continual or frequent communication of a double bind seems to be occurring chronically in schizophrenia producing families. But more broadly for the sake of this paper I should add that the authors stated that only in the extreme would this lead to schizophrenia otherwise "we must expect a pathology to occur" (p. 32). As I will show later, however, the other types of dysfunction have been greatly ignored until now.

This sort of pathology inducing behavior was another part of Haley's analysis of hypnosis. There must not simply be two incongruent messages as in the previous scheme, but there must be incongruent messages at different logical levels. For instance, the hypnotist might say, "Whatever you do, stay awake and do not follow my suggestions." The subject is in a double bind: the suggestion is to stay awake and also the instruction is to not follow any sugges-

41

tions. Thus, following suggestions to stay awake indicates the subject is following suggestions, and hence will be hypnotized. But not following the suggestion to stay awake is an early admission that the subject will go into trance. No matter what the subject does, trance is the result due to the double bind being incongruent on two different logical levels. Words alone do not have to carry the entirety of this message. Tone, inflection, and other nonverbal communication can disqualify the verbal message at a different level.

In a double bind, there is a denial of confliction that cannot be commented on. It is the incongruity of trance behavior that defines a trance. Hypnotists request subjects to voluntarily do involuntary behavior, then to deny the whole process. Hypnotists help subjects participate in the denial, in this creation of double-bind communication. This incongruity in communication is difficult to track. When the hypnotist is working with someone, the subject volunteers for, and gives tacit permission to, the hypnotist to provide contradictory instructions about voluntary behaviors and involuntary responses. This adds to the conflict and to the incongruity.

When this is applied to children in families, there are more ramifications than just those that apply in schizophrenic families. In fact, my interest in visiting and studying with Erickson was always this: Is it possible that the child's behavior is the result of a parental sort of hypnosis? I continually asked this question of Erickson during my visits since the pathological behavior of adults is especially like posthypnotic suggestion being carried out by the subject. In this case the child, as a result of the induction from the hypnotist-parents, could be described as a hypnotic subject carrying out posthypnotic behavior long after the induction is over and the parents gone. R. D. Laing (1967, 1972) concurred in *The Politics of Experience* and *The Politics of the Family*, and Eric Berne (1972) in *What Do You Say After You Say Hello?*. That is why I persisted in my questions of Erickson and finally synthesized his influence and Haley's schemes to answer the question.

CONTROLLED AMBIGUITY

Communicators should know how to control ambiguity volitionally and deliberately, and as a tool when working with people in trance. And, too, we need to be able to censor it out of our communication when it could do harm. To increase thoughtful awareness of our choices about these elements, I recommend practicing the controlled elaboration of ambiguity. By changing the pronouns in our communications, we can change our perceptions of the communication, for example, "I am communicating something to you in this situation." Try saying the following sentence aloud and comparing the statements after altering the first part, "I am communicating." For instance, "My father would tell you to sit down and be quiet right now," compared with "I am telling you to sit down and be quiet right now." Notice the difference when you change the pronoun from "I." Does it make it more or less powerful when you remove yourself from the situation, distancing so that you are not really a part of it? This incongruity is typical of trance communication but also a part of normal daily conversation and child rearing.

Next change both the pronoun "I" and "this message" in the communication. An example is, "My mother never told me anything about a situation like this," compared to "I don't know what to do in this situation." Next, change the "I" and "to you" in the message. For instance, "My mother told my father think for yourself and be sure to tell me what you come up with." Compare that with saying, "I'd like you to figure out what to do and tell me." Note the change in perceived relevance. Sequence and surroundings are more important than the congruency of the statement.

The last part of the exercise is to change the content, along with the pronouns, of the communication in the entire sequence: "I am communicating something to you *in this context.*" For instance, "My mother told my sister that a way to complete your homework would present itself after you are completely through eating dinner." This is found to be a more powerful type of communication. In this example you can see that no aspect of the formula remains unchanged. There is certainly a great deal of ambiguity in that sentence yet it is totally under the speaker's control. As the ambiguity increases, so does the variety of possible responses. In the case of schizophrenics, it doesn't take much reflection to realize that these people are harder to talk to because of the variety of responses one could make to what they are saying.

It may be obvious that alterations such as these are purposefully made within therapeutic stories or metaphors told to clients. While this is not the place to dissect elements that create goal-directed metaphors, the simple idea that a story is about someone else in another context, and may not involve anything that the speaker has said illustrates how each of these elements change to control the ambiguity in a relationship. Such purposeful ambiguity allows a wider range of response from a client. In that way, it frees both the therapist and the client from the rigor of exact and detailed definitions of terms and facilitates ongoing verbal exchange.

INTRODUCING THE WORLD TO ERICKSON

So these contributions about binds, metaphors, ambiguity, and hypnosis are the gateway Jay Haley created for many to discover Milton Erickson. My story about meeting Jay Haley and how he introduced me to Erickson started when I was in high school. I had a dream. I don't remember it at all but what I do remember is that I awoke with an incredible memory of visual clarity and I went to my homeroom teacher and inquired how to make sense of that sort of thing. She sent me to the librarian, who referred me to the card catalogue, suggesting that I look under "symbolism" or "psychology." Frankly, I had never heard the word "psychology" at that point. I didn't know even vaguely what it was. So I went to the psychology section and there were these huge books with long names on them. I almost couldn't tell the author from the title, because I didn't know either one of them, Arietti's "Interpretation of Schizophrenia," Fenichel's "Psychoanalytic Theory of Neurosis," and so on. I wasn't that great a reader at that time, so I found this one thin little green book on the shelf that looked real friendly. I didn't know the psychotherapy word, but I did know the words "strategies" and "of." And there were only three words in the title and it really was the smallest book on the shelf. Also, the cover seemed nice and concise. *Strategies of Psychotherapy*. So that was my introduction to Jay Haley and Milton Erickson.

I read about this man, Haley, who was working with someone named Milton Erickson. He made so many references to Erickson being really old that I concluded he must be dead. But I was so impressed that Haley had gone out to the desert and learned something with this interesting old man, Erickson. The book had an engineering quality to it that I understood. I initially majored in engineering and mathematics, although I finally switched to social sciences because those things were more interesting and challenging. Years after I majored in psychology I ran across Milton Erickson's name again. But it didn't really dawn on me at the time that I had come upon it before. The entire connection became apparent to me and with some impact when I saw Haley's and Richeport's preview of a film, *Milton Erickson: An Explorer in Hypnosis and Therapy*. I had been interviewed and videotaped by them a couple of years before . . . but never thought about it again . . . and I'm watching a tape by Jay Haley about Milton Erickson, and suddenly — I'm in it. And I was led to it by a dream!

Many of us were led to Erickson by Jay Haley. We find references to Erickson in Haley's work as far back as "Toward a Theory of Double Bind," published in 1956, in Haley's early work on the transactional nature of hypnosis, the interactional patterns in schizophrenic families, and finally in *Advanced Techniques of Hypnosis and Therapy: Selected Papers of Milton H. Erickson, M.D.*, edited by Jay Haley in 1967. For those of us who had not discovered the various published papers of Milton Erickson primarily in the *American Journal of Clinical Hypnosis*, Jay Haley's edited volume was a beacon. Indeed, before I first visited Erickson in 1975, it was this volume that provided my greatest source of study about his approach. In 1973, Haley had written the more popular book, *Uncommon Therapy: The Psychiatric Techniques of Milton H. Erickson, M.D.* These publications are probably well known to readers of this book and I need not review them here. I am citing them to emphasize that the widespread awareness and understanding of Erickson's work, and especially in his own words, was created almost single-handedly by Jay Haley in 1967 and 1973. In the history of psychotherapy, this contribution must be recognized as great as those of his own theories on communication.

METACOMMUNICATION

The concept of metacommunication is another important aspect of Jay Haley's early theories of communication. In workshops, I often illustrate this dramatically with a magic trick that starts with an audience member picking a small, finite number between 1 and 20 then telling me and the audience what it is. I then carefully demonstrate exactly how he or she is to count the same number of cards, sort through the deck, and finally read the card corresponding to the chosen number. I then ask the volunteer to replace the chosen card into the deck, shuffle the deck, and hand it to me. With a good deal of drama I proceed to explain that I will produce the chosen card from the deck. However, on my first attempt I fail. I then explain that I will do it on my second or even third attempt. But on each attempt I fail. I fail repeatedly.

Finally, I illustrate that the point of this trick is to illustrate that one thing I learned from Haley's and Erickson's work is that you don't want to try to defeat your client in some things. It's all right to allow your client to defeat you or to teach you things. And, this is especially true for clients who feel they must compete with everyone around them. If they want to try to defeat you at something, let them. Therapy is not about winning or losing. It's about interacting in such a fashion that a beneficial outcome is reached. At that point the audience is generally pleased that the entire point of the magic trick was for me to fail and pass on that wisdom.

I then ask their permission to show a videotape and change the subject. I may announce, "Here's a tape of Haley or Erickson I want to show you." But when I turn on the VCR, it appears that I have made yet another mistake. The videotape is of a news broadcast. Unbeknown to the audience, I have *purposefully* placed this tape in the recorder. The news broadcaster is handed a piece of paper and he then announces as he holds up the piece of paper, "Is this your card?" The piece of paper, of course, is a picture of the card that was originally chosen by the participant during the magic trick!

The audience is always quite astounded at this point. Just when they thought that the purpose of my magic trick was to emphasize the importance of losing, it turns out that the magic trick was even more complex than they could have imagined and I performed it correctly! And so I can illustrate with this trick that while you're losing at one level, it's important if you can win at another level.

So the communication during this trick is saying "I can't do the trick correctly," and the audience is convinced of that. Consequently, the communication of the trick becomes incongruent at two logical levels. On one level I have performed the trick correctly in an extremely complicated fashion, while at another level I have continually apologized and announced that I seem to be unable to do the trick. This sort of communication is the essential foundation of the double-bind communication. (A missing ingredient in this type of entertainment, but which is found in a true client family, is that the audience is not bound to stay in my presence as the child is bound to stay in the care of the parent.) While Haley showed how this type of communication pertains to double binds for pathology, we find it in all kinds of deceptions, such as the kind we enjoy in magic tricks. Magic is a deception frame.

FRAMES

We need to have a common understanding of "frames" to proceed. From the sociology of Irving Goffman (1969) we learn a great deal about frames. Whenever any experience is understood to have started, we know something is happening or has happened. We have framed it. When we frame some event (and therefore experience) we give it meaning. Then, and only then, does it have meaning. It may be that *the* question the human brain is wired-up to address and do something about is: "What's going on here now?" So, were this to be a more serious deception than a magic trick, and a double bind were actually in force, a very important "problem" would be underway: "Is he robbing me?" "Is this a scam?" When you have a scam or deception of any kind, you are dealt an incongruity at the level of communication and metacommunication. Under those circumstances, it's difficult to answer the question "What's going on here now?" until it is over, at which time the frame cue at the end may backward frame the event sufficiently. The problem is that until you know the answer, you don't have understandable experience.

When a strip of experience begins and then ends (and this may be a negotiated choice between the viewer and the sender), what you have is a kind of cueing device that makes brackets for the big frame. Inside that bracketed experience are frame-breaks and sub-frames. This is shown in the illustration below.

Complex Reframing Variables

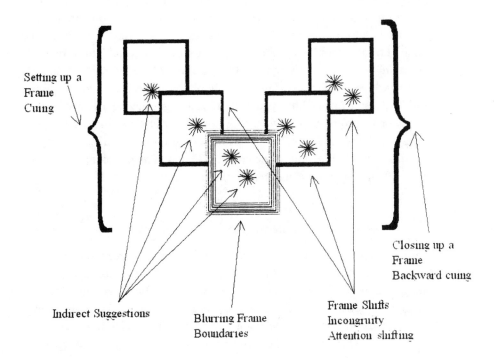

Setting up a
Frame
Cuing

Closing up a
Frame
Backward cuing

Indirect Suggestions

Blurring Frame
Boundaries

Frame Shifts
Incongruity
Attention shifting

If, in the course of framing an experience, you blur where that frame begins or ends (and that's what happens in deception, in the magic trick, in a double bind, and in hypnotic induction) then it becomes a kind of hypnotic experience — at least the beginning of one — in that you begin to rely upon internal experience to try to make things clear. You're hunting for more clues; you're trying to remember the voice tone, looking for the memory of the face, for what you might have done to misinterpret it. As you begin to become more internally absorbed to make sense of things, you experience the introductory stages of trance. This is what often happened when you were talking to Erickson. You could ask him what trance is and not get a simple answer. You would have your pad and paper ready but he would say, "While you were talking to me, you didn't notice you're wearing socks. Hypnosis is a matter of focusing your client's attention where it should be focused. You weren't aware you were wearing a necktie, you weren't aware of the temperature in the room. It wasn't important to you." And imagine that this communication goes on for another six minutes, and at this time your attention is focused on those things, while technically, he is not saying 'I am directing your attention to these things for an explanation of hypnosis.' This is blurred. Is he saying it to you? Is he saying, "Do this now"? You are doing it, but he didn't say, "Do it." Does that mean he didn't say to do it and you shouldn't do it? It doesn't matter how you slice it, you begin having a blurred frame because of the communication Haley's talking about here that really hadn't been noticed before. That is the metacommunication you are receiving at the same time you are listening to the communication. The metacommunication level is ambiguous and incongruent with the message.

DUAL INDUCTIONS IN FAMILIES

In order to look at what experiences come from those transactions we must recognize the contributions of Jay Haley and follow up on the four parts of communication and the double-bind theory. Double binds, communications that discredit other communication, are generally thought of as utterances from one person. But let me walk you back to it with a different twist. In the chart below we have two columns and two rows. Let's say that these represent communication from both 'Parent A' and 'Parent B' and not one person. To show the *content* that is used, which can be the same or different, I have mapped it in different columns. To show the *delivery* that can be alternately or simultaneously, I have mapped that in different rows.

Dual Induction Results

Content Used

		Same	Different
Speech Delivery	Alternately	Focuses conscious and unconscious attention	Dissociates conscious and unconscious experience
	Simultaneously	Overloads consciousness and unconscious takes on the affect	Overloads conscious mind and unconscious makes trance phenomena synthesis

SAME CONTENT, DELIVERED ALTERNATELY

The simplest interaction to recognize is when both parents speak about the same content and alternate speaking. That would sound something like the following.

Parent A	Parent B
Why don't you ever follow through on what you promise, young man?!	
	You are terrible at following through, Johnny.
You told me you would do the yard work before you left. But you didn't, did you?	
	I also heard you say you would do the yard work. You said it while we were in the kitchen.
You also told me you would call if you were going to be late. I have told you over and over to do that!	

	There is a real pattern developing here and I think you should be punished in some manner.
I think I ought to just ground you for about two weeks until you learn your lesson!	
	If you ask me, you should be grounded for at least three weeks.

In the example above, the listener can easily follow the content and track it. In fact, if the content is the least bit relevant to the listener, the listener will be unable to focus on anything other than the content delivered by the parent. This content can be positive or negative, but in either case the conscious and unconscious mind will be captured and focused.

An example of positive content follows for the sake of clarification.

Parent A	**Parent B**
Look at that report card!	
	Johnny, you got straight "As" on this card!
Wow, we are really proud of you for the hard work you've put into your grades.	
	Let me see it again — Wow, you got an "A" in biology, too. I thought you were worried about that.
If you ask me, applying yourself like this deserves a celebration of some kind.	
	I know, let's go to the movies tonight. It's your choice, Einstein.
But even if you don't want to go, that's fine. We are just trying to say, we are very proud of you, Johnny.	
	We couldn't be happier for *you* either.

In this example, unlike the first, the content is all positive. Reading the account and imagining how you would react as a listener ought to be enough information to confirm this view as it becomes more complex. That is, alternately speaking about the same content (positive or negative) will result in the "captive" listener.

The following is an example of dissociation that is common. The two parents can be saying to Johnny, "We love you *and* we hate you." They can give such mixed messages — not as one person as in the "formal" double bind but as a parental unit. Is that not, in many ways, like the double bind when you consider that both parents represent the real world to the child? Let's play with this concept just a bit and say each communication comes from a different parent and can be delivered in two differing ways. That is, the parental team can deliver a message simultaneously or alternately and they can deliver a "same" message or a "different" message as they do. That provides four choices, as seen on the chart.

DIFFERENT CONTENT, DELIVERED ALTERNATELY

What would happen if Johnny comes home from school, and one parent says, "Johnny have you done your homework? You know you have a paper due tomorrow." And Johnny says, "Yes, I'm going to do it." And he walks through the office where the other parent is, who says, "Hey, do you want to order a pizza tonight?" Johnny says, "Yeah, I do, okay, we'll do that." Then he walks back to the kitchen, where the first parent says, "Are you doing your paper yet or are you just wandering around the house?" "Yeah, I'm going to go do that now." He goes to his room, and 'Parent B' comes in and says, "What do you want on your pizza when we order it? Do you want to eat before or after we watch Pinky and the Brain?" And the answer is given. And maybe we start channel-surfing right now, as a prelude to pizza. Now 'Parent A' walks in and says to Johnny, "I thought you were going to do your homework." Then, 'Parent B' walks in and asks, "Did you say you wanted mushrooms on the pizza? — They are on the phone right now!" In this example, each parent has a topic he or she is talking about, and the topic is different, and the parents are delivering it alternately — 'A' then 'B,' 'A' then 'B.' This sort of communication is remarkably common in American homes.

Parent A	**Parent B**
Johnny, have you done your homework? You know you have a paper due tomorrow.	

What do you want on your pizza when we order it? Do you want to eat before or after we watch Pinky and the Brain?

I thought you were going to do your homework.

Did you say you wanted mushrooms on the pizza? — They are on the phone right now!

The parents in this example are speaking about different contents alternately. Furthermore, this is a rather benign example of content and neither parent is being particularly hostile. When parents give different messages alternately, a key element becomes the affect with which it is delivered. As the child dissociates to track both parents, he or she ends up with dissociated ego states. However, if the affect is similar, the child can actually take any learning from either parental instruction and apply it to the content offered by the other — thus learning metaphorically and with great speed. However, if the effect is not similar enough, the child will be unable to integrate and generalize learnings.

But imagine yet another common example of the same variety: different content and alternate delivery, and this time, both are hostile. In such a case the integration can happen but only along a hostile frame of reference.

Parent A

Why don't you ever follow through on what you promise, young man?!

Parent B

I heard from your teachers that you skipped school today, Mister!

You told me you would do the yard work before you left. But you didn't, now did you?

Where did you go — I'm talking to you!

You also told me you would call if you were going to be late. I have told you over and over to do that!

When I ask you a question I expect an answer!

I think I ought to just ground you for about two weeks until you learn your lesson!

Do you hear me? Answer me!

In this example, the parents are focusing the child's attention on the same content and, by speaking alternately, they are locking the child's entire awareness on the topic as he or she tries to integrate the common information. In the earlier chart, we see that the same message, when delivered alternately, produces a dissociation of conscious and unconscious attention so both messages can be tracked and later integrated if the affect is similar. Both parents were giving different messages alternately. If one parent is always hostile, and the other parent, knowing that, wants to correct by being friendly, the child cannot integrate, and dissociates. You end up with dissociated ego states.

SAME CONTENT, DELIVERED SIMULTANEOUSLY

Another common practice is for parents to deliver the same content at the same time. Consider the usual situation in which an award was won by a child. In such a case it is easy to imagine or recall when both parents, excited with joy, are congratulating the child without regard for the other parent's speaking.

Parent A	Parent B
Wow, Johnny, you did great!	First prize, that's terrific!
You did a fantastic job, Son.	I'm so happy for you!
It is almost unbelievable. You just did great.	I'm so proud and happy for you.
I can't believe it. It's just amazing. You did great.	Wow, this is really a great achievement. Congratulations.

In an example like this it should be apparent that the child cannot really follow the communication of either parent. That is, the conscious mind does not grasp the specific content of the communication. All that is conveyed in such communication is the affect and bits and pieces of the content. If the affect is positive, the communication is retrieving and building that positive emotion as an affective resource in Johnny's repertoire of experience. However, if the affect is negative in tone, the same process is at work. That is, Johnny's conscious mind does not grasp the content; he only learns to build the negative affect.

That is, if the content contains an important message, it will, in fact, be lost. Only the affect will be reliably transmitted. So, in the following example, the lesson about security measures will not likely be what Johnny walks away with — rather, he will simply feel like a failure who disappoints his parents.

Parent A	**Parent B**
Johnny, do you call this security?	You have to turn on the alarm when you are going out!
You didn't even lock the doors. That's just stupid.	What's the matter with you, leaving those open?
Did you ever think that this is a responsibility that you have as part of this family?	What were you thinking? Why do you think we were asking you?
This was dangerous and you were irresponsible.	This is the most foolish thing you've done in as long as I can remember!

This sort of parenting is common and yet misunderstood if it is thought to be a good example of a unified front. Instead it creates a child with less conscious attention for the important lesson the parents intend to teach.

DIFFERENT CONTENT, DELIVERED SIMULTANEOUSLY

Making things more complex, sometimes parents agree and sometimes they contradict each other. Looking at the content in terms of binds, it is apparent that there will be a difference in the impact that is made between these two different forms of parental communication. It is obvious that sometimes parents talk, or rather shout, orders of a different content and do their speaking at the exact same time the other parent is speaking. When each parent simultaneously gives a different message, the conscious mind of the listener is overloaded. Dissociation, depersonalization, and regression result; the unconscious mind makes some trance phenomena as a synthesis of it. Consider the following example with Parents A and B using the above example but speaking at the same time:

Parent A	**Parent B**
Why don't you ever follow through on what you promise, young man?!	I heard from your teachers that you skipped school today, Mister!
You told me you would do the yard work before you left. But you didn't, now did you?	Where did you go? I'm talking to you!
You also told me you would call if you were going to be late. I have told you over and over to do that!	When I ask you a question I expect an answer!
I think I ought to just ground you for about two weeks until you learn your lesson!	Do you hear me? Answer me!

It should be apparent that the effect on the listener would be considerably different between this example and those of the alternate delivery above. In the earlier examples the listener would be able to "track" the conversations from both parents, provided the listener could dissociate to keep each as a consistent message. In the last example, conscious tracking would be difficult, if not impossible. As a result, the listener would experience an overload of the conscious mind, and the unconscious experience would simply be to pick up the affect of the speakers. That is, if the parents were proud of the child, the child would learn pride. If the parents were rejecting of the child, the child would learn rejection. It is that simple.

So what if this happens in a family where one parent is just a little odd, like in their mind God tells them this and that? If the content is different and delivered simultaneously, the bits and pieces of the content that are picked up along with the affect can create trance phenomena. This happens most easily when one of the speakers is using references that can easily retrieve trance phenomena. That is, if one parent speaks about what God wants and the other speaks about "talking and talking" but not being heard by the child, it would be predictable that the child would, to some degree, synthesize the two topics and end up with an idea of God talking to them. In other words, the auditory hallucinations of some schizophrenics can be learned in such a manner. A simple test of this can be demonstrated briefly using dual induction in hypnotic trance. In a taped demonstration concerning these various patterns of dual induction (1982), Carol Lankton and I concluded by speaking about different topics simultaneously with the following words:

Carol
(speaking about gardeners
and learning)

Stephen
(speaking age regression
suggestions)

The gardener enjoys the process of waiting for the seeds to come up knowing that she participates. And only a fool gardener would take credit for making seeds come up. Because the seed can't help but unfold according to its natural process. But, the gardener can enjoy it, and watch the garden grow. And, at first when those plants are so tiny it just seems impossible to believe that one day you'll be reaping more vegetables than you know what to do with. And so, cooks use as many vegetables as they know how to use and give the rest away, end up throwing some away and freezing others. Its the same way that all those experiences preceding the actual cooking of a meal are necessary to that meal eventually being served, appreciated and gobbled down. It's the same way with childhood experiences. You learned a lot of things, a long time ago — things you haven't thought about for years but you know that when you first went to school and saw all those letters of the alphabet lining the black board and there were big letters and little letters and you didn't know where to put the loop on the "p" and the "b" and how many humps on the "m" and the "n". Your conscious mind had a concern about how you'd possibly learn all those letters but your unconscious

Now I had a client who came to see me one time in a workshop in Florida. She said she had a lot of anxiety about her mother and I thought that was a problem she certainly ought to have some solution for. You have solutions in the back of your mind. So I asked her to go into a trance and have childhood experience unconsciously and her conscious mind didn't need to pay attention at all. And, she told us with a gleeful smile on her face that she was watching a cow. I said "what"? She said she was watching a cow lie down. And, she had a big smile on her face when she said that. Now I don't know what is so interesting about seeing a cow lie down. You might have thought she was looking at a clown. But, she clearly said a cow. And, she was laughing. I asked who was with her and she said her sister and her brother. And, I asked what they were doing and she said watching a cow lie down. And, that really seemed to me, as a young child. And, I suggested that you take that childhood memory and apply it in a useful fashion so that she was able to find a memory helpful in avoiding that anxiety she felt. And, that way she didn't have to feel that anxiety anymore. But, her unconscious mind took care of it automatically and and her conscious mind never knew.

mind went about the task forming mental images that influence your ability to read and write and memorize for years. And, it's that way with so many learnings. A child first learning to stand up has to learn each and every minute muscle movement and coordination. So many things to learn. And, as each one is learned, your unconscious mind stores it away and makes it automatic. And, soon the child is able to toddle confidently toward the door knob. And, the door knob provides quite a challenge to the young child. Do you push it, pull it, in which direction do you turn it? When the child learns it becomes automatic. There is need to even think about a door knob.

And, her mother never knew that when she was looking at her with a smile on her face she was thinking about a cow lying down.

It should be apparent that the content from each us would have been difficult to follow as it was delivered for about three minutes and spoken simultaneously. We might briefly summarize that Carol began speaking about a gardener planting seeds and went into great detail on how one learns. At the same time Stephen discussed the age regression of a client who recalled visually and behaviorally and emotionally a joyful event. Following these words the client was offered and accepted a rapid reorientation from the trance. He was asked to summarize his experience and he reported:

> I spent most of my time with this gal about five years old, holding her hand and walking down this row in a garden. We were watching things grow and she was asking me questions. Then part of the time I became her and was looking way up at the person who was leading me. It was kind of an interesting switching back and forth. And ... I was aware that you were talking at me but I was actively tuning you out. Well, I was aware you were talking about a chef and a meal and then watching little seedlings grow. At least that's part of what you were saying.

57

He reports, "I was actively tuning you out." In other words, his conscious mind, to avoid being overloaded, did not follow the content we spoke. However, he reported "walking down this row in a garden . . . watching things grow . . . I became her . . ." That is, he took the female pronouns offered by both Carol and Stephen; he age regressed ("become her") following, in part, Stephen's age regression suggestions, and he was walking in a garden interested in watching and being curious following, in part, Carol's suggestions about the garden and learning sets. He effectively synthesized the two pieces of content that he believed he was ignoring and produced an experience of that matching the closest trance phenomena.

The double bind by a single parent occurs when the same parent communicates all by himself or herself. He or she could give one message at one level and another message at another level. So it's little wonder that we have schizophrenic behavior such as hallucinations, age regression, talking to angels, hearing voices, and so on, while the parent disclaims any contribution to that sort of thing whatsoever. There in no malice, but simply through that pattern of communication these effects were created. So, here we see an extension of Haley's original ideas regarding the structure of communication, and the double bind played out or applied in a multi-parent atmosphere that is very common. It suggests strongly that various mental characteristics may result from the chronic communication patterns in the home. These can include a range of experience from depression found in dissociation to psychotic experiences of hallucinations.

INTERACTIONAL BIOCHEMISTRY

I mentioned that Haley's contributions marry interaction with experience and this would lead, ultimately, to each individual's biochemistry. Here I have oversimplified the nonromantic version of the human body that initially came from an idea offered by psychiatrist friend Robert Phillips (1975). This brief introduction should be sufficient to make my point. In the center of the diagram on the opposite page are the lips, esophagus, lungs, heart, stomach, liver, intestines, alimentary tract, colon, etc. And surrounding them on the outside are three tubes that hold us together. These are the musculoskeletal system, the cardiovascular system, and the skin-nervous system. These three support systems wrap the central organs up into a nice little package. These images suggest that we've cut across the human being and put him on a microscope slide. The parasympathetic–dominant nervous system services the central apparatus and the support system is serviced by sympathetic–dominant adrenaline flow.

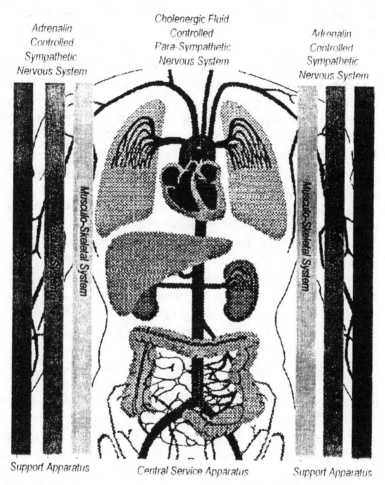

For simplicity we could say that when adrenaline flows as the dominant chemical set, you cathect the skin-nervous system, musculoskeletal system, and cardiovascular system. The rush of adrenaline to these systems provides the support and protection for perception, reaction, strength, etc. Hence the use of the term "support apparatus."

The internal organs are serviced by parasympathetic–dominant, sympathetic nervous system. In this interior, cholenergic fluid floods the central apparatus, relaxing sphincters, causing an increase of cell-wall permeability, so toxins are exchanged with nutrients and oxygen-rich blood and the organs are serviced and relaxed. These I'm referring to as the "support apparatus."

Now referring to the support apparatus, if I cathect adrenaline, I can support myself. If I'm not old enough to do that, someone else supplies that support (since I'm just an infant). The parents supply that support — and they need to do that to the exclusion of their own needs for support at times.

But both systems must alternate in every person to an appropriate degree in order for healthy functioning to occur. That is, the central-needs apparatus sometimes also has to be present and cathected from time to time. Otherwise, the person risks ending up with a Sylvester Stallone's "Rocky," or the "Marlboro Man" type, who presumably never gets tender and has no such needs. On the other hand, if one never cathects the support apparatus, never learns how to do that, or gets comfortable doing that, he or she ends up as a "Barney Fife" or "Woody Allen" type of character who never can be strong.

In a family, if the messages are of the type: "hurry and grow up," "we don't want you whining around here," "big boys don't cry," "don't be a baby," etc., every time the child begins to find a way to express the need for servicing the central apparatus that's not perfectly comfortable for the parents, the child learns to let the chemical trigger become a discriminative stimulus to fire off adrenaline instead. If they can, they become strong when they should have been cared for. And the opposite dynamic is also true.

If the child continually cathects himself with adrenaline (and learns the chemical trigger as a discriminative stimulus to avoid cholenergic dominance and accompanying tenderness), he will (or may) eventually burn up some aspect of one of these three systems. When that happens enough, he gets psoriasis, high blood pressure, arthritis, or hardening of the arteries, etc. — those various diseases that come from overusing subsystems within that support apparatus. Or, if it's done the other way around, one gets damage to the organs of the central apparatus that may include diverticulosis, types of ulcers, spastic esophagus, spastic colon, kidney, liver, or spleen problems, etc.; those kind of things that can come from never giving external support to oneself because of a fear of standing up and being assertive or other adrenaline-based behaviors.

In other words, the chemistry is changed by the ongoing parent–child transactions like the ones discussed here. There is one other combination that's even worse, where one parent says, "You're my little girl/boy, don't ever grow up, I'll take care of you," and the other parent says, "Big boys/girls don't cry, shut up, be strong, be the little man/woman." So you have one parent asking for one, and one parent asking for the other, and the child gets the chemical equivalent of the double bind just discussed. It should be clear that the overstimulation of one or the other chemical set can be produced by the ongoing communication of the parents who discount the child's needs, message, or situation, including incongruity that results in double binds between parents. Further, this overstimulation of one system or understimulation of the other can result over time in the failure of one of the subsystems in sympathetic- or parasympathetic-dominant systems. We see in this not only the development of pathology, as Haley predicted, but the development of somatic symptoms often considered the domain of medical professionals instead of family therapists.

CONCLUSION

In summary, Jay Haley's early contributions included introducing many of us to the methods of Milton Erickson. However, his early work in marrying transactions to experience in observing the impact of interaction on hypnosis and communication in families with a child diagnosed as "schizophrenic" is profound and has not yet been fully appreciated. This observation, as shown here, can help us understand all types of "normal" daily communication and metaphoric messages, but also an entire range of experiential effects within families. Not only can we understand the development of schizophrenic communication but also other characteristic symptoms, such as dissociation, age regression, and any symptom that can be manufactured from the focusing of awareness, retrieval of experience, dissociation, integration, and trance phenomena. Finally, we can even begin to build a model of somatic predispositions, changes, and illnesses in a relatively predictable manner from the extension of Haley's transactional concepts. Such concepts are logical and quantifiable enough to research on large populations thanks to the observations, articulation, and clever schemata begun by Haley.

References

Bateson, G., Jackson, D., & Haley, J. (1974). A note on the double bind — 1962. In D. Jackson (Ed.), *Communication, family, and marriage* (pp. 55–62). Palo Alto: Science and Behavior Books. (Original work published 1963).

Bateson, G., Jackson, D., Haley, J., & Weakland, J. (1974). Toward a theory of schizophrenia. In D. Jackson (Ed.), *Communication, family, and marriage* (pp. 31–54). Palo Alto: Science and Behavior Books. (Original work published 1956).

Berne, E. (1972). *What do you say after you say hello?: The psychology of human destiny*. New York: Grove.

Goffman, E. (1969). *Frame analysis*. Chicago: Doubleday.

Haley, J. (1971). *Changing family: A family therapy reader*. New York: Grune & Stratton.

Haley, J. (1973). *Uncommon therapy: The psychiatric techniques of Milton H. Erickson, M.D.* New York: W. W. Norton.

Haley, J. (1973a). An interactional explanation of hypnosis. In D. Jackson (Ed.), *Therapy, communication, and change* (pp. 74–96). Palo Alto: Science and Behavior Books. (Original work published 1958).

Haley, J. (1973b). Control in psychotherapy with schizophrenics. In D. Jackson (Ed.), *Therapy, communication, and change* (pp. 146–168). Palo Alto: Science and Behavior Books. (Original work published 1961).

Haley, J. (1974a). An interactional description of schizophrenia. In D. Jackson (Ed.), *Communication, family, and marriage* (pp. 151–170). Palo Alto: Science and Behavior Books. (Original work published 1959).

Haley, J. (1974b). Family experiments: A new type of experimentation. In D. Jackson (Ed.), *Communication, family, and marriage* (pp. 261–289). Palo Alto: Science and Behavior Books. (Original work published 1962).

Haley, J. (1974c). The family of the schizophrenic: A model system. In D. Jackson (Ed.), *Communication, family, and marriage* (pp. 171–199). Palo Alto: Science and Behavior Books. (Original work published 1959).

Haley, J. (1976). *Problem solving therapy: New strategies for effective family therapy*. San Francisco: Jossey-Bass.

Haley, J. (1984). *Ordeal therapy: Unusual ways to change behavior*. San Francisco: Jossey-Bass.

Jackson, D., & Haley, J. (1973). Transference revisited. In D. Jackson (Ed.), *Therapy, communication, and change* (pp. 115–128). Palo Alto: Science and Behavior Books. (Original work published 1963).

Laing, R. D. (1967). *The politics of experience*. New York: Ballantine.

Laing, R. D. (1972). *The politics of the family*. New York: Ballantine.

Lankton, S., & Lankton, C. (1982). *A dual induction using dissociation* [Video]. Phoenix: Milton H. Erickson Foundation.

Phillips, M.D., Robert. (1975). *Structural symbiotic systems*. Chapel Hill, NC: Robert Phillips, M.D.

4

A States of Consciousness
Model of Ericksonian Hypnosis[1]

The interrelated fields of hypnotherapy, psychotherapy, and family therapy are experiencing a historical period of growth as a result of innovative techniques created by Milton H. Erickson, M.D. (1901–1980). His contributions are distinctive in many ways but are of special interest for the variety of treatments and interventions they provide. To explicate the uniqueness of his strategic approaches and interventions and increase their availability to hypnotherapists, this paper attempts to place them within a "states of consciousness" (SoC) model of mental processes. This is achieved by providing a guideline that traces the induction process in terms of the alternations in emphasis between conscious and unconscious SoCs. Finally, implications for family therapy are suggested.

Milton H. Erickson is recognized as the master of clinical hypnosis and strategic therapy. His influence has extended beyond dynamic techniques of intervention to reshape the very way we view clients and problems. This paper offers a States of Consciousness (SoC) perspective on clients and problems. Charles Tart produced a definitive essay concerning SoCs as "a unique, dynamic pattern or configuration of psychological structures, an active system of psychological subsystems" (Tart, 1975, p. 5). He added that these states are

---

[1] Lankton, S. (1985). A states of consciousness model of Ericksonian hypnotherapy. In S. Lankton (Ed.), *The Ericksonian monographs number 1: Elements and dimensions of an Ericksonian approach* (pp. 26–41). New York: Brunner/Mazel. Reprinted with permission.

held together or maintained by the loading of awareness/attention with stimuli provided by various tasks, chemicals, and so forth. That is, the stimulation provided by sensory and chemical inputs helps to induce and continue a SoC. Once induced, they are maintained by feedback created by mental monitoring (Tart, 1975, p. 5). In other words, each person does a self-observation that regulates the SoCs. Each SoC can be thought of as a different inner reality with different mental processes, muscle tonus, feelings, and associated actions. Examples are even noticed when a person claims, "I can't function very well yet because I haven't had my coffee," and "I'm not feeling like myself today so my judgment is a little off."

Since Ericksonian hypnosis provides a unique kind of interpersonal stimulation, it is well suited for producing and studying these inner realities. Erickson viewed trance as a state of consciousness in which certain associations were connected in a way that produced an inner "reality." This newly constructed reality expressed a creative recombination of previous learnings (Erickson & Rossi, 1979, p. 464). Those "previous learnings" were learnings that clients had gained in still other uncustomary states of consciousness. For example, in trance (a state of nonordinary consciousness), an adult presenting the problem of bulimia facilitated her cure by calling upon perceptions gained as a young girl when she was walking on a beach and experiencing a different uncustomary state of consciousness (Lankton & Lankton, 1983, pp. 179–184). In trance, a hysterical depression that prevented an adult from normal dating was solved through a reexamination of instructions acquired in childhood (Erickson & Kubie, 1980). These examples illustrate the empirical and therapeutic value in recognizing and utilizing various states of consciousness.

Although these states of consciousness exist "within" the individual, they are created by means of social interaction. Initially, they are created by the client's family (Laing, 1972); "the child is, in effect, hypnotized by his parents" (Berne, 1972, p. 343). In this sense, the concept of states of consciousness can be used as a means of integrating and understanding the interactional dynamics of individual and social experience.

Erickson's epistemological framework interrelates individual and social systems through the process of *intervention*. Because Erickson developed a method of *intervention* rather than a *theory of personality,* his students have been able to avoid those differences created by traditional *theories* of personality and family structure. Erickson's approaches achieved therapeutic impact at several levels of individual and social mental processes:

1.   *unconscious* patterns of experience;
2.   *conscious* beliefs and frames of reference;
3.   *interpersonal* communication; and,
4.   *family organization.*

Ericksonian method is based on the viewpoint that problems arise when clients become "stuck" in a SoC that lacks the resources needed to meet the social and behavioral demands confronting them. In some cases, the operative SoC might actually produce a maladaptive response. Erickson stated that "psychological problems exist precisely because the conscious mind does not know how to initiate psychological experience and behavior change to the degree that one would like" (Erickson & Rossi, 1979, p. 18). Instead of attempting to just remove symptoms, Erickson helped the client utilize and integrate unconscious resources (that usually existed outside the customary state of consciousness and belief system) to meet current life demands. He assumed that problems arose due to an inappropriate response to life's increasingly complex sanctions and role pressures. His therapy, therefore, often did not demand an immediate reduction in a symptom. Rather, his work centered on the development of needed resources. Often the conscious mind of the client would remain unaware of the scope of change so that new learnings did not constitute a threat to the customary state of consciousness.

Observing Erickson in action[2] led to the formulation of ideas about his work in terms of States of Consciousness. His contact with me helped me shape important attitudes and perceptions about people and their experiences that I use diagnostically. I found that certain ideas from the SoC concept helped me apply Erickson's interventions with both individuals and families in a systematic manner.

ERICKSONIAN HYPNOSIS STATED
IN PREMISES REGARDING SOC

I propose eight premises regarding SoC that can be used to bridge the gap between individual and family therapy and at the same time provide a schema for constructing *interlocking system-wide interventions* for use with any client system. I have used some identifying titles for these premises and I will deal with

---

[2] Personal contact, 1975–79, at 1201 Hayward, Phoenix, Arizona.

them individually: (1) requisite existence of states of consciousness; (2) resources and limits in different states; (3) functions of states of consciousness; (4) necessity of shifting between different states; (5) learned induction and maintenance of states of consciousness; (6) social induction and maintenance of SoCs; (7) rules regarding the recombining of experience; and (8) symptom formation and states of consciousness. These premises can help us conceive of a theoretical framework that accomplishes what Erickson's work demonstrated: implicit unity of individual and social systems and the creation of interventions that have a system-wide effect. Each premise will be examined first in relation to social systems dynamics, and then in relation to specific applications in clinical trance work.

1. Shifts in States of Consciousness Are a Fact of Human Life Manifested Socially or Culturally Via Rituals, Sanctions, and Rules of Conduct

People of every culture shift between various stages of consciousness throughout normal daily activities. Religious rituals, for example, are experienced differently from labor activities. In America, terms such as *work, weekends, vacation, prayer, studying, hanging out,* and so forth, denote more than different ways of structuring time; *each involves a recognizably different state of mind.* Cultural rituals constitute recorded rules concerning the methods for *"proper" induction and maintenance of consciousness.* The special words said at a marriage ceremony or during church prayer are examples. Another example is the conflict that arises if, while *hanging out,* an individual has thoughts about ambition and employment matters. Usually, speaking about these thoughts will result in a mild form of ridicule or punishment. Those thoughts are thus culturally controlled; certain mental states are expected to be in operation at certain times.

Many subtle aspects of culture can be seen as sanctions that guide conduct within different states of consciousness (Goffman, 1967; Laing, 1967; Pearce, 1974). These subtle aspects concern the "customary" hours for conducting business, proper social conduct, the length of a school hour, the duration of television broadcasts, highway speed limits, and even beliefs about the nature of "reality." The total effect of the direct and subtle regulation of consciousness is, in fact, the fabric of the culture. Rituals and rules of conduct are merely the outward manifestations.

2. Various SoCs Within the Individual Contain Discrete as Well as Overlapping Sets of Resources and Limitations. The Use or Misuse of These Sets Will Determine the Utility or Liability of Any Particular SoC

Different states of conscious awareness are known as ego-states (Fenichel, 1945, p. 223) and, as such, involve a sense of awareness, identity, history, and specific social impact (Berne, 1966). For example, at times we act, think, and feel as we did as children and at times we act, think, and feel as our parents did (or might have in the situation). Other states of consciousness or unconsciousness may also be created in which some of these aspects may be changed or nonexistent. Whatever the case, in each particular state of consciousness certain resources or potentialities are available and certain limitations are imposed. Other resources and other limitations are found in other SoCs. Some resources and limiting experiences can be shared by several SoCs.

Throughout normal daily activities, an individual experiences some alterations of discrete states within the normal waking state. These alterations are described in terms of moods, feelings, musings, daydreams, reflects, and so forth. All are groupings of experience that allow for certain problem-solving interactions with the environment. For example, feeling, thinking, and acting like a parent may be most useful when value judgments are necessary and, likewise, a SoC that feels, thinks, and acts like a child is most appropriate for meeting the social demands at parties. The use or misuse of these various alterations will determine whether or not a SoC functions as a resource or a liability within a particular environment at any specific time.

3. The Function of Shifting SoCs if Problem Solving

Shifting SoCs makes it possible for a person to synthesize new combinations of past experiences as needed in different life situations: It is the process that makes resource retrieval possible. A normal waking state of consciousness is composed of several discrete states of consciousness. Shifting these discrete states is part of natural problem-solving activity for each individual. A particular SoC makes possible the use of specific sets of such functions. The example in the following section will further clarify this observation.

4. Shifting Between Different SoCs Is Necessary for Optimal Survival, Creativity, and Intelligent Survival

People *must* alter their states of consciousness in order to interact with their environments and each other in an effective and optimal manner. As an example, take the businessperson who solves a difficult problem on the tennis court. The scenario usually goes like this: He or she has been unsuccessful in solving a problem after working hard for hours in a particular SoC (maintained by caffeine and other stimuli from the office environment). Finally, he or she goes out for an energetic game of tennis during which the answer is conceived.

States of consciousness are *induced* and *maintained* in conjunction with the particular characteristics of each new context. Thus each SoC produces an opportunity for a novel solution to a problem because the mentation and mechanisms that operate within it organize experience in different ways.

5. Shifting and Altering States of Consciousness Is Learned

The ability to alter and stabilize consciousness is learned. The learning can occur on either conscious or unconscious levels, or a combination of both. As with any other skill (e.g., playing piano, skating, penmanship, etc.), the type of learning that occurs results in either efficacious or inefficient and inappropriate performance.

We expect that people would tend to induce and maintain the SoC they consider to be the most beneficial, prosperous, attractive, etc. Also, people will attempt to induce or maintain it in the best manner possible for them. A common example is found with individuals who complain that they "procrastinate." The illustration I use concerns the task of writing a dissertation. Often writers will complain that they do everything *except* sit down to write. They may decide to postpone writing (for just a moment) until they first clean the office, organize a bedroom drawer, take out the garbage, get a snack, read the paper, wash the windows, and so forth. Eventually, life demands take over and the time they might have used to write the dissertation has been squandered. This procrastination can be viewed as an induction ritual that is being used to prepare the SoC for writing. It could be speculated that the writer is using the lesser tasks to load his awareness with the stimuli that produce the SoC for mastery of the intended task. This is an example of the person doing his best to induce a SoC in the manner in which it was learned even when doing so is less effective than desired.

We can see this point again demonstrated in an example of pathological conduct involving child abuse. If, for instance, a child abuser finds most of the resources he needs in a SoC which is characteristically associated with certain levels of bodily tension, judgmental internal dialog, breathing patterns, voice tones, and so forth, he will select social and physical conditions that further maintain the SoC with those behaviors. Should he experience a zone of comfort normally associated with that SoC, he can be expected to apply those same behaviors even more intensely in an attempt to maintain the "world as he knows it." Thus the abuser may resort to shouting, striking, and abusiveness to maintain his unique problem-solving level of efficiency. His attempts to overemploy clumsy methods of maintenance will strain psychological mechanisms and lower the operational quality of his performance of social conduct. In other words, he may beat, shout, and abuse rather than discuss, listen, and negotiate. It can be seen that, in part, the function of some symptoms may be to continue the preferred SoC through lack of a better learned choice for control of conflict and tension. Finally, another type of symptom development results as the stressed physical and psychological mechanisms are chronically overused in this effort.

6. Social Stimuli Induce and Help Maintain SoCs

People use one another to help induce SoCs. This is true for even the "normal daily" SoC. Social systems (e.g., families) help maintain each member's preferred SoC and get other members to act so as to help maintain their own. Members maneuver other members into assisting in the maintenance process. Maneuvering can be done by agreeing on beliefs, rituals, and experiences, or it may be done by resorting to ulterior and defensive behavior (Berne, 1966; Goffman, 1967; Laing, 1967, 1970, 1972). Inductions of SoC are done by means of conscious, planfull maneuvers, such as seduction, manipulation, courtship, child rearing, psychotherapy, hypnotherapy, and family therapy. In contrast to these consciously deliberate methods, it is also done by means of unconscious automatic strategies such as defenses and repetitive "game" sequences, as well as by means of ordinary daily transactions.

> In the family situation, however, the hypnotist (the parents) are already hypnotized (by their parents) and are carrying out their instructions, by bringing their children up to bring their children up . . . in such a way, which includes not realizing that one is carrying out instructions, since one instruction is not to think that one is thus instructed. (Laing, 1972, p. 79)

7. Recombining and Shifting Experience Within SoCs Is Rule-Governed

There is a saying that: "You can't get there from here." This is also true for mental processes: Some mental processes are directly interconnected while others are not. It may be easy to switch from Set A to Set B, but impossible to go from Set A to Set M. For example, a person may be able to go from *wondering* to *self-doubting*, but it is unlikely he or she could switch directly from *self-doubting* to *joy* even though these may all be normal waking state experiences for the person.

"Rules of recombining" different SoCs for each individual vary greatly. The verbally abusive man who can't smile and apologize during an angry exchange may be able to smile during other circumstances. But within his normal state of consciousness, rules of recombining prevent him from a verbal altercation with the display of a smile. He may have learned no way to get from *tension* to *smiling* in a social situation. A further example is the common situation where two family members are quarreling and, in the heat of the exchange, one of them is able to answer a ringing telephone and sound pleasant. The other family member cannot. One might say there are no "roads" in his or her "map of experience" from argumentative behaviors to pleasant behaviors. The rules of recombining are idiosyncratic for each individual.

8.   Symptom Formation Results from a Misuse of SoCs

The inability to maintain a SoC and shift among appropriate SoCs creates stress. Moments of stress invite an overuse or misuse of maintenance mechanisms or resources available in any given SoC, which results in symptomatology. An example of this process is the stress that occurs with sleep deprivation. It is well known that the misuse of caffeine or other chemicals as a means of maintaining a waking state will produce various short-term symptoms ranging from irritability to paranoia.

The development of symptoms in a family member often serves the function of evoking and maintaining otherwise unstable SoCs among other family members. In extremely rigid family systems, the emergence of symptomatic behavior is a highly symbolic unconscious product of such "transpersonal collusion" (Laing, 1972, p. 99). An example of this conduct is seen when a child develops a school phobia and the anxieties of the parents are displaced as concern for the youngster. The more rigid the family system, the more the symptom localized in a single individual will serve as a metaphoric statement of the family stress.

ERICKSONIAN APPROACH TO INDUCTION

Thus far we have looked at individual and family systems in terms of a SoC model. Now we will examine these aspects that relate to Erickson's work with hypnosis and families. Having presented the premises derived from my study with Erickson[3] in terms of a SoC model, we can now examine how shifts in states of consciousness (SoC) occur during clinical trance.

Erickson considered hypnotic trance to be a state of heightened, internally concentrated awareness that had its less specialized correlate in the form of the "common everyday trance" (Erickson & Rossi, 1979), which most people experience intermittently as a matter of course throughout the normal daily cycle of shifts in consciousness. Erickson conceptualized hypnosis as a state of consciousness in which *ideas* were better communicated and exchanged in a manner superior to normal waking-state consciousness. Erickson used indirect forms of communication as a means of stimulating creative, independent thinking in his clients. His multileveled suggestions would constellate networks of associations that culminated in a cohesive, unified trance experience. Erickson and Rossi (1979) commented on this phenomenon:

> Associating suggestions in such interlocking chains creates a network of mutually reinforcing directives that gradually form a new self-consistent inner reality called "trance." It is construction of such interlocking networks of associations that gives "body" or substance to trance as an altered state of consciousness with its own guide-posts, rules, and "reality." (p. 464)

The net result of these many associations may be experienced consciously to varying degrees. Much of the therapeutic process, however, remains unconscious in the normal waking state. In either case, the unconscious associations create the therapeutic basis of the trance that results. But the induction of the trance state is the first important step.

---

[3] These premises are the conclusions from numerous personal observations of Erickson's work that initiated my understanding of each of the premises. The scope of the present article makes it impossible to describe all these observations.

71

Tracing the Induction Process

The following guidelines[4] have been particularly useful for tracing the induction process. They reflect the change in *emphasis* Erickson often evoked in states of conscious and unconscious processes during a hypnotic induction. The actual steps of induction overlap extensively, and there is no artificial break in the stages as implied in this guideline. Major shifts in emphasis can be traced through these stages:

1. *Orienting the client to trance.* The goal of this first phase is to find a natural method to relax the client's normal waking-state conscious. This is accomplished by ensuring that the client is physically and psychologically prepared for trance. Part of the preparation involves identifying and dispelling myths the client may hold concerning hypnosis. To facilitate this phase, the Ericksonian therapist often uses stories that demonstrate the common experience of trance on both personal and cultural levels. Observations will be shared of cultural and personal behavior upon which the first several premises were formulated. These often include: the requisite existence of states of consciousness, resources and limits existing in different states, the function of states of consciousness, and the necessity of shifting between different states for problem solving. The therapist might say, for example, "Everyone knows how to daydream," "Sooner or later everyone drops into a trance and examines things from a different angle," "Every child knows the importance of imagining and the value of wonder," "It is important to forget things now and then," and so forth.

    To the extent that education of the client involves the use of stories from the therapist's life or evokes memories from the client, a fixation of attention is initiated and step one is essentially complete.

2. *Fixating attention and rapport.* The goal at this phase is to disrupt the customary waking SoC by attaching the client's attention onto a story, body sensations, or an external object. The reader will recall that there is an

---

[4] A more extensive discussion of this outline can be found in S. Lankton and C. Lankton (1983), *The Answer Within: A Clinical Framework of Ericksonian Hypnotherapy* (pp. 131–177). New York: Brunner/Mazel.

"inducing" force from outside stimuli and from the client's conscious feedback and that this maintains his or her normal waking state.

While classical hypnotic approaches fixate attention on the goal of relaxation, the Ericksonian approach recognizes that many individuals *struggle* to achieve relaxation and in so doing, actually *increase* the stability of their waking state. This struggle against relaxation (or giving up other familiar patterns of behavior), in fact, prevents many people from going into trance with "classical" induction techniques (Spiegel, 1972). An important aspect of Erickson's therapeutic contribution was his development of the *utilization approaches* to hypnotic induction whereby *any* presenting behavior is accepted and utilized as a trance-inducing agent (Erickson, 1980c, pp. 177–205). The importance of the utilization approach is underscored here as the basis for assuming that most individuals can experience trance.

For example, when Erickson told the compulsive pacer to pace the floor even more, the client's usual SoC was no longer applicable. The tension of his customary interpersonal role was dispelled. He was no longer at the mercy of the usual maintenance control created by verbal struggle with those who encouraged him to relax nor did he have the bodily struggle that ensued when he attempted to relax. The client's habitual social and cognitive role became the object of his observation rather than an object for struggle. Thus, his customary SoC reality perceptions and conscious beliefs were not reinforced *vis-à-vis* his struggle with a hypnotist demanding or encouraging that he relax.

3. *Dissociating conscious and unconscious processes.* The next major goal is to create a state in which the client's attention is dissociated and polarized by using language that contrasts the functioning of conscious and unconscious processes in a way that the client can understand. Again, this involves indirect techniques, including the use of anecdote and metaphor, to direct and educate the client about the functioning of unconscious thought processes. In order to illustrate I will present a portion of an actual induction.

There are a number of ways you can go about altering your state of consciousness. You might even open your eyes while in the trance and check out the room, and close them again. Realize that you put yourself in trance by stimulating mechanisms that are known to you. Your conscious mind's probably not likely to be able to articulate what those are but your unconscious can use them nonetheless. Your conscious mind may be attempting to have no thoughts to concentrate but your unconscious will still synthesize experience in a unique way. And your conscious mind might think you can create a situation similar to previous trance but your unconscious is more than likely creating a unique synthesis that reflects this particular moment. Sooner or later your conscious mind will seize upon an idea or an image. It will be interesting if that's the same as what your unconscious will be sorting through. Usually your conscious mind begins a line of thought and your unconscious will continue the line of thought to its culmination. That way your conscious mind is free to skip to a new idea. It really would be difficult for a person to say whether or not the next idea chosen by the conscious mind is simply an epiphenomenon of your unconscious experience. You might prefer to think that your unconscious experience is guided by a sequence of willfully chosen conscious thoughts. You certainly can willfully focus your mind on one of your hands. It appears that your right hand has a general sense of catalepsy and dissociation that it already displays. To a lesser degree, so does your left hand.[5]

As this example shows, educating the client's customary SoC about the functioning of aspects of other (unconscious) SoCs creates a duality of thought and begins to sensitize the client to ongoing differences between conscious and unconscious mental processes. It is desirable if this results in a splitting of attention and creates two effects at once. First, it weakens the integrity of the rigidly held conscious waking state beliefs by involving the client in phenomena that are occurring beyond the limited scope of normal waking consciousness. Observing the previously unnoticed associations and processes that accompany trance requires the client to seek a new framework that will give meaning to them. In the example above this may be most apparent where the therapist guided the client to notice how an idea is seized and to notice a growing dissociation in his hands. Clients will attempt to employ previously held attitudes about what hypnosis ought to be in order to make this integration. Since the Ericksonian therapist holds the premise that experiences in

---

[5] This is an excerpt from an induction done by the author at a workshop, August 3–12, 1984, in Albuquerque, NM.

other SoCs can be utilized as beneficial resources, he or she supports and guides the client in formulating a favorable view of unconscious potential. In operational terms, the guidance may be as subtle as saying, as in the example, that the unconscious synthesizes ideas and carries out thoughts. This implies an active and ambitious quality. Or, in other cases, it may be more explicit, as in, "I wonder if you are aware that your unconscious can work with comfort and ease."

The second effect of creating dual conscious and unconscious mental processes is achieved to the extent that awareness is focused on nonordinary (to the customary SoC) experiences. When the therapist selects the experiences and focuses awareness in this manner, the interaction serves to structure the fabric of the induced SoC and "give substance" (Erickson & Rossi, 1979) to the trance state. This brings the therapist to the final step in the induction: drawing together and stabilizing the elements of the nonordinary SoC into an experience of therapeutic trance.

4. *Ratifying and deepening the trance.* Ratification of trance involves gaining clients' understanding of the fact that they have achieved a nonordinary SoC that can be used for therapeutic purposes. This is easily accomplished by focusing awareness on the many alterations that have occurred in facial muscles, reflexes, respiration, and so forth. As ratification "sinks in," a feedback loop is created whereby clients begin sustaining the trance state on their own. At the ratification stage, clients have placed their awareness on their own internal processes and their consciousness has been educated and oriented toward a positive problem-solving frame.

Let us look at one simple example. If the therapist has suggested the dissociation and levitation of the right hand but the client has levitated the left hand, the situation can go as follows: The therapist points out to the client that not lifting the hand that was suggested indicates that he or she does not follow "irrelevant suggestions." The implication is that the levitation is what is meaningful, while the handedness is inconsequential. Further, the lifting of the left hand indicates that nonordinary processes are occurring, whereas a lifting of the suggested right hand would indicate a less special response. Thus, the client has the nonordinary experience of his or her hand levitating, which in turn inclines the client to further monitor such instances. Thus clients can place attention/awareness on how they are following only relevant suggestions, and a feedback mechanism is set in operation. Also, clients monitor how much nonordinary processing is occurring, which, in turn, operates as another client-conducted feedback loop helping to maintain the trance.

Trance deepening may be facilitated by the presentation of several types of techniques (the confusion technique, indirect suggestions, binds, and so forth) aimed at increasing the noticeability of nonordinary processes. If awareness for the novel processes increases and residual monitoring of the customary SoC decreases, then clients will be able to sustain their own trances. Otherwise, the therapist must provide the stimulation that focuses the client's awareness to maintain the trance state. At this point in the process, the therapist can now turn most of his or her attention to the actual therapy that will be carried out in the trance state.

5. *Using trance to elicit and associate experiences.* Although this article deals primarily with the *induction* of SoCs, perhaps a few words on the *therapeutic process within trance* are in order. In the same manner that Erickson utilized subsystems of noncustomary SoCs to induce trance, his hypnotherapy also involved the use of these same mechanisms. He might, for example, use the mental mechanism of memorization of multiplication tables to help clients more thoroughly learn a feeling of self-worth within trance. That is, clients could more systematically examine the experience of self-worth by applying the method of scrutiny that was learned in the activity of memorization.

Once an altered SoC is established, experience from other SoCs can be incorporated into the trance. Determination of which experiences are needed is suggested by the diagnostic assessment and the contracted therapy goals. The needed experiences are often elicited with indirect suggestion, anecdotes, binds, and metaphors which, provide an altered frame of reference that stimulates clients to entertain the possibility of–or the reality of–novel experience. Finally, the elicited experiences are arranged into a network of associations that help clients form a new "map of conduct" derived from a recombination of past perceptual, emotional, and behavioral patterns. Although the outcome of these changes will be known in part to the conscious mind in the normal waking state, it is not possible or necessary to know all of the new changes in the "map." By analogy, when new roads are built in a city, it is not necessary for the citizens to know all of the pillars and supports, nor even all of the destinations that can be reached by the new structures. It is sufficient for them to know how to get where they want and need to go.

When the associations are made and sufficiently reinforced for the session, the trance can end. It should be emphasized that the Ericksonian approach *does not* rely upon direct suggestions aimed at reducing the symptom. Instead, it aims at building resources by which the "whole" person can become equipped to handle the demands that may have created the context within which the symptom developed. Since symptoms are a signal that an individual or family is responding in a limited way to the strains being placed on existing SoCs, treatment is a matter of bringing necessary outside resources into the customary SoC.

6. *Reorienting the client to the waking state.* Whether reorientation is rapid or gradual, it resolves the temporary suspension of the normal waking state. At this stage the therapist has a final opportunity to assist clients in developing amnesia, posthypnotic behavior, and/or other trance phenomena that may be part of the treatment plan. Determination of the proper *therapeutic* arrangement for reorientation may be a complex matter (Lankton & Lankton, 1983).

The actual reorientation of *consciousness* is, by contrast, rather easy. Once the client's attention/awareness is directed away from the trance experience, with the therapist reinforcing the shift in direction, the habitual mechanism that creates the normal waking state will reassemble. The client will begin to feel "normal" again but this customary SoC will perhaps have some new perceptions within its familiar boundaries: These will be the learnings that were gained in the trance and partly or fully brought back into the conscious waking state under the hypnotist's guidance. Of course, the Ericksonian therapist will be cautious to provide necessary explanations and positive frames for the customary SoC to interpret any potentially hurtful material that is being integrated from noncustomary SoCs.

IMPLICATIONS FOR A SOC MODEL
OF FAMILY THERAPY

As the influence of Erickson's work becomes increasingly appreciated, his techniques become more frequently used and the opportunity arises for development of a unifying theory. The increased use of his approach is stimulating an integration between the induction of the clinical SoC and the function of family systems. Erickson's major departure from classical hypnosis involved his technique of retrieving resources from SoCs that could be used to induce trance adequately (even creatively). These same resources would now be available for therapeutic use in the client's normal waking state. This paper has attempted to unite those aspects of Erickson's approach that deal with individual and social functioning under the rubric of "states of consciousness," and to demystify the mechanics of trance induction via the reformulation of it in terms of a SoC model.

Trance phenomena in family therapy and family life, "common everyday trance" experience (Erickson & Rossi, 1981, p. 48), and the therapeutic employment of states of consciousness are similarly becoming demystified and unified into a variety of clinical settings (Ritterman, 1983; Lankton & Lankton, 1983). The analysis provided in this paper primarily applies to the therapeutic use of hypnotherapy with individuals but the same principles also can be applied to Ericksonian work with families.

We have seen how therapists can help to induce new SoCs out of current consciousness. A further analysis could show how these same principles are unwittingly followed by parents as they hypnotize their children. One might easily see how, in family therapy, the use of paradoxical prescriptions and the refusal to play the expected role in the family drama would parallel the fixation phase of the induction process described above. A strong connection between this analysis and the dynamics of family therapy is the subject of other writing (Lankton & Lankton, 1986).

CONCLUSION

For now, the author has sought to demonstrate Ericksonian principles of therapy within a SoC model. This paper analyzes a typical form of Ericksonian induction and relates that analysis to eight premises about SoC. In so doing I hope to provide a bridge between the seemingly divergent fields of hypnotherapy and family therapy. Understanding the function and effect of Ericksonian interventions on the varying and shifting states of consciousness that shape experience can help therapists achieve a more natural, accurate, and efficacious application, and hopefully can also help researchers design and implement increasingly scientific studies of these techniques.

References

Berne, E. (1966). *Principles of group treatment.* New York: Grove.

Berne, E. (1972). *What do you say after you say hello?.* New York: Grove.

Brown, D. P., & Fromm, E. (1977). Selected bibliography of readings in altered states of consciousness (ASC) in normal individuals. *International Journal of Clinical & Experimental Hypnosis, 25,* 338–391.

Erickson, M. H. (1980a). Initial experiments investigating the nature of hypnosis. In E. L. Rossi (Ed.), *The collected papers of Milton H. Erickson on hypnosis: Vol. I. The nature of hypnosis and suggestion* (pp. 3–17). New York: Irvington.

Erickson, M. H. (1980b). A special inquiry with Aldous Huxley into the nature and character of various states of consciousness. In E. L. Rossi (Ed.), *The collected papers of Milton H. Erickson on hypnosis: Vol. 1. The nature of hypnosis and suggestion* (pp. 83–107). New York: Irvington.

Erickson, M. H. (1980c). Further clinical techniques of hypnosis: Utilization techniques. In E. L. Rossi (Ed.), *The collected papers of Milton H. Erickson on hypnosis: Vol. 1. The nature of hypnosis and suggestion* (pp. 177–205). New York: Irvington.

Erickson, M. H. (1980d). Hypnotism. In E. L. Rossi (Ed.), *The collected papers of Milton H. Erickson on hypnosis: Vol. 3. Hypnotic investigation of psychodynamic processes* (pp. 21–26). New York: Irvington.

Erickson, M. H. (1980e). Hypnotic psychotherapy. In E. L. Rossi (Ed.), *The collected papers of Milton H. Erickson on hypnosis: Vol. 4. Innovative hypnotherapy* (pp. 35–48). New York: Irvington.

Erickson, M. H., & Kubie, L. S. (1980). The successful treatment of a case of acute hysterical depression by a return under hypnosis to a critical phase of childhood. In E. L. Rossi (Ed.), *The collected papers of Milton H. Erickson on hypnosis: Vol. 3. Hypnotic investigation of psychodynamic processes* (pp. 122–142). New York: Irvington.

Erickson, M. H., & Rossi, E. L. (1979). *Hypnotherapy.* New York: Irvington.

Erickson, M. H., & Rossi, E. L. (1980). Autohypnotic experiences of Milton H. Erickson. In E. L. Rossi (Ed.), *The collected papers of Milton H. Erickson on hypnosis: Vol. 1. The nature of hypnosis and suggestion* (pp. 108–132). New York: Irvington.

Erickson, M. H., & Rossi, E. L. (1980). The varieties of double bind. In E. L. Rossi (Ed.), *The collected papers of Milton H. Erickson on hypnosis: Vol. 1. The nature of hypnosis and suggestion* (pp. 412–429). New York: Irvington.

Erickson, M. H., & RossI, E. L. (1980). The indirect forms of suggestion. In E. L. Rossi (Ed.), *The collected papers of Milton H. Erickson on hypnosis: Vol. 1. The nature of hypnosis and suggestion* (pp. 452–477). New York: Irvington.

Erickson, M. H., & Rossi, E. L. (1981). *Experiencing hypnosis: Therapeutic approaches to altered states.* New York: Irvington.

Erickson, M. H., Rossi, E. L., & Rossi, S. I. (1976). *Hypnotic realities. The induction of clinical hypnosis and forms of indirect suggestion.* New York: Irvington.

Fenichel, O. (1945). *The psychoanalytic theory of neurosis.* New York: Norton.

Goffman, E. (1967). *Interaction rituals.* Chicago: Doubleday.

Huxley, A. (1956). *The doors of perception and heaven and hell.* New York: Harper & Row.

Juhasz, J. B. (1979). Theories of hypnosis and theories of imagining. *Academic Psychology Bulletin, 1*(2), 119–128.

Laing, R. D. (1967). *The politics of experience.* New York: Ballantine.

Laing, R. D. (1970). *Knots.* New York: Random House.

Laing, R. D. (1972). *Politics of the family and other essays.* New York: Random House.

Lankton, S. R. (1985). Multiple embedded metaphor. In J. K. Zeig (Ed.), *Ericksonian psychotherapy, Vol. 1: Structures* (pp. 171–195). New York: Brunner/Mazel.

Lankton, S. R., & Lankton, C. H. (1983). *The answer within.* New York: Brunner/Mazel.

Lankton, S. R., & Lankton, C. H. (1996). *Enchantment and intervention in the family: A framework of Ericksonian family therapy.* New York: Brunner/Mazel.

McCabe, M. P. (1978). Hypnosis as an altered state of consciousness: I. A review of traditional theories. *Australian Journal of Clinical Hypnosis, 6,* 39–54.

Morgan, A., & Hilgard, J. (1978). The Stanford hypnotic susceptibility scale for adults. *American Journal of Clinical Hypnosis, 21,* 148–169.

Pearce, J. C. (1974). *Exploring the crack in the cosmic egg.* New York: Simon & Schuster.

Ritterman, M. (1983). *Using hypnosis in family therapy.* San Francisco: Jossey-Bass.

Rogers, C. R. (1961). *On becoming a person.* Boston: Houghton-Mifflin.

Shor, R. E. (1972). Three dimensions of hypnotic depth. In C. T. Tart (Ed.), *Altered states of consciousness* (pp. 257–267). New York: Doubleday.

Spiegel, H. (1972). Eye roll test for hypnotizability. *American Journal of Clinical Hypnosis, 15,* 25–28.

Tart, C. T. (1975). *States of consciousness.* New York: Dutton.

5

Ericksonian Systems Approach[1]

There are no entries entitled *family* or *systems,* in the indexes of Erickson's collected papers (Erickson, 1980), or in Erickson's collected lectures and seminars (Rossi & Ryan, 1985; Rossi, Ryan & Sharp, 1983), or in any book authored by him (Cooper & Erickson, 1954; Erickson, Hershman, & Secter, 1961; Erickson & Rossi, 1979, 1981; Erickson, Rossi, & Rossi, 1976). It is intriguing that Erickson is well known for his creative and pioneering contributions to family therapy in books by Bateson (1972, 1979), Fisch, Weakland, and Segal (1983), Haley (1973, 1985), Madanes (1983), Watzlawick (1976), and so on. Although Erickson himself never offered a family systems formulation of his work, his diagnostic and intervention strategies did, in fact, utilize an implicit general systems theory, or ecosystems theory, or cybernetic-type theory. It is therefore the purpose of this paper to provide a new schema for understanding Erickson's intervention strategies with individuals and families within the context of a systems framework.

Three volumes by Jay Haley — *Uncommon Therapy* (1973), *Conversations With Milton H. Erickson, Vol. 2: Changing Couples* (1985), and *Volume 3, Changing Children and Families* (1985) — are family therapy oriented books containing verbatim transcriptions of Erickson's work. They are noteworthy as

---

[1] Lankton, S. (1988). Ericksonian systemic approach. In J. Zeig & S. Lankton (Eds.), *Developing Ericksonian psychotherapy, state of the arts: Proceedings of the third international Congress on Ericksonian Approaches to Psychotherapy* (pp. 417–437). New York: Brunner/Mazel. Reprinted with permission.

rigorous attempts to place Erickson's work in a family developmental framework. While they make extensive reference to various aspects of the family by means of the cases presented, this is possibly more reflective of the editor's intention than of Erickson's original focus. Erickson's work in many areas, it seems, functions as a projection screen for theorists, for the raw material or data they frame in varying conceptual formulations. Certainly, this is true regarding his highly creative approaches to individuals and families, which others have discussed in terms of specific systemic factors (Lankton & Lankton, 1983, 1986; Ritterman, 1983). In this chapter I will present an Ericksonian systems approach to working with individuals and their families by examining three main areas of concept and intervention. Part I presents a framework of family systems that identifies both the developmental factors and the interactive variables that create an ongoing feedback loop, characteristic of cybernetic systems, and culminates in the family's daily life experience. Part II discusses how presenting problems and symptoms can be identified in terms of the four levels that comprise the family's ongoing interaction dynamics. Part III discusses an Ericksonian approach to designing "system-wide interventions" — interventions that reflect and encompass the cybernetic dynamics that underlie all family experience.

PART I:
A FRAMEWORK OF FAMILY SYSTEM DYNAMICS

Ongoing Developmental Issues

Illustrations 1 and 2 depict the impact of various interventions on different arenas of the individual and family system. These illustrations are intended to provide guidance for conceptualizing systemic intervention regardless of the number of clients being seen. A family, an individual, or an organization of any size can be viewed as going through continuous cycles of stability and instability (see Illustration 1, center portion). For example, at the family level the birth of a child or the relocation of a home is a period of noticeable instability when contrasted with times that are characterized by homogeneous routines and a relative redundancy of daily living patterns. For the individual, graduation from college, a new job, or a physical illness are examples of such unstable periods.

There are stages of development through which a family will traverse over time (see Illustration 1, top portion). The family cycle of stability/instability is

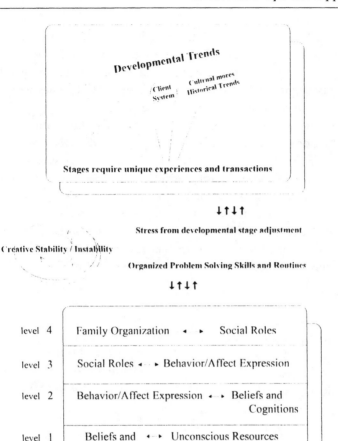

most often initiated by the changes brought on by the requirements of particular developmental stages. At each new stage of development, novel experiences or alterations in the usual types of experiences and transactions must be learned. For instance, when the birth of a baby signals a change in the family to the child-raising stage of development, hundreds of new experiences, transactions, and behaviors must be learned, postponing one's gratifications for the sake of the child's needs, learning to ask for help with the child, being able to experience joy in the child's growth, acquiring a vast array of caretaking skills, and so forth.

If these experiences are readily available as resources due to previous learnings, the disorganization within the family system is relatively short and the transition to a new organization is relatively easy. Conversely, to the extent that the resources are not available, the disorganization becomes more debilitating. Resolutions to the disorganization will come eventually with the implementation of problem–solving mechanisms and techniques used individually and collectively by the members of the family.

This process of problem solving is what takes the family system from a condition of instability to one of stability. I have depicted problem solving as the pivotal dynamic of the family system and have further detailed the levels of system dynamics (see bottom portion of Illustration 1 and expansion in Illustration 2) as the areas of primary emphasis in this chapter. The reader will notice that this discussion deals with only one direction of influence. Although it should be clear that there is a mutual influence between the entries on both sides of the chart, and the arrow points both ways, therapy deals with the social influence on experience and these arrows proceed from the social to the personal.

Building Social Interface
Ambiguous Function
    Assignments
Blocking Communication
Family Structure Metaphor

Total client/family system viewed from 4 levels of behavioral complexity

Paradoxical Prescription
Self-Image Thinking
    Metaphors
Identity & Role Metaphor
Skill Building Assignment

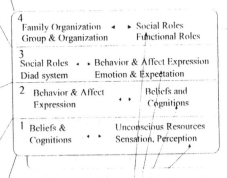

4   Family Organization ◄ ► Social Roles
    Group & Organization   Functional Roles

3   Social Roles ◄ ► Behavior & Affect Expression
    Diad system   Emotion & Expectation

2   Behavior & Affect   Beliefs and
    Expression ◄ ► Cognitions

1   Beliefs &   Unconscious Resources
    Cognitions ◄ ► Sensation, Perception

Affect Metaphor
Behavior Metaphor
Behavior Rehearsal

Reframing
Relabeling
Attitude Metaphor
Confusion

Indirect Suggestions
Therapeutic Binds

Illustration 1

Family systems dynamic chart. Illustration 1 depicts the multi-level cybernetic interaction taking place within individuals and their families. The developmental stages that influence the family cycle of stability/instability present problems to which the family must respond. The problem-solving skills that, in turn, must be marshalled will be a complex product of four interlocking levels of dynamic family interaction: On each level, the first variable determines the parameters and expression of the second variable. Family Organization delineates and delimits the roles each family member assumes; Social Role limitations, in turn, shape all forms of communication and behavior; Communication and Behavior then circumscribe the range and flexibility of beliefs that are acceptable; and these Beliefs, in turn, affect the accessibility of the individual's Unconscious Resources and processes.

Illustration 2

System-wide interventions. Illustration 2 highlights the various forms of interventions that can be used at each level in designing a systems-wide approach to family therapy.

Ongoing Family Systems Dynamics

Illustration 1 shows how system dynamics relate at different levels of complexity. Specifically, it shows life experience interlocking in a matrix of developmental trends and interactive dynamics that can be understood to span the internal experience of single individuals, to coupled partners, to family structures, to informal social networks, socializing institutions, and social-cultural and economic environments. It depicts an ecosystemic approach to human problems, since the theory expands and extends a general systems theory by offering an understanding of the historical influences on populations of environments, families, and individual personality.

Personality can be seen as the natural dynamic of a system: It is the behavior that has the highest frequency of occurrence. Using this definition, it is understandable why the field of psychotherapy has been inclined to consider *personality,* a semantic *construct,* as a reality that comprise behaviors, roles, belief systems, thoughts, perceptions, sensations, and unconscious experiences. All these factors are, to me, different interactional aspects of human systems that reflect different levels of conception of the same system. These different conceptions are related to one another in a logical arrangement shown on the Family Systems Dynamics Chart.

Each level that is placed below another (Illustration 1, bottom) is relatively simpler in organization; each higher level is built in more complex ways from experiences below it. It is useful to remember that none of these levels of conceptualization gives a fully correct interpretation of the system. *Each level is constructed as an alternate perspective.*

Finally, since therapy is in the business of enhancing problem solving, it is necessary in this chapter to explain only the relationships which illustrate the greatest degree of social constraint and, hence, the greater impediments to problem solving. That is, this chapter is contending that family organization delimits social roles, despite the general awareness that the opposite is also true. The reason for this focus is simply that family organization is more complex — it is a larger category, it is a group of social roles. Change or lack of change at the organizational level can create broad alteration in many social roles, whereas a change in a single role may not have such a sweeping impact on the family organization.

In a similar hierarchical manner, social roles delimit communication. Yet, acquiring new communication can affect the way a role is played and the absence of an entire set of communication can limit the performance of a social role. However, social roles are themselves sets of communications and behaviors. Legitimizing a new social role has a pervasive affect on the relatively simpler subsets of communication and behavior. It might be accurate to say that first-order change to variables on the left-hand side of the chart (Illustration 1, bottom) creates second-order change in variables on the right-hand side of the chart. It is for this reason that unidirectional arrows have been used.

Let us use an example of a child's being born into a family in order to trace this dynamic, interactive process through the entire chart.

Family organization shapes social roles

Level 4 of Illustration 1 begins with family organization, which is, of course, a result of influences at a more complex level "above" the top of the chart — that is, the level of cultural mores and historical trends that dictate the range of family organizations that are acceptable. Societal values are in flux in many cultures. A representation of this flux in our current American society can be seen in the existence of group marriages, homosexual couples, single-parent families, serial monogamy, spouse swapping, "singles" condos, and so forth. This change of values loosens the controls on the organization of families and thus affects styles of decision-making and roles that are allowed within the families.

My four-year-old son has red hair. Nearly every stranger has one or two things to say to him, usually beginning with "Where did you get that red hair?" What's my son going to think as a result of such comments? Is he always going to be aware that everybody sees his red hair first? Some people are further moved to tell him what it means to have red hair: "Oh, you're going to be sensitive," "You're going to be handsome," "You're going to be angry," or, "You're going to be creative." This is an example of social structure from cultural norms reaching directly into the family and inducing (or trying to induce) a certain role as well as a receptive family order for that role. The comments may become roles that my son can learn to play.

Once a family organization is formed, it either begins to push at existing social boundaries or stays solidly in the middle. In both cases it *will delineate the degree of role diversity that is possible for its members.* An example: The statement, "Chris, you don't like potatoes. Give them to your brother," teaches Chris about what *she does not like and what she is supposed to do about it.* This type of transaction occurs countless times in a multitude of ways in most families. Transactions become conflicted when they violate the needs or the ecologically adaptive options of family members. Ackerman (1958) once wrote that *intra-psychic* conflicts originate as *interpersonal* conflicts. I think this is an example of what he meant. Parental conflict can occur in any number of arenas: verbally stated beliefs, perceptual predispositions, behavioral modeling, physical abuse, and so on.

As an example of shaping perceptions that become a role into which a child gets trained, let's imagine a parent who sees only the clumsy things his son does and then says, "I have a son who is a klutz." The parent would then "prove" the statement by continuing to perceive only clumsy movements in his son's active reporting of behavior. Those perceptions then would become true for the parent and true, to some extent, for the child. When this kind of transaction occurs, families often think they are commenting innocently on reality when in fact they are *inducing* reality. They are shaping roles so that their children will fit into the family structure of perceptions and action. They may even be shaping lifetime personality characteristics.

Social role shapes communication

The social role aspect of personality delimits the communications that individuals will make. Communications (verbal, nonverbal, emotional, behavioral, etc.) will most frequently occur as a part of a constellation of action. Behavior that is not a part of a constellation tends to not occur. The connection to the next two levels of beliefs and unconscious resources can be illustrated with a brief example of how roles limit communication options.

"Jane" is a girl we have sometimes employed for babysitting. She is from a strict religious family in which it is desirable for children to accept passively the parental beliefs and values. Because of the rigid rules in this family, the children have remained extremely dependent. They have been inculcated with injunctions against developing their own perspectives, and they have been shielded by the parents from the world of different opinions and beliefs. Of course, the children were not allowed to engage in any kind of assertive or aggressive behavior that resembled anger. For example, while Jane was babysitting for us, someone walked up and took a chair from the porch of our condominium on the beach. My former wife, Carol, asked her what had happened to the chair. In response Jane whined, "Oh, that guy over there took it." When Carol asked, "Why didn't you tell him to give it back?" Jane said, "Oh, I couldn't do that."

Why couldn't she speak up to the intruder? She was never given a role for being assertive, aggressive, or angry. None of the roles familiar to her included even the occasional option of demanding anything from anyone, even in response to such blatant wrongdoing as that of the chair-stealing incident. Jane's engraved roles then delimited the range of communication available to her. She had learned to play an almost exclusive role of subservient victim and her communications were congruent with this role.

Communication shapes beliefs

Such *communications* are the interface between *roles* allowed by the family and the next level of the system — the level of *belief and unconscious resources*. The same girl, Jane, later tipped a plate of spaghetti onto one of our dining room chairs and said, "Oh, I always do that." The kinds of communication that she is allowed, that which she rehearses to herself, and for which she is reinforced for delivering, determine the kinds of belief systems she then formulates — for example, "I am the kind of person who always spills things and makes a horrible mess." We know this from the idea of cognitive consonance: Get a person to defend a position on a debate and he or she will modify previously held beliefs to be more consonant with what is being defended. (Modeling and attribution are, of course, still other ways of learning beliefs and cognitive structure. In this model, those learnings would usually affect the level of social roles.)

Once Jane has formulated such a belief system, unconscious resources that could mediate contrary experiences will not impinge upon her normal waking state. Or if they do, they are considered a conflict and an indication that thera-py is needed. This is the way in which *beliefs* (lowest level of chart) delimit *unconscious resources* and unconscious experience. Even if Jane happens to feel aggressive impulses, she believes she is not the kind of person who can have them, so she denies having them. In the same way, a person who believes he cannot be confident in front of a group spends all of his time noticing his lack of confidence when he is in front of groups! Similarly, a person who believes he has ringing in his ears hears that background ringing that we all tend to ig-nore. A belief is a way of saying, in effect, "This range of experience is the only range of stimuli I can notice." Then, millions of other stimuli are not no-ticed. This is not to say that a simple change in beliefs is all that is necessary. Indeed, Erickson's work suggests that we should intervene at each level of the system, since each level contributes a reinforcing aspect to the situation.

Interface of Developmental Trends and Ongoing Family Systems Dynamic: A Case Example

A final example will show how developmental trends interface with family organization, role limitations, communication, and beliefs. This is the case of Paul, a 31-year-old man who came to therapy because of anxiety attacks. He was about to get married and wanted to be rid of the attacks that had plagued him intermittently since adolescence. Now that he was to marry, he wanted to "clean up these problems."

Interviewing revealed that he had been shy and unassertive throughout adolescence and young adulthood. Paul's wife-to-be was somewhat bossy and was now making all the choices about the wedding and giving him very little voice. For him, each stage of his development from adolescence to "about-to-be-wed" had been handled with the same general constellation of resources to solve problems — his shyness and unassertiveness. Thus, when developmental stress caused disruption in Paul's normal stability, his problem–solving resources failed to include appropriate assertiveness skills. Paul's consistently unassertive appearance and conduct produced an overall characteristic of consistency that one might call "personality." Here we see the cycle of stability/instability (middle of Illustration 1) being influenced simultaneously by the stress of de-velopmental stages (top of Illustration 1) and by the use of problem–solving skills (at the bottom of Illustration 1).

The dynamics of this man's problem–solving abilities can be further dis-cussed in terms of beliefs and unconscious resources (depicted at the bottom of Illustrations 1 and 2). Both his family of origin and the family he was forming through the new marriage were organized around the placement of overt decision-making and assertiveness skills in the hands of others. Thus, his power to make changes in either family order would probably come as a result of his symptom formation. This symptom and its control would take shape over the years as the gap widened between his available assertiveness, and the need for using it.

Since role limits control the range of a person's communications (Illustration 2, level 3), his characteristic role of shyness did not allow for any random or occasional assertiveness. When his stress increases, so does his "symptom" of increased weakness or victim-like behavior (and not violent outbursts). At the next level (Illustration 1, level 2), communication/behavior form limits on beliefs; hence, we find that he has in fact formed a belief of himself as inadequate. He formed a self-concept that he consciously recalls from as early as adolescence. In these roles of shyness and inadequacy, he decided that he was inferior to several "normal" boys and did not compete in sports, academics, or social activities with them. This stance, according to him, led him later to drop out of college. Even upon returning to college several years later, he did not major in the field he truly desired due to thoughts that he could not handle it.

At the lowest level on the chart, again, we see that beliefs delimit unconscious resources. The beliefs he holds about his conduct and abilities make it difficult for him to perceive the assertiveness and aggressive impulses he might generate unconsciously in appropriate situations. It is very possible that the anxiety he experiences is his cognitive interpretation of his poorly formed perception of aggressive impulse.

The "Family Systems Dynamic Chart" helps clarify the interlocking levels of influence in the human system, as well as serving as a practical guide for therapeutic intervention. There are two ways to use this chart as a functional guide: 1) as a means of identifying and understanding presenting problems and symptoms, and 2) in designing system-wide treatment. I'll discuss each area separately.

PART II:
IDENTIFYING PRESENTING PROBLEMS AND SYMPTOMS

Problems brought to a therapist's office most often can be identified and located into one or another level on the Family Systems Chart. Problems are usually described in terms of conflicts taking place between coexisting elements on a particular level. For example, conflicts between *family organization* and *role limits* might be worded as, "Johnny is not fitting into the family due to his school behavior." Problems between *role limits* and *communication/behavior* might be expressed as, "I am so ashamed of my conduct," or, "Johnny has not been himself lately (he is influenced by his peers)." Another recently blossoming expression of conflict on this level is, "How can I balance my career and child-rearing demands?" Or, a converse conflict: "I don't know what to do with my time now that the children have left home."

Problems of incongruence between allowed communication/behavior and held beliefs might be expressed as, "I don't know how to be happy," "I'm anxious all the time," "It's just my nerves," and so on. Conflict on this level also includes the absence or presence of communication/behaviors (including emotional behaviors) that are not in keeping with the conscious belief system. An example is someone who believes he should perform better (absence of behavior) or a person who shows every sign of strongly suppressed emotional reactions (presence of behavior). Still another way of expressing such a conflict is, "I don't cry — I can't cry." In these statements we see the recurrence or absence of a behavior that in turn reinforces a belief and shapes a perceptual predisposition.

Problems exemplifying the lowest level of conflict in our system commonly occur as discrepancies between beliefs and unconscious resources and activity. An example would be, "I've been having these awful thoughts about harming people." Here the client is essentially saying that unconscious impulses are impinging on the disallowing belief system. Yet another way to express conflict on this level is in comments such as, "There is no emotional problem, but the doctor who treats my allergies says I should see a psychotherapist." Again, the belief system successfully denies the possibility of stimulated unconscious emotional factors contributing to the allergy.

At first glance, this chart helps us to make sense of a particular symptomatic conflict in the context of the broader *systems picture*. It appears to give us a sense of where to intervene: Identify the level and you've identified the point of intervention. Unfortunately, such a first glance would be misleading. Each of these levels of data organization gives, by itself, an incomplete picture of the human system of which it is a dynamic part. The entire range of events and experiences at all levels is, in fact, involved in the difficulty. The event is merely most conveniently characterized or measured at the one level where the conflict arises.

A therapist who is an ardent adherent of one or another therapeutic discipline might be quick to identify the existence of a problem at a particular level and perhaps overlook or underestimate the influence of other levels that are contributing to the problem. This is especially true of therapists who treat only symptoms and fail to consider their developmental context. I suspect this is why some psychotherapists devalue the importance of family therapy, or why radical family therapists say that we can't study or treat the individual outside of the family. Change the family organization and you change it all or you change the most important piece. In these instances, intervention at the family level of data organization is clearly emphasized.

Different therapeutic approaches tend to emphasize one or another level, without focusing on the interactive relationship actually taking place among all the levels. For example, Bob and Mary Goulding have suggested name changes for some of their clients (Goulding & Goulding, 1979). In following the therapeutic directive and changing their names, clients have a convenient symbol for indicating that they will present a different *role* to the world. I met a man whose name was "Twig." The Gouldings suggested a change and he decided to change "Twig" to "Forrest." These are examples of intervening at the level of social roles. Where Twig had been inconspicuous and unimpressive, Forrest is confident; Twig was dying and Forrest is living.

Some therapies have been greatly influenced by psychodrama, which focuses on acting out emotional states and responses within various *social roles*. Gestalt therapy, for one, relies strongly upon intervention at this level of (emotional) *communications/behaviors*. I locate therapies that deal with emotion in the communications area because emotion is a form of relational communication or behavior. Emotion is movement outward. A careful reading of Perls shows that he believed primarily that "emotional explosion" and "organismic self-regulation" would solve an individual's problems (Perls, 1947, 1973; Perls, Hefferline & Goodman, 1951). The same is true to an even greater extreme for other "feeling therapists" (Hart, Corriere & Binder, 1975).

Proponents of this type of therapy tend to devalue the function of cognition belief systems. Perls called it "phony" (Perls, 1979, p. 59). In fact, his therapy goal was to break into and evoke an explosion of core feelings in order to change the way clients presented themselves. In this framework, clients' belief systems were only an inconvenience. But, is there a price to pay for "letting it all hang out" emotionally, to the exclusion of all other levels of psychosocial functioning? Doesn't the marathon attendee go home and bump headlong into a family that is at odds with the newly sanctioned conduct?

On the other hand, there are other therapies that emphasize change at the level of beliefs. Ellis (1973) skillfully convinces clients that problems are a result of irrational belief systems — and as unconscious impulses, sociometric variables, family power dynamics, and other interactive factors are virtually ignored. Similarly, for analytic therapists (Langs, 1973), emphasis is placed on the cognitive level of organization; conscious thoughts are elevated as the pivotal point of behavior change.

The cognitive behaviorists, such as Lazarus (1976), however, have a systematic way of viewing belief and thought that gives them more breadth and scope. Thought is not regarded as rational or irrational, as contaminated or secondary, but rather as a discriminative stimulus that can determine the target for therapy when what follows the stimulus is maladaptive. Nevertheless, the primary interest of this type of therapy is located on the circumscribed level of cognition and belief in the individual and tends to again place "pathology" *in* the individual.

Conversely, body therapies, though obviously aware of the etiological influences from the family, tend to center their work on increasing the range of unconscious experience that is allowed into cognition-belief systems by manipulating the body in a variety of ways (Alexander, 1969; Baker, 1967; Feldenkrais, 1972; Lowen, 1958, 1965, 1972, 1975; Reich, 1945, 1951).

In this discussion it is not a matter of who is correct and who is incorrect. Every one of these is correct *in part*. It also may be partly correct to say that the proper answer is more than merely combining all of the psychosocial levels. The participant-observer dichotomy is only a semantic reality; any of these therapeutic frameworks constitute a kind of participation — a therapist making these categorizations about a family also tends to induce that reality in the family or the individuals.

So the matter is not which approach is the truest, but rather *how we can best operate in a systemic manner with families and individuals*. It is here that the Ericksonian approach to psychotherapy makes the greatest contribution. Whereas most therapists tend to favor one or another level of psychosocial interaction as a means of conceptualizing presenting problems and creating appropriate interventions, Erickson perceived and intervened at each level of organization in a very large number of his reported cases and did not place "the problem" *in* the person or *in* the family.

PART III:
DESIGNING SYSTEM-WIDE INTERVENTIONS

Erickson developed a range of interventions that accomplished different goals at different levels of the family system. In the course of therapy with any particular family, he used most of them. I have indicated these interventions along the left side of Illustration 2. Before discussing them, it would be useful to comment on Erickson's general ideas regarding the roles and interface of conscious and unconscious processes and resources as they impact both individuals and families.

Erickson seemed to value the unconscious mind more highly than the conscious mind because it was the conscious mind that concocted the limiting beliefs. Simply stated, this means that certain consciously held beliefs and thoughts stop people from searching for resources they may actually be able to use. For instance, the belief that "I can't be happy and trusting" will stop the individual from experiencing the components that make up *happy* and *trusting*. Another example is expressed in the cliché transaction: (Person A) "Why don't you try going dancing and getting out a little bit more?" (Person B) "Oh, I make such a fool of myself whenever I try to dance," or, "Oh I couldn't do that — I'm so uncoordinated." In this case the respondent will not allow the natural gracefulness of the body a chance to express itself because the belief system continually finds ways of choosing only those ungraceful moments to notice, remember, and recreate.

Although Erickson often sought to depotentiate or bypass the limitations of the patient's conscious mind, he nonetheless did not ignore or devaluate the subjective importance of consciously held beliefs. He honored the client's need to either receive an explanation regarding treatment or to not receive one. He worked *with* the conscious mind rather than through direct confrontation against it. This single element of his approach gave rise to techniques of communication that have been termed *reframing*, *relabeling*, and *therapeutic metaphor*. It is my intention to provide a more comprehensive overview of Erickson's techniques and to illustrate how specific types of techniques were used to intervene at specific levels of individual and family organization.

Level 1 Interventions

Level 1 of Illustration 2 shows unconscious resources interacting with beliefs. To effect changes at this level, Erickson used interventions that were based upon indirection. For retrieving unconscious resources, he recognized that interventions that stimulated unconscious search would be essential. The ambiguity inherent in metaphor, indirect suggestions, and various types of binds can stimulate unconscious activity in a therapeutic direction. Hearing a therapeutic metaphor, for example, activates types of cognition and behaviors that are difficult to delineate experimentally. These include: comparison, contrast, memory, association, congruity checking, identification, attributions selection, and so on. Similarly, indirect suggestions and binds (and the unconscious stimulation they create) constitute the "glue" that holds together a variety of internal associations. For example, indirect suggestions and binds about feeling confident might sound like this:

"Your conscious mind certainly knows a lot about confidence that you couldn't explain consciously. I doubt that anyone here could articulate consciously how to begin to feel a sense of confidence. Usually you don't notice. It may begin with an alteration of your body posture. Everyone has heard the phrase, 'breathing deeply, sigh of relief.' But a conscious mind never really knows how your unconscious can go about regulating your body experience and change it to be more comfortable."

Continued listening to such indirect verbalization results in continued unconscious associations to the words. Unconscious processes such as memory, association, anticipation, congruity checking, identification, and others continue too. Intervention at this level does not produce change in belief systems, nor in communication patterns, nor in roles the client commonly assumes. Unconscious resources are simply retrieved — in this case, it would be experiences of confidence.

Reframing, relabeling and attitude metaphors (Lankton & Lankton, 1986) are interventions that urge clients to conceptualize beliefs differently. A well-known example is that of the recently married couple who consulted Erickson because of the husband's failure to consummate the marriage despite his previously active sex life. The bride considered this situation to be a sign of his not loving her; to her it meant that the marriage had been a mistake. After two weeks the wife had consulted an attorney for an annulment. Erickson reframed the situation by asking her if she had considered what a compliment her husband had paid her: "Well, evidently he thought your body was so beautiful that he was overwhelmed by it. Completely overwhelmed. And you misunderstood that and felt he was incompetent. And he *was* incompetent, because he realized how little capacity he had to really appreciate the beauty of your body." Erickson explained separately to the husband that the fact that she overwhelmed him was proof that she was the right woman for him; and she was the one overwhelming girl for him (Haley, 1973, p. 157).

In this intervention, no retrieval of unconscious material was elicited for change. Rather, a new cognitive framework was presented to facilitate both family members' recognition of the potential for a loving experience (instead of feeling bitter and incompetent) in the future. The husband was then seen alone for further therapy to that exact end. A lengthy discussion of a metaphoric method used by Erickson to elicit change as an attitudinal level can be found elsewhere (Lankton & Lankton, 1986, pp. 193–198).

Level 2 Interventions

This brings us to the next level of Illustration 2 — that of communication and the limits it places on beleifs. Interventions that affect this level include behavior protocols, affect protocols, behavioral rehearsal, and simple illustration. Erickson would sometimes have clients rehearse the very symptom that had brought them in for therapy. For instance, he had a girl who sucked her thumb learn in the office how to suck it better. There are numerous accounts throughout Erickson's *Collected Papers* (Erickson, 1980) illustrating in metaphorical ways the proper manner of shopping for presents, gift giving, standing up to a spouse in a quarrel, and so on.

In addition to these behavior-change metaphors, some metaphors are designed specifically to elicit emotions. Notable among these is the story of how Erickson helped his mother say goodbye to the farm and how this story evokes sadness in the listener (Lankton, 1978, and modified in Lankton & Lankton, 1986, pp. 285–288). Emotion can be aroused indirectly by metaphor (Lankton & Lankton, 1986, pp. 198–203) and non-emotional behaviors can also be brought into the foreground by the use of metaphor (Lankton & Lankton, 1986, pp. 203–205). Each of these techniques has the common goal of sensitizing the client to a new method of feeling, communicating, or behaving. This type of change is independent of the cognitive adjustment on Level 1 that may preclude or support it.

Level 3 Interventions

Interventions which exemplify Erickson's awareness of the social role level of dynamics (Level 3) include the interventions of building *self-image thinking* and prescribing *paradoxical prescriptions*. Roles become solidified when they are conceptualized as roles by the individuals who live the behaviors. Erickson frequently created changes in clients' self-image thinking (Lankton & Lankton, 1983, pp. 312–344).

One such case was that of a "dumb moron" named Harold (Haley, 1973) was was dealt with by being sent on a number of assignments. These assignments included learning to play the piano, taking dance lessons, and going to a barn dance to test his progress. Harold was not led to believe that these assignments would get him into the normal stage of courtship (which he needed to attain but which he found highly threatening); rather, he was allowed to believe that these tasks would further his goal of becoming a good manual laborer, a goal which did not threaten him. At the dance, Harold decided that he was "not so bad after all." At his next office session, Erickson used hypnosis to extend this sense of competency into the future where Harold would need it again and again. Changes in role conduct thus produced concomitant changes in self-image. Stories about the progress of Harold are, in fact, therapeutic metaphors that help clients create a change in their own self-image thinking.

Self-image thinking is another level of intervention aimed at the area of social role development and its influence on communication. Self-image thinking can be facilitated in metaphor with specific guided imagery, or with indirect suggestions and "assignments," as in Paul's case. Family members are taught to think about themselves in positive, goal-directed visual rehearsals as a method of problem solving. This may involve systematically building the body image of all family members by assisting them to visualize themselves acting out certain capabilities and by helping them imagine scenarios of themselves playing different roles (Lankton & Lankton, 1983, pp. 312–344).

The use of paradox also belongs on this third level. The therapist using paradox tells a client to keep doing what he or she is doing (the presenting symptom or dynamic), but for a different reason. In this way, the role or the family organization can be changed to some degree. Consider the earlier case of the girl sucking her thumb (Haley, 1973, pp. 195–202). The parents bring her in to see Erickson after she has been labeled aggressive by a previous doctor for sucking her thumb. They are a very religious family and *aggressive* is a disturbing word to them. Erickson begins by telling the parents that no matter what the girl does, they should ignore her thumb sucking. Thus, he is setting limits on the family transactions. He then brought the girl into his office and, while the parent waited in the living room, he presented her with paradoxical instructions to continue sucking her thumb and to do it better! From her family she had acquired a role of having no control over her thumb sucking and, therefore, had acquired yet another role as a psychiatric patient. Erickson's use of paradox completely transformed this role. The paradoxical intervention — which was to keep doing the same behavior but to do it better — was to be done to "irk" her parents. That is, the same behavior would now be used for the role of making them angry, *and* there would be no way they could stop her from expressing this aggressive thumb sucking.

Let us take a closer look at how this intervention affected role limits within the girl's family. At first the girl's conduct says, "I'm a person who is accidentally sucking my thumb and can't help myself. It's my unconscious aggression." Then, she has to take the role of, "I'm going to really irk my parents with this and do it really well." So the same behavior becomes a different role because of a different motivation. Paradoxical interventions change the role that is being played by changing the context or the motivation for the behavior.

Level 4 Interventions

Blocking transactions, as when with the parents of the thumb sucker were told to ignore her, obviously affects the manner in which power can be channeled in a family. It is difficult to reestablish the rules in the family when normal avenues for communication are no longer open. This is a desirable situation that allows a learning of new social roles and congruent communications. Other interventions at this level include *ambiguous function assignment* (Lankton & Lankton, 1983, pp. 136–152) and *family structure change metaphors* (Lankton & Lankton, 1983, pp. 207–208). Both stimulate clients to begin to think about reorganizing the family structure.

A cogent example of intervention at this level was the case about the overprotected young woman whom Erickson ordered to move away from her mother and aunts without even telling them her whereabouts. In addition, she was told to get an apartment with three other girls and to regularly drive around with them in the car without regard for where they were going (Erickson & Rossi, 1979). Here we see an example of a very *direct* intervention, which is in contrast to the *indirect* approaches discussed as means of evoking change in the lower two levels of the chart. The family organization is literally disrupted by the girl's move; role selection is now confused as the disorganization affects and determines the boundaries of roles for each family member.

DISCUSSION

When a change in family organization creates a confusion about rules, there is also a flux regarding which roles will be tolerated. Further, once roles have become temporarily in flux, a tolerance for new communication arises. This new communication via behavior or emotion will be temporarily acceptable to the conscious mind to the degree that changes in attitude also have been stimulated. Finally, the entire package of small changes at each level can be interwoven via indirect suggestion and binds that create a set of operational changes that reverberate through the entire system at each level. This, indeed, constitutes my view of Erickson's systemic approach to therapy: he was capable of stimulating small changes at each level of the system, and each small change supported and reinforced the small changes at other levels.

This approach to therapy with a family system is analogous to assembling a toy spring horse: If all the screws in the frame and on the horse are loosened, the essential springs can be added easily. However, if all the screws remain tightened, a great deal of resistance to proper construction is created. Without much resistance, then, Erickson's systemic approach allows the entire system to gradually shift to allow specific, new problem-solving resources to emerge that can help the client creatively adjust to the demands of developmental pressures.

I have attempted to focus specifically on Ericksonian interventions in regard to the variables depicted on the charts. Yet the reader will certainly recognize how interventions from Behavior Therapy, Psychodrama, Gestalt Therapy, Rational Emotive Therapy, and so on, will also apply. It is my intent to use learnings from Erickson's systemic approach as a means of furthering therapists' abilities to intervene effectively regardless of the "school of technique" used. To that end, this chapter has provided a latticework that relates interventions to different levels of psychosocial and familial organization. These levels of organization that occur within the entire family system are further related to the cycle of stability/instability that families experience as they traverse the various developmental stages in life. The usefulness of the chart can be evaluated operationally by how well it guides therapists to understand symptom formation and subsequently to intervene in an orderly way at all major levels of family experience.

References

Ackerman, N. (1958). *The psychodynamics of family life*. New York: Basic Books.

Alexander, F. (1969). *The resurrection of the body: The writings of F. Matthias Alexander*. New York: Delta Books.

Baker, E. (1967). *Man in the trap: The causes of blocked sexual energy*. New York: Avon Books.

Bandura, A. (1969). *Principles of behavior modification*. New York: Holt, Rinehart, & Winston.

Bateson, G. (1972). *Steps to ecology of mind*. New York: Ballantine.

Bateson, G. (1979). *Mind and nature: A necessary unity*. New York: Dutton.

Berne, E. (1961). *Transactional analysis in psychotherapy*. New York: Ballantine.

Cooper, L., & Erickson, M. (1954). *Time distortion on hypnosis*. Baltimore: Williams & Wilkins.

Ellis, A. (1973). *Humanistic psychotherapy*. New York: McGraw-Hill.

Erickson, M. (1980). *The collected papers of Milton H. Erickson on hypnosis: Vol. 1. The nature of hypnosis and suggestion; Vol. 2. Hypnotic alteration of sensory, perceptual and psychophysical processes; Vol. 3. Hypnotic investigation of psychodynamic processes; Vol. 4. Innovative hypnotherapy*. Edited by Ernest Rossi. New York: Irvington.

Erickson, M., Hershman, S., & Secter, I. (1961). *The practical application of medical and dental hypnosis*. New York: Julian Press.

Erickson, M., & Rossi, E. (1979). *Hypnotherapy: An exploratory casebook*. New York: Irvington.

Erickson, M., & Rossi, E. (1981). *Experiencing hypnosis: Therapeutic approaches to altered states*. New York: Irvington.

Erickson, M., Rossi, E., & Rossi, S. (1976). *Hypnotic realities: The induction of clinical hypnosis and forms of indirect suggestion*. New York: Irvington.

Feldenkrais, M. (1972). *Awareness through movement: Health exercises for personal growth*. New York: Harper & Row.

Fisch, R., Weakland, J., & Segal, L. (1983). *The tactics of change: Doing therapy briefly*. San Francisco: Jossey-Bass.

Goulding, M., & Goulding, R. (1979). *Changing lives through redecision therapy*. New York: Brunner/Mazel.

Haley, J. (1973). *Uncommon therapy: The psychiatric techniques of Milton H. Erickson, M.D.* New York: Norton.

Haley, J. (1985). *Conversations with Milton H. Erickson, M.D., Vol. 2: Changing couples; Vol. 3: Changing children and families*. New York: Norton.

Hart, J., Corriere, R., & Binder, J. (1975). *Going sane*. New York: Jason Aronson.

Keeney, B., & Ross, J. (1983). Cybernetics of brief family therapy. *Journal of Marital and Family Therapy, 9*, 375–392.

Langs, R. (1973). *The technique of psychoanalytic psychotherapy: Vol. 1 & Vol. 2.* New York: Jason Aronson.

Lankton, S. (1978). Personal communication with Milton H. Erickson, August.

Lankton, S., & Lankton, C. (1983). *The answer within: A clinical framework of Ericksonian hypnotherapy.* New York: Brunner/Mazel.

Lankton, S., & Lankton, C. (1986). *Enchantment and intervention in family therapy: Training in Ericksonian approaches.* New York: Brunner/Mazel.

Lazarus, A. (1976). *Multimodal behavior therapy.* New York: Springer.

Lowen, A. (1958). *The language of the body.* New York: Collier.

Lowen, A. (1965). *Love and orgasm.* New York: Collier.

Lowen, A. (1972). *Depression and the body: The biological basis of faith and reality.* New York: Coward, McCann & Geohegan.

Lowen, A. (1975). *Bioenergetics.* New York: Coward, McCann & Geohegan.

Madanes, C. (1983). *Strategic family therapy.* San Francisco: Jossey-Bass.

Perls, F. (1947). *Ego, hunger and aggression: The beginning of gestalt therapy.* New York: Random House.

Perls, F. (1973). *Gestalt approach and eye witness to therapy.* Ben Lomond, CA: Science and Behavior Books.

Perls, F. (1979). *Gestalt therapy verbatim.* Lafayette, CA: Real People Press.

Perls, F., Hefferline, R., & Goodman, P. (1951). *Gestalt therapy: Excitement and growth in the human personality.* New York: Dell-Delta Books.

Reich, W. (1945). *Character analysis.* New York: Simon and Schuster.

Reich, W. (1951). *Selected writings: An Introduction to orgonomy.* New York: Farrar, Straus & Giroux.

Ritterman, M. (1983). *Using hypnosis in family therapy.* San Francisco: Jossey-Bass.

Rossi, E., & Ryan, M. (Eds.). (1985). *Life reframing in hypnosis: The seminars, workshops, and lectures of Milton H. Erickson, Vol. 2.* New York: Irvington.

Rossi, E., Ryan, M., & Sharp, F. (Eds.). (1983). *Healing in hypnosis: The seminars, workshops, and lectures of Milton H. Erickson, Vol. 1.* New York: Irvington.

Satir, V. (1979). *Peoplemaking.* Palo Alto: Science and Behavior Books.

Watzlawick, P. (1976). *How real is real? Confusion, disinformation, communication.* New York: Vintage Books.

Brief Therapy

6

Ericksonian Strategic Therapy[1]

DEFINITION

Psychotherapy is the branch of social science that makes a practical application of the principles of psychology, group dynamics, and sociology for the improvement of individual experience, social behavior, and performance. The practice often involves the reduction, or amelioration, of conflict and maladaptive patterns of cognitive, emotional, and individual and family behavior. The practice of psychotherapy or family therapy is primarily reliant upon verbal communication and may involve varying degrees of active involvement from either the therapist or the client, depending upon the specific approach being employed.

QUALIFICATION STATEMENT

The Ericksonian strategic approach is a method of working with clients emphasizing common, even unconscious, natural abilities and talents. Therapy goals are built upon the intelligence and health of individuals. It works to frame change in ways that reduce resistance, reduce dependency upon therapy, bypass the need for insight, and allow clients to take full credit for changes.

Most problems are not viewed as internal pathologies but as the natural

---

[1] Lankton, S. (1990). Ericksonian strategic therapy. In J. Zeig & M. Munion (Eds.), *What is psychotherapy?: Contemporary perspectives* (pp. 363–370). San Francisco, CA: Jossey-Bass. Reprinted with permission.

result of solving developmental demands in ways that do not fully work for the people involved. The Ericksonian strategic approach is distinctive in that it is associated with certain interventions upon which it relies heavily during extramural assignments and therapy sessions. These include skill building homework, paradoxical directives, ambiguous function assignments, indirect suggestions, hypnosis, reframing, metaphors, and therapeutic binds. These are not so much interventions as characteristic parts of the therapist's interactions with clients. As such they are used to motivate clients to actively participate in changing the way they live with themselves and others.

The rationale for strategic therapy, which credits Milton H. Erickson (1901–1980) as its ephemeris, is threefold. The main tenets affect the practice of therapy as well as the way in which problems and people are viewed. Problems are not seen as inside a person's head. Rather, there is a depathologizing of problems. Problems are thought to be the result of disordered interpersonal relations. Consequently, diagnosis is an activity that frames the presenting problem in terms of the developmental and interpersonal climate experienced by the individuals and their families. Likewise, therapy is directed toward making a creative rearrangement in relationships so that developmental growth is maximized. Accompanying the reduction of the pathology-oriented diagnosis is a corresponding reduction in so-called resistance.

Additionally, in strategic therapy, the therapist is active and is ultimately the one responsible for initiating therapeutic movement. This is accomplished by introducing material into the therapy session and by the use of extramural assignments. That is, therapy does not wait until clients spontaneously bring up material; rather, the therapist often sets the pace and challenges clients to grow and change.

Finally, strategic therapy is interested in getting clients moving. This movement will be in their lives outside the therapist's office, and the use of office time is directed to that end. Assignments are, of course, delivered in order to have clients carry out chosen acts between the sessions. Hypnotherapy and the use of anecdotes, metaphors, and indirect suggestions are designed to motivate clients during sessions to carry out new relational behaviors or congruently engage in the homework assignments. It is from the learning brought by new actions and not from insight or understanding that change develops. Consequently, a client's understanding or insight about a problem is not of central importance. The matter of central importance is the client's participation in new experiences and transactions that congeal developmentally appropriate relational patterns.

An Ericksonian approach to therapy, which can be considered a subcategory of strategic therapy, is centered upon an integration of family therapy and hypnotherapy. Often these areas are seen as extremes with little convergence. Although Erickson's approach grew in these two areas independently, there are philosophical underpinnings for an integrated approach in the work of Gregory Bateson, Heinz Von Foerster, and other epistemological thinkers who emphasize the need to depart from the linear causality essential to the medical model of therapy. Erickson's work, perhaps better than that of any other modern clinician, embodies this goal. The following psychological processes common to both hypnosis and family therapy delineate the notable differences and major strengths of an Ericksonian approach in this regard:

- *Nonpathology-based model.* Problems are seen to be a part of, and a result of, people's attempts to adapt to the changing needs of their family and social network. It is inaccurate and inconvenient to define an individual as having a problem "in his head." Rather, symptoms often are seen as the essentially natural mechanism that has been used to calibrate a system (for example, the family) that has made a particular adjustment to developmental demands.
- *Indirection.* Indirection concerns itself with helping an individual or members of a family discover talents and resources, options and answers, seemingly without the aid of the therapist.
- *Utilization.* This involves making use of common understandings and behaviors that clients bring to the office so that these may be a part of the motivation or reinforcements of therapy.
- *Action.* Clients are expected and encouraged to get into action related to the growth or change that is sought.
- *Strategic.* Therapists are active and take an instrumental role in setting or initiating the stages of therapy.
- *Future-oriented.* Therapy is directed to how clients will act and experience in the immediate present and future rather than being focused on what they did in the past or what they will do about what they did in the past.
- *Enchantment.* Therapy activity engages the mind and appeals to clients as a pleasant challenge.

Techniques used with an Ericksonian approach vary depending upon the case being treated, but several unique interventions are associated with the approach and had their origin in Erickson's practice. These include paradoxical assignments, ambiguous function assignments, skill-building assignments, therapeutic metaphors, anecdotes, conscious-unconscious dissociation, hypnotic induction, therapeutic binds, indirect suggestion, and reframing.

While diagnosis and assessment often are conducted in a conventional manner, the treatment plan usually involves shifting attention away from the identified problem or the identified patient. These techniques are used to help establish a conducive setting for therapy, establish rapport, elicit conscious and unconscious treatment contracts, and shift attention to strengths that are needed to carry out therapeutic assignments. Therapists do not usually construct artificial reinforcement paradigms to help build new behavior but rather rely upon the inherent reinforcements found in the natural satisfaction of living functionally and coping creatively with the pragmatic or profound aspects of one's developmental tasks. As these changes in developmentally appropriate relations are put into action, problems cease and satisfaction is found, or further diagnosis and treatment planning are formulated and carried out to that end.

CRITIQUE STATEMENT

Specific advantages of the Ericksonian strategic approaches to therapy center around the flexibility of its treatment model. We see this element in two major arenas: the unique overall treatment of each case, and the ability to bypass or avoid the resistances to change that direct approaches often elicit. These two aspects will become more clearly important as we examine the major criticisms of the approach.

The major strength of the approach lies in its reliance upon careful observation of clients' methods of thinking, experiencing, and acting, and upon tailoring interventions to match the unique history and actions of the client moment by moment in each session. To the extent that this occurs, resistance is nonexistent or minimal, and client participation is high. It follows that applications of the approach make intervention possible with some of the historically most difficult client populations.

Certain criticisms naturally arise with this model, and these criticisms can be classified in the following three ways: (1) the paucity of research on the approach and the difficulties the approach provides to researchers; (2) difficulty in obtaining necessary skills, training, and supervision to bring practitioners to competency levels with the approach; and (3) possible concerns for the ethics of client manipulation or informed consent. These interrelated concerns are illustrated below.

Research paradigms are most easily applied to approaches that are redundant, use well-defined interventions, and conform to the epistemological view of linear causality. While this often has been a classical problem for the social science researcher, the more individualized an approach becomes, the greater will be the research problem.

An Ericksonian strategic approach aims at being scrupulously unique with each client and therefore does none of those things that would facilitate application of existing research paradigms. Rather, each metaphor, each paradox, must be delivered with an ongoing sensitivity to the special needs of the listener (this is called the *utilization approach*). This need for a uniqueness during application eschews the redundant patterns that lend themselves to research. That is, a metaphor delivered in therapy to one individual at a certain time may elicit a grief reaction while the same metaphor at another time or to another individual is not likely to have the same result. This creates, of course, a difficulty in measuring the effect of a specific intervention. Likewise, interventions are changed slightly for each individual, and thus it is in the uniqueness rather than the commonality of the intervention that the therapeutic bond is made and from which the real efficacy of the approach arises.

Similarly, indirect suggestions for action (*indirection approach*) are used to elicit motivations. These will be carried out by individuals when they are closely matched to immediately existing behavior and experience (utilization). However, delivering those same suggestions to a group of individuals will not yield the same results for each person owing to the differences between their motivations, personal histories, degree of pain, and so on. Commonly, research paradigms are built upon generalizations about individuals, whereas the most successful Ericksonian approaches are built upon the uniqueness of individuals.

The participatory quality of the Ericksonian approach derives from an epistemological framework of circular organization known as recursion. This is radically opposed to the historical notion that observers have objective knowledge about a subject independent of themselves. The traditional medical model relies upon knowing that certain behaviors make the subject a "neurotic," a "borderline personality," and so on, and then giving medication to the individual to cure this internal pathology. An Ericksonian approach, on the other hand, recognizes that the perception of individuals is not based on an objective perspective. That is, therapists who speak the experiential language of a client will not find the client resistant, and therapists whose language is, for instance, psychiatric, will find all clients (except some psychiatrists) to be resistive. Hence, treating a person for being "resistive," "crazy," "antisocial," and so on, would be an epistemological error that comes from overlooking the role played by the participating (rather than observing) therapist and the social context. This epistemological difference, then, requires a research paradigm that is not based, as our current model is, upon linear causality (observer-based treatment).

This brings us to another difficulty: the question of consent. While it is easy to intellectualize about a different epistemological approach, in the moment-by-moment pragmatics of therapy we must be effective and accountable. Often effective intervention is done when resistance is lowest — a situation that often occurs when the limitations of conscious biases and beliefs are bypassed by means of indirect interventions.

Effective intervention with a bleeding arm does not require informed consent, although consent often can be easily obtained for such obvious troubles. In therapy, however, resistance is often created in situations involving personal growth into areas where clients have doubt or are fearful to proceed. For instance, standing up for one's own needs in the face of an intrusive parent, while necessary, may be easy to teach (and even to carry out) but may be met with much resistance and anxiety on the part of the client.

Requiring prior conscious consent before eliciting motivations for actions such as these may effectively stop therapy. In these situations, the Ericksonian approach frequently works from the knowledge that clients follow the suggestions that are most relevant for them and that prove to be in their best interest. Hence, an unconscious contract based on tacit or implicit approval can be obtained from a client and resistance springing from conscious insight and deliberation can be avoided. But once again, this may raise questions of ethics and informed consent as they have been viewed historically.

Related to this issue is the need for good training and supervision of Ericksonian strategic therapists and the difficulty inherent in measuring effectiveness of training and performance in the absence of easily obtainable and relevant research. Therapists in Ericksonian training must learn to be comfortable and confident, often with less verbal feedback than in other approaches. They must learn to rely upon highly trained and developed observation to a greater extent.

Independent of these criticisms, much excellent research is being done and published. And although no two interventions are alike, Ericksonian strategic therapy remains accountable because of its emphasis on pragmatic and reality-based goals for clients. Furthermore, despite the uniqueness of each intervention, well-specified protocols or intervention patterns exist, are becoming more widely known, and may provide the basis for further refinements on effectiveness and therapy outcome. Finally, as the profession continues to grow following the current trends created by the changing therapeutic paradigm, it is expected that the Ericksonian strategic approach will continue to flourish.

7

Using Hypnosis in
Brief Therapy[1]

Hypnosis can be an effective tool in many areas of brief therapy. This article briefly reviews some of the controversies and dichotomies in modern hypnosis. Discussing the induction of hypnosis with conscious and unconscious dissociation, the article takes a closer look at the construction and language of several types of indirect suggestions and therapeutic binds. General conditions for using hypnosis for situations of anxiety, performance building, and recovery from trauma-created limitations are summarized. The article ends with a short discussion of the danger of using hypnosis with certain people and a reminder to seek professional training and supervision.

While it may be difficult for therapists within a strict behavioral practice to foresee their use of hypnosis, it may be just as difficult for strict psychoanalytic-oriented therapists to recognize how hypnosis could fit into their practice without violating principles of counter-transference. However, strategic and brief therapists can purposefully or even unwittingly use the communication skills, perceptions, and experiential phenomena that are essential pillars of hypnosis. This article will address the use of clinical hypnosis by strategic- and brief-oriented therapists.

---

[1] Lankton, S. (2001). Using hypnosis in brief therapy. *Journal of Brief Therapy*, 1: 17–31. Reprinted with permission.

Hypnosis as it is practiced today is best understood as a tree with two branches. These branches often continue to grow apart despite many efforts to integrate them. The two branches are the traditional scientific study of hypnosis and the ever-changing clinical practice of hypnosis. Historical hypnosis probably owes its survival to scientific work that described, defined, and isolated its pertinent variables. Of course, research has been conducted since the work of Berheim, Charcot, and Freud near the beginning of the last century. Recent research in hypnosis has been addressed by authors such as Milton Erickson (1979), Irving Kirsch (1975), William Kroger (1977), Ernest Hilgard (1965, 1961), Andre Weitzenhoffer (1953), Martin Orne (1959), Sarbin and Coe (1972), Erika Fromm (1972), Herb Spiegel (1972), Robert Shor (1962), T. X. Barber (1979), and many others who have contributed to the journals of the *Society for Clinical and Experimental Hypnosis* and the *American Society for Clinical Hypnosis* for several decades. In all of this rigorous investigation, several controversies still abound within the research community.

Questions as to whether hypnosis is a "state" and whether it is dependent upon interpersonal influence and other environmental factors still await decisive answers. While an operational definition can be offered, there is still a question as to whether the operational definition should be based upon an individual's responsiveness to standardized suggestibility scales. Finally, there is the question of how to measure the existence of hypnosis at all, as no physiological correlates have been isolated that would distinguish hypnosis from a waking state.

Interestingly, hypnosis is more like a waking state than it is sleep. Hypnosis can be operationally defined as a *time-limited state of concentration typified by heightened internal focus with a reduction of external foci such that alterations in perceptual, cognitive, emotional, muscular, and visceral experience can be effected.* Scientific definitions of hypnosis, however, are often based on the use of suggestion. Usually the use of direct suggestion has been described as hypnotic when the subject responds in an unconscious or involuntary manner to the content of the suggestions used by the therapist (Weitzenhoffer, 1953). The basis of hypnosis defined in this manner relies upon an individual's ability to respond to suggestibility scales in a standardized manner (Barber, 1979; Eliseo, 1974; Hilgard, 1965; Shor & Orne, 1962; Spiegel, 1972; Weitzenhoffer & Hilgard, 1963). Conflict often results with clinicians who find that most of their clients can respond to hypnotic language and demonstrate hypnotic phenomena. Yet the scientific research has indicated that only half of the population should be susceptible to hypnosis. Erickson (Erickson & Rossi, 1979) believed that any individual who didn't have severe brain damage was hypnotizable. Paraphrasing him, I've often pointed out that any individual who can be socialized can be hypnotized.

Clinical hypnosis also has two branches. One branch grows in the direction of scientific standardized scales and direct suggestion with involuntary responses from a limited number of clients in the population. The other branch of the tree grows toward the use of hypnosis in a clinical setting with nearly any individual being a potential subject and the focus being upon any form of language that can be perceived to be making an impact consistent with the definition of hypnosis in the operational sense. This clinically oriented group consists of professionals who are somewhat less bound by some of the scientific evidence and how they apply it in practice, including the group of therapists who found support in Erickson's work.

The difficulty in researching Erickson's approach to change results from its being highly individualized. It may be more appropriate to say that practitioners can be studied for their ability to succeed by using various techniques rather than saying an independent entity called "hypnosis" can be researched. Also, the research that lends itself most easily to outcome validation pertains to diagnostic disorders that are most easily codified. These include anxiety disorders, phobias (Crawford & Barabasz, 1993), traumas (Spiegel, 1993), certain habits (Gardner, 1978), and a range of physiological events such as slowing bleeding (Bank, 1980) and anesthesia. However, hypnosis has been successfully used for a wide range of other cases, including pain (Barber, 1977; Lankton & Lankton, 1986), depression (Yapko, 1992), various adjustment disorders, sexual dysfunction (Araoz, 1982; Craselneck & Hall, 1975), family communications (Lankton, 1986), physical performance enhancement (Nugent, 1989a), mind/body (Rossi, Ryan, & Sharp, 1983), and even psychosis (Erickson, 1979b). This article will briefly discuss the induction and introduction of hypnosis in a session and its application in only three of these areas: anxiety, performance, and trauma recovery.

THE INDUCTION OF HYPNOSIS

There are many ways to induce hypnosis. The definition of hypnosis includes increasing internal absorption and decreasing attention to external foci that will accompany a reduction of critical analytic mechanisms in a manner that enhances the change in the various parameters mentioned above. Any engagement between the therapist and the client that begins to focus attention inward will, in fact, appear to be the beginning stage of trance induction. Therapists familiar with the double-chair technique of Gestalt Therapy may recognize that the result of that intervention satisfies the criteria for the beginning of an induction of hypnosis. Therapists who ask clients to close their eyes and try to recall a dream in detail and therapists who ask clients to role-play a situation of the past or the future have focused the client's attention inward and begun that type of engagement that can constitute the first stages of induction.

A formal induction usually requires clients to be seated with their arms and legs uncrossed and their attention focused on a progressive relaxation throughout the body. As the relaxation is deepened, the therapist often uses counting backwards to help the client develop an expectation that the internal focus is also going deeper. This sort of formal induction is perfectly acceptable; however, the aforementioned methods may be much more consistent with a client-centered approach that utilizes the client's presentations and concerns; I prefer this type of approach.

It is not necessary for clients to close their eyes to achieve a deepened, heightened internal concentration. However, this is usually more easily accomplished when eyes are closed. Clients should be offered all suggestions with an understanding that they can follow those that are relevant, modify those that can be modified to become relevant, and ignore those suggestions that seem to be irrelevant. All clients, through this type of participation, are responding to their own connection to the therapist, or in a way, hypnotizing themselves. It may be helpful to most clients to understand that they are in control of engaging or disengaging from the therapist's influence with suggestions and they are "hypnotizing themselves." In this way, all hypnosis can be seen as self-hypnosis.

Finally, a degree of increased dissociation begins to occur in response to comments about unconscious experience. Phrases such as the following may be used to facilitate that dissociation with the client: "Your conscious mind can listen to the things that I say while your unconscious begins to identify those ideas that are relevant for you." "Your conscious mind may be listening and sorting through your experiences while your unconscious relates in a global fashion to the experiences that you need." And, "your conscious mind may be following a certain train of thought while your unconscious reacts symbolically or follows an entirely different train of thought that's useful for you." In this manner, therapists direct the conscious mind to experiences that are easily validated and basically true for the client at that time. Thus, the induction is very individualized. Comments regarding the unconscious mind of a client are generally more global, contain a great deal more ambiguity and, regardless of attempts by therapists using direct suggestions, will involve a certain vagueness. This sort of vagueness can be elaborated and controlled by the use of therapeutic stories or indirect suggestion. A discussion of either of these techniques is beyond the scope of this article but can be found elsewhere (Lankton & Lankton, 1983, 1986, 1989).

Indirect suggestion can be an important part of accomplishing both the internal absorption and the dissociation. While these have been referred to earlier, the following section will give a brief glimpse as to what some of those forms of suggestion are and how they are formed. Six common forms of indirect suggestion and four common forms of therapeutic binds are representative of the large number of ways in which indirection can be codified.

OPEN-ENDED SUGGESTIONS

Open-ended suggestions take the form of increasing the degree of ambiguity for any element in a sentence that would otherwise be a direct suggestion. In common language usage, it's usually an open-ended suggestion that introduces a topic. For example, an open-ended suggestion such as, "Everyone can find a way to record information that's important," could have been formed from the direct suggestion "Write this down." Since it's an open-ended suggestion, the degree of compliance by the client is irrelevant. Instead of telling the client what to do, it initiates the client's own search process for a discovery of what's relevant — if that happens to be writing down what's been said, then an exact fit between the otherwise direct suggestion and what the client decides will have been made. But that's unusual. Open-ended suggestions are a prime example of how indirection is designed to be client-centered and to facilitate helping clients discover their own understanding of what's relevant and useful to them, with the therapist still retaining an element of control, yet avoiding an authoritarian relationship.

IMPLICATION

The form of implication is that of a simple or complex presupposition which also states a desired goal. For example, "After you write this down, we'll continue." This example uses presupposition syntax of the word "after," followed by the goal of taking notes by writing. Other presuppositions are: "Since this is the first time you've been in trance, close your eyes," and "After your trance is over, we'll do some talking about it" or "One of the first things you'll want to do in trance may be formulating a sense of comfort." In each of these examples, simple or complex presupposition was followed by a statement of the goal.

QUESTIONS OR STATEMENTS THAT FOCUS AWARENESS

Suggestions that focus awareness can take the form of questions or statements. Statements such as "I wonder if you'll be going into trance soon" or "I don't know if you've discovered how comfortable you are" have the effect of helping clients notice the portion of the sentence that highlights the goal and yet offers the sentence in a manner that seems to be rhetorical rather than strongly exclamatory. This form can also occur in questions such as: "Have you noticed how relaxed you are yet?" "Do you think you'll begin thinking about the goal that we spoke of?" While these questions seem rhetorical, in order to consider them the client must focus awareness as prescribed in the suggestion.

TRUISM

Truisms state something that is essentially undeniable. Such sentences usually begin with phrases like "All children" or "all people" or "in all cultures . . ." For example: "All people have their own way of going into trance," "Every child uses imagination to think about ideas," "In every culture, people problem-solve in a unique way."

ALL POSSIBLE ALTERNATIVES

Suggestions stating all possible alternatives can take several different forms but generally have the common aspect of listing many different ways or times in which a problem can be solved or a goal can be reached or experienced. For example, "Your eyes may close suddenly or they may close slowly or you may close them and open them repeatedly, maybe you'll squint for some time or it's possible that you'll have your eyes closed without realizing it and in some cases even have your eyes open and think that they're closed." Another example pertaining to relaxation could be "You may relax systematically from your head to your feet or you may relax from your feet to your head, perhaps you'll discover some portions already relaxed and relax adjacent parts of your body, or it's possible that there will be a gradual relaxation all over your entire body at once, or possibly random limbs and muscle groups will relax in a more spontaneous manner or perhaps it will happen differently." In all possible alternative suggestions, it is advisable to have one of the alternatives state that the client will not do any of those on the list because, in fact, you are trying to list all possible alternatives, including the alternative that nothing of that nature will occur. In this form of suggestion, the therapist's list helps clients recognize that there are many ways the goal can be achieved and that they have a choice in how they personally express themselves. Therapists continue to establish an egalitarian relationship or client-centered relationship with the client rather than forcing an authoritarian and heightened compliant relationship.

APPOSITION OF OPPOSITES

This form of suggestion emphasizes that the occurrence of a desired goal may proceed paradoxically against some behavior that is generally seen as its opposite. For example: "The greater a degree of tension you have in your muscles, the more profoundly you may relax," "The longer you have been confused about the issue, the more rapidly an idea may come," "The greater your uncertainty has been, the stronger your conviction may be." Clients can redirect and use energy previously devoted to avoiding or resisting to drive an equally strong, willful experience or behavior in the direction of their change. No reason or logic should be given for this paradox but rather clients should be allowed to discover for themselves how it becomes true for them. With indirect suggestion, the goal is not to make people behave in a particular way but rather to help stimulate their own thinking and experience in such a manner that they determine for themselves exactly what's relevant and how it's relevant for them.

BINDS OF COMPARABLE ALTERNATIVES

The first of the four therapeutic binds is Binds of Comparable Alternatives. In this type, two alternatives are provided so that clients may choose which is best for them and in the process of making either choice, the actual desired goal is accomplished because it was presupposed by both choices. For example, "You may want to try these ideas in your family before you go to work; however, it may be best for you to try them after work." In this case, the presupposition of trying the therapeutic material with the family exists for the client whether or not an attempt is made before or after work to implement the behavior. "You may go into trance by closing your eyes or you may wish to keep your eyes open" also presupposes going into trance regardless of the condition of the eyes.

CONSCIOUS/UNCONSCIOUS THERAPEUTIC BINDS

The Conscious/Unconscious Therapeutic Bind takes a form that is somewhat like an algebra expression with an "x" and "y" variable, one for the conscious and one for the unconscious. The form of the sentence is that the conscious mind may do "x" as the unconscious mind does "y." There are three things to consider about such a sentence. The first is what goes in place of the "x." It is a good idea to place a word that refers to something that clients can verify with their conscious mind. Some verb of mental activity such as wonder, discover, know, investigate, or find works very well in the position of "x" especially when there is only one specific therapeutic goal at that moment. What goes in place of the "y" in the formula is exactly what the goal is or some sub-portion of the goal at that moment. For example, if the goal happens to be to feel more comfortable spending time around one's new employer, the suggestion may state: "Your conscious mind may be surprised to discover how your unconscious will bring a feeling of relaxation around your new employer." If the goal is to relax in trance and recover a memory, the sentence could be formed as "Your conscious mind may be relaxed while your unconscious investigates that memory." The third thing to consider with conscious/unconscious therapeutic binds is how the conscious and unconscious parts of the sentence are connected. There are a variety of causal links, such as "and," "as," "since," "while," and "because," that can connect the two events.

DOUBLE DISSOCIATIVE CONSCIOUS/UNCONSCIOUS THERAPEUTIC BINDS

This form of bind is exactly the same as the previous one except that it accommodates two goals by duplicating and reversing variables on the conscious and unconscious as that phrase is repeated. An example of the formula is "Your conscious mind may do "x" as your unconscious mind does "y" or your conscious mind may do "y" as your unconscious mind does "x." When "x" and "y" represent two different goals they can or may become inexorably linked together by this type of verbal production. For example, if the goal is to feel comfortable and relaxed as you visualize interacting in a job interview, the sentence becomes "Your conscious mind may be comfortable and relaxed as your unconscious rehearses how you will conduct yourself at the job interview or perhaps your conscious mind will rehearse how you will conduct yourself at the job interview while your unconscious mind is comfortable and relaxed."

Therapeutic bind is especially apparent in this sort of sentence. The client in trying to determine whether or not the first part or the second part of the sentence is the most true has, in fact, associated comfort and relaxation and visualizing the job interview. The only way to escape making the bind become true is to simply pay no attention to the actual content of the indirect suggestion used by the therapist — hence the understanding that these are "therapeutic binds."

PSEUDO NON-SEQUITUR BINDS

The last form of bind is a pseudo–non-sequitur bind. A true non-sequitur question such as "Do you walk to school or carry your lunch?" may at first appear to be appropriately well formed as a question, but actually bears no connection between the elements provided for choice and is therefore a non-sequitur. In a pseudo non-sequitur suggestion, two apparently different choices are provided for the client; however, the choices are simply the same option with a rewording. This form differs from the bind of comparable alternatives because either choice is exactly the same choice. For example, "Do you think you'd like to go into a trance or would it be better to simply achieve an altered state appropriate for your learning today?"

Using Suggestions

No goal is likely to be reached by the utterance of a single suggestion but the goal could be addressed by each type of suggestion to facilitate varying kinds of mentation and therefore enhance the possibility that clients will respond in a way that is meaningful to them and consistent with the therapeutic goal delineated by the therapist. A brief example of an induction using these suggestions might go as follows:

I don't know whether or not you've been in trance before. After you reorient from trance we can discuss it. You can go into trance in your own way. Everyone goes into trance in a way that's unique for them. You might develop an altered state that's appropriate for learning today or maybe develop a deep clinical trance. And you can do that rapidly, or suddenly, or you can go into trance and come out and go back in again, or you might simply gradually drift into a deep trance, or perhaps a medium trance, or nothing at all. You can go into trance with your eyes open or closed. So let your conscious mind really wonder what the first thing your unconscious will do as you turn your attention inward. You may find that your conscious mind is able to make some sense of things that your unconscious focuses on as you turn your attention inward or maybe your conscious mind, in turning your attention inward, will allow your unconscious mind to find some things that it can focus upon. Because every human being has the ability to orient his or her experience toward that which is relevant. And the longer time you've spent in confusion wondering what to do, the more rapidly you may embrace the direction that seems right for you.

The suggestions in this hypothetical induction are given as examples to facilitate an understanding of trance induction and how it might be developed using indirection in a client-centered fashion in the clinical setting. Greater detail and study and supervised training are always necessary for the appropriate and ethical use of hypnosis in therapy.

Some clients will develop a rather profound and immobile state within three to five minutes while other clients may only develop such a state after 20 minutes of such suggestion. The depth of trance is less important than the relevance of the trance. The relevance of the trance will increase the degree of internal concentration and therefore increase the depth of trance. Each trance is individualized to the client and standardized inductions should be avoided as much as possible. The state of internal absorption, the presence of some degree of ambiguity, and dissociation of the conscious mind establish a situation of communication with the client that is most conducive to helping that client focus upon and amplify various experiences. Since brief therapy is interested in focusing upon client resources, that state of concentration and focus can be used to solve current life situation problems. Both of these aspects of mentation become the focus of the therapeutic part of the hypnosis. This article does not intend to replace supervised training or in-depth study of hypnosis. It only intends to facilitate a cognitive understanding about hypnosis as it is created and introduced in therapy sessions. Primarily, the focus should be on questions about which resources are useful to concentrate upon and in what way to accomplish various goals, such as reduction of anxiety, performance increase, and the beginning steps of trauma recovery.

ANXIETY SYMPTOMS

Hypnosis research is replete with studies concerning the reduction or elimination of anxiety, performance anxiety, sexual performance anxiety, and various other anxiety-based concerns. Hypnosis is usually performed with a concentration on relaxation. The ability to increase relaxation and comfort in this manner contributes to temporary relief for many clients. In fact, if nothing more were accomplished than learning to relax periodically throughout one's day, a number of self-regulatory mechanisms may be automatically triggered (Rossi, Ryan, & Sharp, 1983). The internalization of a habit for self-hypnosis could bring about this sort of stress reduction in one's life. However, that's not the use of hypnosis for anxiety reduction to which this article refers.

In general, the sources of anxiety can be seen as coming from one of two dynamic ideologies. The first is that which is represented in classical dynamic psychology theory. This pertains to an increase of anxiety as defense mechanisms begin to fail and threatening feelings, thoughts, or impulses begin to penetrate into the conscious mind. The second type of anxiety results from an inability on the part of the client to access and organize needed experiences in the context in which they are needed. The types of experiences a person may need at any given moment range from cognitive, perceptual, emotional to behavioral and complex groupings of these into various roles. The greater the degree to which the environment demands a certain type of perception or experience for smooth operation, the greater the anxiety will be for the individual who is unable to access or retrieve that experience. The general rationale and tactics for these two different dynamic ideologies of anxiety will be discussed separately.

Anxiety based upon the inability to produce needed experiences in desired contexts is most conducive to change in clinical hypnosis. The method of intervention is to help the person identify and retrieve the needed and desired

121

experiences but this process is influenced by the conceptualization of the problem and/or background experiences of the client in question. Looking at an example to illustrate this will highlight both of these aspects. Consider the case of a client with an inability to perform sexual intercourse and in this case, let's also say that the individual desires to perform and has no other questions regarding sexual orientation. The therapist using hypnosis would have gathered sufficient information about the client's needs, desires, and history, would have contracted with the client to use the session for this purpose with the mutual understanding of a goal, and may have chosen to induce hypnotic trance.

So far so good. The first problem would arise when the therapist used either direct or indirect suggestion to ask the client to remember, retrieve, or reexperience the perceptions, emotions, and sensations related to previous sexual performance. Painting the goal with such broad strokes, conceptualizing it with such a global term as retrieving previous sexual performance would be certain to fail with the client who has no previous history of sexual experience or sexual performance. It simply could not be possible for the client to reach into his or her past and produce an experience that has not previously been performed. With such an intervention then, we can see both sides of the common error that can occur. For example, conceptualizing the problem or solution too globally or too generally prevents resource retrieval. Furthermore, attempting to retrieve too large a chunk of experience and, in the case illustrated, calling for an experience that does not exist in the client's historical repertoire, may lead to failure and frustration. However, the same client with the same goal would most likely be perfectly capable of experiencing all of the components that make up sexual responsiveness, such as the ability to fantasize, to be excited, to increase one's heart rate, to alter one's breathing, to be tender. The client would even be able to experience the physiological components of mucous membrane stimulation, the ability to look at another person, and the ability to combine these various pieces of experiences and label them with the term chosen by the client to represent sexual arousal. These various subcomponents of physiology, cognition, perception, and labeling would most likely exist in the historical repertoire of all adult clients. Combining this with the memory of rapid physical movement and rhythmical physical activity begins to approximate sexual response to a sufficient degree that it can be organized and brought into the foreground. Associating this experience in the context in which it is to be performed and desired is a matter that will be discussed shortly. But in this example, it is enough to have illustrated that the success or failure of the strategy of using hypnosis in therapy may largely depend upon the methodical and tactical planning of the therapist and the selection of incremental stages and steps that will help the client reach the stated goal. Unless there happen to be other learned limitations to experiencing these retrieved resources, this general tactic should be successful in time with any client who is capable of establishing the hypnotic relationship with the therapist.

When there are learned limitations regarding experiences we find that the client has a situation that parallels the other dynamic ideology for generating anxiety, that is, an internal conflict. The breaking down of successful defense mechanisms often leads to the experience of anxiety due to this very reason. So, a hypnotic tactic or strategy that becomes most appropriate for individuals with this second type of ideology has to do with properly handling and dealing with these previously learned limitations. In such cases, the actual learned limitations can take a number of different shapes depending upon the unique client. For any individual who has successfully learned a limitation about experience, we should expect that those learned limitations include nearly every aspect of human functioning from role to behavior to emotion, cognition, perception, and visceral response as well. However, each individual will have a different emphasis on any of these experiential subsystems. One individual may have a very strong cognitive component such as a religious belief that it is improper to engage in sexual activity, while another individual may have a very strong visceral experience that may have been the result of an early punishment. Therapists must determine for each unique individual what that unique set of limitations is.

Once those limitations have been identified, the direction of therapy proceeds in such a way as to reevaluate the need for those previously learned limitations or to perceive and discriminate times in which those limitations are still needed and times in which those limitations are no longer needed. This learning often involves a recognition that more options are available to the adult than were once available at the time the limitation was learned and imposed. In some cases, resources that are available to the adult that were not available to the child include things that had been disallowed and avoided. At other times it may be cognitions and interpretations of sensations and their various peculiar combinations that uniquely exist for each individual and form the unique gestalt relevant to that client. As the client with anxiety difficulties learns to no longer inhibit more appropriate, useful, and adaptive responses and experiences, the client also will find it is possible to have the desired and necessary experiences in the context in which they are demanded. Habits for these behaviors and experiences can be learned and practiced within the context of hypnosis so that laborious mental deliberation is not needed each time a client desires to reduce anxiety. In fact, the ability to habituate or condition these sets of resources and unlearning previously learned limits constitutes one of the major assets of hypnosis.

HYPNOSIS FOR BUILDING PERFORMANCE

Related to the goal of improving one's ability to function with desired resources and without anxiety is the task of performing in the desired fashion with these resources. Using hypnosis to improve performance has been researched especially as it pertains to sports and gymnastic performance (Nugent, 1989a, 1989b). However, the type of behavioral and perceptual change necessary for tasks and stunt performances translates very well to a tool that will help enhance interpersonal performance in any situation, from test taking to job interviews to social conduct in general. Self-image thinking is a device to be learned in trance for the client to use consciously at other times (Lankton & Lankton, 1983, 1986, 1989). Self-image thinking consists of using certain mental mechanisms for imagination, experience association, and posthypnotic suggestion to build a conditioned set of responses to anticipated stimuli. Some research (Meichenbaum, 1997) has confirmed that this type of behavioral fantasy rehearsal is more rapid and more successful for reducing test-taking anxiety than systemic desensitization techniques. The following list summarizes the minimum necessary steps for accomplishing the intervention of building self-image thinking for a client and rehearsing through desired performance situations.

I.   Build a Central Self-Image.
1.   Once the client has accomplished entering into a state of hypnosis, suggest relaxing as much as possible and establishing a secure and comfortable sense of well-being.
2.   Ask the client to visualize an image of the self that is currently accurate.
3.   Having previously identified at least three desired experiences, ask the client to begin systemically recalling a time when those experiences were being used.
4.   Ask the client to revivify, age regress, or in some other fashion go back in time and reexperience the perceptions, thoughts, and feelings of each of those desired experiences.
5.   As each experience is revivified and felt, ask the client to notice small

changes in posture, facial expression, and breathing and add this identified feature to the original image of the self-created image in step 2 above.

6. After each of the desired experiences has been identified, revivified, felt, and located symbolically with some visual change of the original central self-image, ask the client to add to this image another human figure in the background, maybe the figure of a child, parent, spouse, girlfriend, boyfriend, or any person who would support the client with these resources. This constitutes creation of the central self-image part of self-image thinking.

II. Create and Rehearse Various Scenarios in an Approximation to the Most Feared Scenario.

1. The client is to let the background of the central self-image fade into a visual movie. This movie consists of allowing the social aspect of the central self-image to be replaced by circumstances that are relatively conducive to the image of the client with the resources and the feelings and behaviors relevant to those resources continuing within the visualization. For example, the client might let the central self-image fade into a visualization that depicts a celebration of his/her own birthday with people at a party who would be willing to allow the client to continue interacting with the desired resources the client chose for the central self-image. As the client watches this scenario unfold, the instruction is to continue to feel the desired resources, watch the image of the self with those desired resources, and imagine the auditory track that would congruently accompany the observed behavior. In this way the client is beginning to develop a complex imagination in a congruent fashion regarding emotions, behavior, and social interaction that are all centered around desired experiences. Simultaneously, desired resources are being experienced while having the behavioral rehearsal and imagining the interaction. Finally, each of these elements is becoming somewhat associated with the anticipated stimuli that would be present during such an event.

2. The client changes the scenario to imagine the background becoming a more neutral, and therefore somewhat less supportive situation. Still the client retains the desired experiences and continues to watch a visualization of the self with those desired resources while hearing the auditory soundtrack that would accompany it. A neutral situation in

this scenario might be interacting with sales clerks in a department store.

3. The client changes the central self-image again and imagines the background becoming slightly more potentially difficult. The background might depict events that would occur when there was an argument in the family. The client maintains the feeling of the desired resources and visualizes the self holding on to those feelings. Consequently, the unfolding circumstances will be reviewed in a manner that is somewhat uncommon.

4. The client unfolds still another scenario from the central self-image in which the desired target situation represents the most previously anxiety-producing experience possible for the client. Once again, the visualization, auditory, and emotional experiences are all held constant during the visualized behavior rehearsal. In this manner the performances and cues for the proper performance are being rehearsed verbally, visually, emotionally, and behaviorally.

Each of these rehearsed presentations is being associated with the anticipated stimuli that will actually occur during future situations in which the client wishes to have these desired resources constant. Asking the client to provide a 10- or 20-minute self-image thinking process such as this will facilitate the reduction of anxiety, the presence of the desired feelings, and even the proper anticipated performance in all of these scenarios. Repeatedly processing such imaginational information as this will increasingly guarantee that the scripted performance be carried out by the client at the proper time. Obviously, this sort of technique can be accomplished by almost anyone. The visualization does not have to be lucid nor does the experiencing of the desired resources need to be in a full age regression. The greater the degree of concentration in each of these sensory areas, the greater the accomplishment will be for the client on a single rehearsal. Fantasy behavior rehearsals such as these can be used for one's own performance, as well as to maximum productivity during various social interactions for enjoyment or for business or in a family setting. With the proper resources being retrieved, such self-image thinking has an application for a wide range of problem-solving situations from sexual performance to insomnia, dieting, study and test taking, job interview behavior, and so on.

OVERCOMING TRAUMATIC LIMITATIONS

Often brief therapists are asked to help clients overcome the results of traumatic limitations that have occurred in the distant past or even in the relatively recent past. One of the greatest limitations for clients in doing this has to do with the need for recall of unpleasant physical or emotional experience as they process the information related to the trauma. For example, a person who has been involved in a train derailment accident may remember some of the information that occurred as screaming, some of the information as visual facts of the terrain and the location of cars and bodies, and some of the information as physical, emotional detail such as her own fear or pain and discomfort. When the client is attempting to problem solve and needs to recall traumatic experience, she therefore recalls the experience in each of the sensory modalities in which it was stored. In other words, she sees some of the visual data, remembers the sounds of some of the auditory data, and actually reexperiences the pain, discomfort, and emotional stress that were stored as feeling and bodily data. The absolute necessity for a person to problem solve using experience from the past will guarantee that the client rehash the experience of the trauma and in turn will guarantee some degree of reexperiencing of the physical and emotional aspect of the trauma itself. For this reason, the very act of problem solving that the client uses will become part of the limitation for overcoming the trauma when using talking therapies or even pharmaceutical interventions.

However, hypnosis can facilitate a rapid reorganization of knowledge about the trauma so that little or none of the dysphasia needs to be reexperienced during the process of recall or the act of problem solving. In brief, once the client has used hypnosis to facilitate dissociating emotional experiences away from the traumatic memory and recoding aspects of the physical experience into visual experience, the client will no longer have to feel discomfort during the act of thinking about the trauma. Therefore, any real need to rethink the trauma for court cases or for future planning or for reassessing one's self in the process of normal growth can be done without any degree of retraumatization. It is the author's understanding that what can be accomplished using hypnosis in this fashion is essentially parallel to what occurs in the normal growth and socialization process as one overcomes the painful limitations brought on by earlier traumas. However, the hypnotic intervention makes it possible for this socialization and relearning to take place in a minimum number of sessions and with a great deal more confidence and control that the outcome will be achieved.

The ideas for intervening presented so far in this article have provided sufficient outline to make it possible to briefly summarize the tactics necessary for helping clients overcome these major limitations of trauma. Once such major limitations are overcome, the client can more easily proceed with making proper adjustments to other community resources, doing this sort of grief and forgiveness work that is typical for traumas and using other aspects of talking therapy to grow beyond the difficulty. Major steps in this intervention are as follows:

SIMPLE ASSOCIATION/DISSOCIATION FOR TRAUMA RECOVERY

The steps necessary to establish a simple association/dissociation experience are similar, but slightly more precise than those listed above:

1. The client needs to establish a hypnotic trance.
2. If not already accomplished, the client needs to have the conscious experience distracted from the painful aspect of the traumatic memory.
3. Feelings of security, confidence, and other desired resources need to be retrieved for the client. Note that these feelings of security may be found in the client's past as mentioned before and can even be found so to speak in the client's future by presupposing with the client that at some time in the next couple of months, there will have been a full recovery and desired feelings will be available at that time. In this manner, the client's imagination proceeds into a future state rather than receding into a past memory. Either way the result is much the same.
4. The client needs to be instructed to literally see and hear *only* events of the past unfold. During this unfolding the client is able to retain the desired resources while seeing the events of the past entirely visually or hearing aspects of them in the auditory manner. At any time the client may need to stop and restrenghten resources in order to proceed with security and comfort.
5. The client should be instructed to make self-nurturing and self-educational comments to the projected part of him- or herself from the traumatic experience. That is, if a victim of violence is being seen in a darkened alley, suggest words for the client to say to that self regarding the intent to be cautious and protective in the future. Nurturing com-

ments are to be offered as if speaking to the self in the past that this violence is not of the self's own doing and so on. More information on this can be found in Lankton and Lankton, 1989.

6. The client should be instructed to view the events that took place in the past and to unfold them in reverse chronological order from most recent to the most distance aspect of the event. By running the event in reverse chronological order, the conditioned aspect of imagery is broken down so that the painful experience that followed event A now precedes event A and the classical conditioning of the sequence of experience no longer holds the same difficulty for the client that it may once have held.

7. The client should be asked to reintegrate this dissociated part back into him- or herself and to in some way connect the learning of those events into a uniform scheme that continues to be useful and facilitate growth. The therapist needs to check on the success of this intervention by asking the client to once again imagine parts of the trauma and find out whether or not in so doing the client has a sense of being freed from the actual impact of pain that preceded the intervention.

COMPLEX ASSOCIATION/DISSOCIATION FOR TRAUMA RECOVERY

In the case of traumas which have been so severe that the client is unlikely to be able to find a secure enough posture while reviewing the trauma, a more complex type of dissociation should be used. This consists of asking clients not to see the events of the trauma or themselves during the trauma but rather to see a representation of themselves that in turn views other representations of the self. It is this second representation removed from the client, who is actually instructed to review the events of the past.

This is somewhat difficult to articulate but might be better understood by imagining that the client sitting on a couch against the wall may envision a younger self, preferably one who was quite resourceful, sitting in a chair several feet in front of him. The person who is sitting in the first chair is to communicate with the client on the couch through the client's imagination by a head-nod (or similar cue). That is, the client is to ask for that representation to demonstrate an understanding of what to do next in a compliance that's been accomplished by watching for that image to have a head-nod occur as a signal to the client on the couch. In turn, that imagined person should be asked by the client on the couch to imagine still another representation a few feet in front and that representation again be a resourceful part from the past. It is this second imagined person who is to see the trauma and not the client on the couch. The client on the couch may be watching, say, a 23-year-old college graduate from the past in the chair nod his head that he is seeing a 10-year-old athlete that he once was sitting in front of and it's this 10-year-old athlete who is to be instructed to see the events of the trauma. As the 10-year-old athlete sees the events of the trauma, he will presumably nod his head so that the college graduate can see that occurring and nod his head to the client on the couch. This may all seem somewhat impossible but it works quite easily for the general population of trauma victims who are in trance. At no time should the client on the couch actually see the events of the trauma and he should be instructed to only allow these imagined images from the past to "see" the events of the trauma. Reviewing the trauma for whichever imagined self is handling that task should be conducted in the manner similar to that described above in the simple association/dissociation experience.

Similarly, once it is completed, all parts should be reintegrated into the self. Sometimes it is valuable and important for a previously lost experience to be brought back to the adult client. That is, some degree of playfulness or trust or sexuality or the ability to be angry or to cry may have been separated off during the trauma. This experience will actually be available to the client in this complex dissociation and can be brought back to the adult client on the couch by asking for some sort of a trade to be made between the protection and nurturance of the adult client being passed along the pipeline to the image in the trauma and asking that the adult receive the experience passed forward while experiencing making the desired trade for the younger part in the trauma.

For example, through the multiple images between the client and the younger client and the image of the trauma, a trading of resources can be negotiated that may involve the ability to have tears being passed forward from the younger part of the trauma and received by the adult on the couch as the adult on the couch experiences a sense of verbalization and sense of tenderness and acceptance directed toward the younger part in the trauma. Each part is guided to identify the resources that are needed and facilitated in making this imaginary trade.

While this entire matter is somewhat metaphoric, what we can be sure of that happens under these circumstances is that the client is actually activating neurons that in some way relate to the trauma but doing it in a fashion that complicates imagination with images of the self as a resourceful person who handled successfully other difficult events such as college and athletics. For each client, these successes will be at different ages and deal with different topics, of course. While those experiences are being retrieved and neurons related to them are being activated, the client is imaging the usefulness of some of the experiences that had once been encapsulated in the traumatic memory. In the trading of experiences, associations are made to the resources with the previously lost experience so that one triggers the other to some degree. For most clients the previously lost experience becomes available and does not in any way remind the client of weakness or threat of the trauma. Hence, the lost experience is reintegrated into the current and future repertoire of the client's behavior and emotional life.

The use of hypnosis to secure an ability for clients to associate with strength and other positive resources in such a short period of time helps empower them and prepares them to continue the remainder of the therapy needed for trauma recovery, such as grieving, forgiving, and other social behaviors.

DANGERS OF HYPNOSIS

There are very few contraindications to the use of hypnosis. The two most obvious categories of contraindication include psychosis and the extreme borderline client. The issue of greatest importance in these cases is the ambiguity of the relationship in light of increased rapport. Hypnosis is also a state of heightened rapport. As such it presents a challenge to anyone who already experiences difficulty with social boundaries. A borderline diagnosis for some individuals usually suggests a deficiency in understanding where the client stops and another person begins. Therapists run the risk of exacerbating this very problem when they use hypnosis with such individuals.

Dr. Erickson liked to remind his students that hypnosis does not hurt people but rather that reckless and unethical therapists hurt people. Seen interpersonally, hypnosis is a special context for communication that offers a chance for intense and accurate pinpointing of experience. In order to make the most beneficial and ethical use of hypnosis in brief therapy, therapists should obtain ample qualified training from recognized professionals and follow the training with supervision.

CONCLUSION

Brief therapy is a field of therapy that addresses a wide range of problems and attempts to meet the challenges of change by emphasizing and drawing upon the resources and strengths of clients. Hypnosis is a tool for creating a heightened attention and amplification of such experiences and it is therefore increasing in popularity among practitioners. It is necessary to obtain qualified training but the rewards are likely to be found immediately in such areas of practice as cases related to anxiety and stress, overcoming trauma, performance, and related issues. While research is currently conducted in hypnosis, more active attempts to develop research protocols that apply to highly unique therapists and clients may allow us an opportunity to better unite research with clinical practice and provide a sounder and more ethical foundation for clinical practitioners as well.

References

Araoz, D. (1982). *Hypnosis and sex therapy.* New York: Brunner/Mazel.

Arnold, M. B. (1959). Brain function in hypnosis. *The International Journal of Clinical and Experimental Hypnosis, 7,* 109.

Bank, W. (1985). Hypnotic suggestion for the control of bleeding in the angiography suite. *Ericksonian Monographs, 1,* 76–89.

Barber, J. (1977). Rapid induction analgesia: A clinical report. *American Journal of Clinical Hypnosis, 23,* 112–118.

Barber, T. X. (1979). The Barber Suggestibility Scale and the Creative Imagination Scale: Experimental and clinical applications. *American Journal of Clinical Hypnosis, 21,* 84–108.

Cassleneck H. B., & Hall, J. A. (1975). *Clinical hypnosis: Principles and applications.* New York: Grune and Stratton.

Crawford, H., & Barabasz, A. (1993). Phobias and intense fears: Facilitating their treatment with hypnosis. In W. Rhue, S. Lynn, & I. Kirsch (Eds.), *Handbook of clinical hypnosis* (pp. 311–337). Washington, DC: American Psychological Association.

Eliseo, T. S. (1974). The hypnotic induction profile and hypnotic susceptibility. *The International Journal of Clinical and Experimental Hypnosis, 22,* 320.

Erickson, M. H. (1980). Hypnosis — its renaissance as a treatment modality. In E. L. Rossi (Ed.), *The collected papers of Milton H. Erickson on hypnosis* (Vol. 4, pp. 52–75). *Hypnotic investigation of psychodynamic press.* New York: Irvington.

Erickson, M. H., & Rossi, E. L. (1979). *Hypnotherapy: An exploratory casebook.* New York: Irvington.

Erickson, M. H., & Rossi, E. L. (Eds.). (1980). *The collected papers of Milton H. Erickson on hypnosis; Vol. 1. The nature of hypnosis and suggestion.* New York: Irvington.

Fromm, E. (1972). Ego activity and ego passivity in hypnosis. *International Journal of Clinical and Experimental Hypnosis, 18,* 79–88.

Gardner, G. G. (1978). Hypnotherapy in the management of childhood habit disorders. *Journal of Pediatrics, 92,* 834.

Haley, J. (Ed.). (1967). *Advanced techniques of hypnosis and therapy: Selected papers of Milton H. Erickson, M.D.* New York: Grune & Stratton.

Hilgard, E. R. (1965). *Hypnotic susceptibility.* New York: Harcourt, Brace.

Hilgard, E. R. (1966). Posthypnotic amnesia: Experiments and theory. *International Journal of Clinical and Experimental Hypnosis, 14,* 104–111.

Hilgard, E. R., Weitzenhoffer, A., Landes, J., & Moore, R. (1961). The distribution of susceptibility to hypnosis in student population: A study using the Stanford Hypnotic Susceptibility Scale. *Psychology Monographs, 75*(8), 1–22.

Lankton, S., & Lankton, C. (1983). *The answer within: A clinical framework of Ericksonian hypnotherapy.* New York: Brunner/Mazel.

Lankton, S., & Lankton, C. (1986). *Enchantment and intervention in family therapy: Training in Ericksonian approaches.* New York: Brunner/Mazel.

Lankton, C., & Lankton, S. (1989). *Tales of enchantment: Goal-oriented metaphors for adults and children in therapy.* New York: Brunner/Mazel.

Kirsch, I. (1990). Changing expectations: *A key to effective psychotherapy.* Pacific Grove, CA: Brooks/Cole.

Kirsch, I. (1985). Response expectancy as a determinant of experience and behavior. *American Psychologist, 40*(11), 1189–1202.

Kroger, W. (1977). *Clinical and experimental hypnosis.* Philadelphia: J. P. Lippincott Company.

Meichenbaum, D. (1977). *Cognitive behavior modification: An integrative approach.* New York: Plenum Press.

Nugent, W. (1989a). Evidence concerning the causal effect of an Ericksonian hypnotic intervention. *Ericksonian Monographs, 5,* 35–55.

Nugent, W. (1989b). A multiple baseline investigation of an Ericksonian hypnotic approach. *Ericksonian Monographs, 5,* 69–85.

O'Neil, H., Jr. (1978). *Learning strategies.* New York: Academic Press.

Orne, M. (1959). The nature of hypnosis: Artifact and essence. *Journal of Abnormal and Social Psychology, 58,* 277–299.

Orne, M. (1962). On the social psychology of the psychological experiment with particular reference to demand characteristics and their implications. *American Psychologist, 17,* 776.

Rossi, E., Ryan, M., & Sharp, F. (Eds.). (1983). *Healing in hypnosis by Milton H. Erickson*. New York: Irvington.

Sarbin, T. R., & Coe, W. C. (1972). Role-theoretical analysis of hypnotic behavior. In J. E. Gordon (Ed.), *Handbook of clinical and experimental hypnosis* (pp. 319–344). New York: Macmillan.

Sarbin, T. R., & Coe, W. C. (1972). *Hypnosis: A social psychological analysis of influence communication*. New York: Holt: Rinehart, and Winston.

Shor, R., & Orne, E. (1962). *The Harvard Group Scale of Hypnotic Susceptibility, Form A*. Palo Alto, CA: Consulting Psychologists Press.

Spiegel, H. (1972). An eye-roll test for hypnotizability. *American Journal of Clinical and Experimental Hypnosis, 15*, 25–28.

Weitzenhoffer, A. M. (1953). *Hypnotism: An objective study in suggestibility*. New York: Wiley.

Weitzenhoffer, A. M., & Hilgard, E. R. (1963). *Stanford Hypnotic Susceptibility Scale, Form C*. Palo Alto, CA: Consulting Psychologists Press.

Wolberg, L. R. (1948). *Medical hypnosis, Vol. I: The principles of hypnotherapy*. New York: Grune and Stratton.

Yapko, M. (1992). *Hypnosis and the treatment of depressions: Strategies for change*. New York: Brunner Mazel.

8

Just Do Good Therapy[1]

UNDERSTANDING AND JOINING

Perhaps the greatest problem with therapy is attempting to make it conform to a theory or paradigm. Often, therapy is judged by the language it uses or its conformity to a school (e.g., family therapy, Erickson therapy, cognitive therapy, brief therapy, or whatever). In so doing, therapists and clients become the servants of the model instead of using the model to serve clients and therapists. This paper addresses what I believe makes therapy "good therapy" from three standpoints: 1) the relationship, 2) the therapy practice, and 3) my experience as a client. It is intended to help us maintain perspective and to keep our attention on designing unique treatment for each unique client-system.

As an example of this initial process I want to share an experience that became a personal breakthrough in understanding how to apply Milton Erickson's work in my practice. In 1969 at a crisis intervention center, The Listening Ear, in East Lansing, Michigan, my role included training volunteers in empathy skills and also working with people who were having what were euphemistically called "bad drug trips." The typical action went something like this.

---

[1] Lankton, S. (1989). Just do good therapy. In S. Gilligan & J. Zeig (Eds.), *Brief therapy: Myths, methods, and metaphors* (pp. 62–77). New York: Brunner/Mazel. Reprinted with permission.

CLIENT: [walking — for lack of better word — into center]

LANKTON: "Hi! Can I help you?"

CLIENT: "Oh, no, man ... I shouldn't have come here."

LANKTON: "Oh really ... nah, this is a safe and comfortable place to be."

CLIENT: "Yeah, but the walls are moving and the room is getting smaller."

LANKTON: "Oh, I wasn't thinking about that. I was pretty relaxed. Does it seem that way now?"

CLIENT: "Yeah, I can't stand it. I got to get out of here."

LANKTON: "Wait, let me see!" [moving near the head of the client] "Oh, yes, I see what you mean. The walls do seem to be moving. They are moving like, sort of like waves. Yeah, it's like the waves of the ocean, sort of. I love the ocean, don't you?"

CLIENT: "Eh, yeah. I do."

LANKTON: "I think the shadows on the wall make it look like waves rolling in to the beach. That always makes me feel comfortable. I just love sitting in the sun on the beach and watching the waves. Don't you? Do you feel like that, too?"

CLIENT: "Yeah, I really do. It does sort of seem like that."

LANKTON: "Yeah, and the warmth of the room is the sunlight that makes you just relax and watch the waves and dream happy daydreams. Do you know what I mean?"

CLIENT: "Yeah, I do. Yeah, I remember that. Yeah. [long exhale and pause] I'm glad I came in here."

LANKTON: "Yeah, me too. It's nice talking with you. What is your name?"

The subsequent conversation was about the drug that had been taken, and also indicated how much longer I would need to continue this manner of careful communication. Though perhaps somewhat amusing, this example illustrates something of deep significance about understanding and joining, namely, how therapists may, to paraphrase Dr. Erickson (personal communication, 1976), proceed by putting one foot in the client's world and leaving one foot in their own world. After joining in this way, clients are guided or motivated to create an alternate, more desirable reality that contains sufficient resources for coping.

This example does little to illustrate how to further help such a person enjoy life without taking dangerous drugs. Nevertheless, it is an effective beginning. There is no need to stand at a distance and analyze clients. The act of doing so might well produce more bizarre and dangerous results. To create those results and exacerbate the problem further by attributing them to the client, perhaps placing him in a diagnostic niche, could be destructive. Yet, this is exactly what occurs repeatedly in many treatment situations.

In the example, I treat a person-in-relation-to-his-environment. In this regard, the case represents a situation similar to the ones we routinely encounter with individuals and families. A difference is that usually therapy clients have less altered perceptions and less dramatic, but longer-lasting behaviors. Their perceptual distortions are merely harder to spot, since they do not often "leap out" at the therapist. In either case, however, the posture of the therapist needs to be actively engaging, motivating, and guiding. Joining in this way involves temporarily embracing the reality experienced by each client.

Trusting Yourself and Others

I hold certain things to be real, true, and meaningful, and other things to be untrue, unreal, and meaningless. However, I do not need to constantly verify these beliefs. I can consider "reality" from the senses and beliefs of others during therapy. I can believe "as if" something were real, that the walls are moving, and so on. The more I take on "as if real" the beliefs, perceptions, and feelings of others, the more I learn to experience and act in the world as they do.

And, this is where I sometimes place limitations. This empathy is not always pleasant, and in some cases it is potentially harmful to my beliefs. That is, I would usually be willing to experience an understanding of the reality of headaches, back pains, depressions, anxieties, and even some hallucinations experienced by others — because I know how to touch on those experiences and move away from them. I can hold onto myself and my beliefs and lead clients and myself elsewhere. But I would not want to *know*, in the experiential sense of the word, how a person desires to do terrible acts of violence, betrayal, or hatred.

Although it does not happen often, there are several types of clients with whom I won't join. For instance, I would not attempt to move my "head and heart" near a murderer and attempt to feel, see, touch, hear, smell, and believe the world from his or her senses. Therefore, I would not attempt therapy with such an individual. Were I to do so, I would be working without the asset of my intuitions; I would hide my intuitive self to keep it safe from the pain of a certain psychological trickery or fate. And, when I hide that intuition, I am looking at clients through a telescope instead of a microscope — doing surgery with a shovel instead of a scalpel. In other words, I can't and won't work as effectively with such a client.

Basically, I will join with and, to some extent, know the world of my clients in most cases. As I join bit by bit, I also suggest, elaborate, and guide the client from the world I experience at the time into a different world. This different world is not mine but one I can simulate as a result of knowing something of the clients' experiences. This co-created world is the therapeutic goal for the session, as it can be used to guide clients to novel attitudes, affect, behaviors, and self-perceptions. At the end of the therapy the novel experiences should lead clients to a problem-free world and leave me in mine.

Liking Clients

Liking one's clients is a well-known aspect of therapy, but it bears repeating that if you do not like your clients, you cannot feel "with" them. While this may handicap your work, it will most certainly be observed by clients. Some clients will be more sensitive to social cues and, by this subtle behavior, be provoked into a further rejection of their experience. Defensively, they will become more entangled in the limitations and defenses that produced the problems and brought them to therapy.

It is best, if one does not trust or like a client, to refer him/her elsewhere. (If you find this happens often, refer yourself there too!) What I find I like best about people is their ability and willingness to learn and take joy in learning. Somehow, when I find that a person has a spark of curiosity and a joy in discovering something, anything, I can follow that inspiration and help him/her use it as a part of therapy. Furthermore, the courage to learn, which is demonstrated by the client, is an inspiration to me. This is what I most respect about my clients.

Creating Reality

When clients conceptualize themselves in the world in ways that are self-limiting, one can, with confidence, take the position that the conceptualization held by the client is not true. It may be true for the client but it is not the only truth. And it is important to remember that same dictum when we conceptualize clients' problems: If we conceptualize clients as limited we are mistaken and need to rethink our position.

As an example, I want to relate an incident with my son, Shawn, when he was 15 months old. At that time he could say very little. In fact, it seemed that the only thing he said at that age was "... want this!" He came into the kitchen one day as I was putting the groceries away and pointed to the laundry detergent box and said, "... want this." I offered the box but he repeated his singular verbalization. To make a long story short, I offered everything on the countertop to him and he continued to request something else. As a good mental health professional would do, I picked him up and asked him to put his finger on what he wanted because I could not quite understand him. He placed his finger on the box of laundry detergent! The box displayed a picture of a magnifying glass and, beneath that, a magnified view of some brown fabric fibers. I thought he must be making a request for a magnifying glass and I made an offer to get him one. He refused it. I even went and got one for him thinking that he merely did not know the word for it. He refused it and pointed and said, "... want this."

Now, any reasonable parent would have been inclined to set him down and tell him to go play elsewhere with the instruction "there is nothing here you need." Had I done this, he would have thrown a fit: He was so determined and he would have been frustrated. And if he had thrown a fit, I would have been tempted to say to myself, "He is being a brat." I might have even told my former wife, Carol, about the incident when she came home and we would have both "remembered" several other times when he seemed to "have a mind of his own" and thus concluded that, in fact, he was a brat.

What did transpire, however, was quite different. He put his hand on the magnifying glass in the picture. I looked at the "fabric" below it and wondered, "What in the world could this look like to him?" I said, "Do you want a pretzel?" And, he replied, "Yes, Daddy, a prentzel" — saying it incorrectly and thus indicating that he did not know the word. Then he hugged my neck tightly and said, "I love you, Daddy." This was not a manipulation to get a pretzel — it was clear that he was getting one. This was a way of saying, "I know you respected my observation enough to stick with me and figure this out and thank you for believing in me." I concluded he was very smart and persistent.

Now the point is this. Is he a brat or is he smart and persistent? Whatever I decided that day, reinforced by Shawn's behavior, and my future perceptions, would have become the "truth." This is what we do with our clients repeatedly for better or worse. We label them and think we have observed reality. We have, along with them, cocreated reality. If we decide that a person is stuck because of his or her marital situation, it becomes a truth we must "cure." If we decide that the person needs medication because of depression, it becomes the truth we must work against. If we decide the person needs a relationship in order to show minimum coping, it becomes the truth. If we decide the person is passive–aggressive, it becomes true. And finally, if we decide our clients have made the best choice they know how to make to cope with the world they perceive, it becomes true. We cocreate the world of choices and limitations with our clients.

Correcting Ineffective Means and Imaginary Ends

What most clients present as a problem is often the result of their attempts to reach ill-conceived goals with ineffective problem-solving means. It may be that a man tries to secure a sense of respect by acting jealously, hoping that his wife will eventually cry, apologize, and reiterate that she loves him. Meanwhile, his wife may be hoping that he will admit his tender and weak side and ask her for help, and in so doing make her feel needed. The results will be disastrous. Both are using ineffective means in their attempt to achieve imaginary ends.

Why? Because the man could respect himself and not seek self-respect by means of his wife's external praise, and the woman could realize her own importance rather than artificially gaining importance by seeing herself as worthy because she is needed by her husband. Each wants something from the other in order to complete a missing part of their perceived reality, but they could change the reality so the missing part didn't have to come from outside of themselves. Also, of course, they could each give more attention to the other if the interpersonal requests were more understandable and they were each willing. There is choice.

Therapy must assess the clients' goals and help each person employ the necessary methods (or means) for achieving these goals. If we believe that clients are attempting to achieve something of value with ineffective interpersonal tools, we will be less likely to label frustrating behavior as crazy.

I recently saw a family whose teenage girl believed herself to be dating "Simon" from the rock group Duran Duran. She was doing this dating via a self-described psychic "channel," who was, in fact, a neighbor girl dressing in a suit jacket and speaking with an British accent. (The "channel" was being seen by an HMO therapist. Now it is possible that we could call my client a "teenage schizophrenic" and attempt to "forbid" her to continue this "dating" — this was, by the way, the demand made on the "channel" by the HMO therapist.) But I saw her as basically normal and doing an appropriate thing for a teen — learning to date. This was an especially courageous undertaking for her, considering that her father was extremely withdrawn as a result of a neck injury 20 years earlier. He had not had sexual relations with her mother for 12 years. He had had no income for 20 years and showed no affection in the home. He was bitter and quick to provoke hostile rejection from others.

Despite this, these two girls were attempting to do a very normal thing and had only used ineffective means to do this dating. My patient's goal in dating was also slightly skewed or imaginary — that is, it would have been all right to date a regular boy, but she constructed a rock superstar companion to make herself special. Seeing this problem as the use of ineffective means to an imaginary end reduced the attribution of pathology to my clients and propelled me to a treatment direction that was realizable. Working initially with the father and mother, I was able to help him feel pride about himself and guide him to what soon became a process of giving more attention to his daughter. The impact on the daughter's conduct apparently followed, as she was soon receiving phone calls from "real" boys and had a casual date with one within a month's time. But, the actual therapy done is another story and this case is only being used to illustrate the importance of using therapy to help clients correct their use of interpersonal means to desired and realizable ends.

Using the Session to Motivate Clients

The work done in a session might best be seen as motivating clients to relate and experience the world differently. Sometimes the discussions and metaphoric communications in therapy remind clients of past experiences. However, I do not conceive of work done in therapy as getting closure on the past, even when clients might be reliving situations concerning their parents. Instead, I understand this therapy to be eliciting a complex and experientially grounded motivation to relate differently in the present. For example, getting angry at a father in imagination during trance might provide a motivation to express anger appropriately toward a husband in the present. That outcome is possible, especially to the extent that therapists are sensitive to helping clients make the events connect.

The same is true for any other elicited behavior, cognition, memory, or fantasy. Optimally utilized, these events produce motivation for action in the present. I consider the metaphorical framework of having clients talk to the children they once were or deal with a parent "as if" in the past, a means for eliciting cognitive, emotional, and behavioral aspects of *motivation*, which must be linked to the extramural life of the present family with assignments and other means.

Helping Clients Diversify Problem-Solving Skills

When clients improve, their families can turn their motivation toward something other than the previously identified symptom. What will have emerged in place of the problems will be hard to predict since, often, the entire balance of the family will have changed. The individuals will begin relating differently. I see this as gaining new problem-solving options.

Perhaps the term "problem-solving options" deserves additional explanation. I see people as involved in an ongoing process, usually outside of their awareness, of adjusting to developmental ecosystemic demands. The tools that are used to meet those demands are the experiences found at several levels of analysis. All the experiences and behaviors we can conceptualize in families are tools that can be used to creatively meet the demands of life. For example, asking for help will sometimes be used to solve problems. Other times, the solving of problems may best be accomplished with divergent abilities, such as nurturing a spouse or disaffiliating with an anger.

When clients change, they will relate differently, and then their symptoms — the anxiety, fears, depression, insomnia, sexual dysfunction, loneliness, drug dependence, domestic violence, and so on — will have a diminished place in their lives. These problems, which often represent ineffective attempts to reach ill-conceived goals, will not be used. Good therapy helps clients solve current problems differently.

Helping Clients Stay Better

In my model it is important to help clients use these tools to stay better. The reinforcement that maintains new experiences and behaviors comes from both internal and external sources. When people reinforce themselves for behavior that is also reinforced by the social system, the behavior becomes stable. There are four factors or levels of needs to consider, and each one can influence any of the others.

1.   Developmental and biological growth needs.
2.   Expectation and self-monitoring (self-administered positive/negative reinforcement, self-image).

3. Social sanctions (family and peer).
4. Demands of the larger environment (neighbors, cultural, etc.).

To the exent that there is a match between the needs and sanctions of different levels, there will be creative health. Therefore, it seems that good therapy will be a matter of helping people gain and/or use perceptions, cognitions, feelings, and behaviors that address the developmental biological needs and the ecosystem demands.

Therapy can be conceived of as a way to help clients create change in *each* of these areas *specifically* and accountably. The field of therapy has become sophisticated enough that we can help clients elicit and respond with feelings they have not previously used for problem solving, reshape inappropriate cognitions with useful ones, rehearse changes in their self-concept, solidify new roles, reorganize family structure to support these changes, and so on (Bandura, 1969; Berne, 1966; Ellis, 1971; Goulding & Goulding, 1979; Lankton, 1980; Lazarus, 1976; Lowen, 1975; Madanes, 1987; Meichenbaum, 1977; Moreno, 1972; Perls, 1947, 1973; Wolpe, 1948, 1982; Zeig, 1987). Clients continue to change or stay better by making gains in these areas. The wider the array of specific changes that therapy helps clients make in each of these, the better will be the therapy.

DOING THE THERAPY

There are several factors vital to doing good therapy. At one level, the factors I am about to describe are common knowledge. But at another level, they need to be reemphasized because all too often therapists forget to do these things.

Identifying the Problem

I once worked with a couple who said they were concerned with the infrequency of their love making. They didn't need to say more. I had heard how it can be when one has been married for a while. I figured they were not having sexual relations for weeks at a time, and I must have talked to them for 30 minutes assuming this. Finally, I felt a need to get specific and asked them how bad it was. The husband answered: "Three times a day." Since that day I have been extremely sensitive to the need for finding out, specifically, what clients mean about how a complaint is a problem for them.

Getting and Understanding a Contract

After finding out what the presenting complaints are, I do not assume that clients want to change them. The most common problem that I have seen in supervision is that therapists can't tell me concisely what their clients think they are trying to accomplish in therapy. The therapists don't know in which direction to exert energy, and clients grow somewhat impassive about what happens in the session. Under these conditions you can be certain that clients don't think about therapy during the extramural hours and fail to carry out assignments given to them.

In addition to getting a contract for the general treatment goal, find out what clients think they will accomplish if they reach this goal. Don't assume. If the client says she wishes to get away from her mother, ask her, "Why in the world would you want to do that?" If the client says he wants to get rid of his anxiety, don't assume you know why. Don't assume it is desirable to not feel the anxiety. Maybe it is. But ask for a deeper understanding of this goal. Ask, "What do you want to do when you feel less anxiety?' Or, "Do you think you can do everything you do and have less anxiety?" Or, "Why do you think it would be a good idea to have less anxiety?" Ask until you get the client's understanding.

This is equally appropriate when the presenting problem shows emotional pain. When a client cries and says, "I have to separate from my mother," we cannot conclude that we know something about the request. We still must say, "You sure look sad when you think about that and say that you need to separate. Go ahead and take some time to cry if you need to. But tell me what you mean by 'separate' and why in the world you would want to do something like that."

Getting Clients Active

In the last example, my question was, "Why in the world would you want to do that?" Such an inquiry is concerned with why this issue is a *problem* and implies the need to be active. That is, despite the fact that the problem presented by the client is upsetting, why does it constitute sufficient need for therapy? Clients, in answering this real naïve concern that I present, can be expected to devote more energy to the change process right from the start. Initial questioning can be motivating.

This energy is utilized in the therapy as clients become active. I ask clients to do assignments between almost every appointment. I have noticed that even the smallest and seemingly inconsequential performance between sessions amplifies the work done in each session. For instance, having a married couple change the location of five pictures hanging in their home each night for a week turned out to be an extremely meaningful task. The husband, with a rigid "macho" persona, said he thought this was being done to illustrate to him that he ought to be comfortable and even excited about change. His wife, who had been fighting him for her independence, said she felt the assignment illustrated the importance of working *with* her husband instead of against him. In another instance, an unmarried male client who complained about insecurity was given a small Indian Kachina doll that he was to carry with him everywhere he went throughout the week. He returned to my office informing me he realized this meant that, as long as he had his imagination, he could not be insecure! I certainly didn't know that!

In such cases, clients making small changes at home and small changes in relating to the world form the attitude that *they* did the therapy. These clients avoid that dreadful passivity that typically makes therapists feel they should work harder. The motivated client becomes an active client, and the active client helps the therapist make therapy good therapy.

Challenging the Obvious

Once I have expressed my general ignorance about the nature of the problem and begin to understand why *this* person or family wants to change something, I still wonder why they don't just do something different. This common sense position is similar to the joke about the man who says, "Doctor, every time I do this it hurts," and the doctor responds by saying, "Well, don't do that anymore."

I have clients say, "You mean I can just get a divorce?" "You mean I can just pick up and move?" and so on. I have had clients who said they wanted to feel more confident about going to college but then decided that they really didn't want to go to college at all. I have had clients who initially wanted to have less anxiety in their job eventually decide that they didn't want to be in that line of work at all. And there have been clients who wanted to get along better with their spouse but then decided that they did not want to be married after all.

What these situations have in common is that I did not stay with the initial request. Instead, I took the position of "I don't understand how this is a problem" and raised questions about the "obvious." And finally, I asked, "Have you considered not doing it at all?" (not going to college, not keeping the jobs, not relocating, not being married).

I do not suggest the change of careers or marriages flippantly. Certainly these things are very serious undertakings. Any client who simply said, "Great idea! I'll do it that way" would find me even more inquisitive than I had initially been. But therapy that is begun when therapists are unclear in their definition of the problem and the motivation of the clients is poorly conceived therapy. I suggest that we inquire about both the problem and the motivation and use the resulting process and content to help clarify and build a productive working relationship.

Using Developmental Assessment Therapeutically

It is important for therapists to assess obvious developmental influences, but they should avoid introducing the obvious developmental needs in such a way that problems are magnified. I recently had a client who complained of anxiety he had about dating. The man, aged 24, was only five feet, two inches tall. I empathized about how hard dating can be. However, I wondered why, since it is a universal problem, he was seeking therapy for it. He said he wanted to marry and have children one day and he seemed to be no closer now than he had been several years ago. I again agreed that it could be frustrating but asked what the hurry was, whom he wanted to date, what part of dating behavior seemed connected with his anxiety, what he was anxious about in dating, and so on. I realized that he was not mentioning his relatively short physical height. I was aware that many people consider height an attractive feature in courtship and yet he had not mentioned his lack of height once in his discussion of problems. I wanted, therefore, to explore the topic, but without introducing more anxiety.

In saying something like, "I wonder if you are concerned that women prefer a taller man," a therapist runs the risk of reinforcing the client's existing fears. Therefore, they become even more true than they were in his silent imagination. Can't we say the obvious in a constructive way? I could step into his world and begin to unhook myself from being as upset as he seemed to be. In realizing how he was (or I could be) hooked in his dilemma, I began to see how to get unhooked. I said, "You didn't mention when or how you had first discovered your height might be an asset in dating." To this he haltingly replied that he had not really thought of being short as an asset and asked what

I meant by the statement, since he thought women usually prefer taller men. He was somewhat fascinated that, while I was "with him," I viewed his height contrary to the popular view. In short, it seemed that the implied suggestion reinforced his hopes about his worth. He began telling me how being 5'2" might, in fact, be an asset.

One of the most obvious aspects of therapy is that clients must adjust to developmental demands. When a family brings a teenager for therapy, I look at the family system to determine its structure. I investigate whether the parents are communicating in a way that will facilitate building a stronger dyad as the daughter leaves home. I wonder if their relationship is romantic, sexual, and caring; I assess their ability to ask for and deliver nurturing with each other; and I wonder if interests shared as a couple exist to the extent that they can turn attention away from their children. I examine each individual's experience of pride, joy, and other feelings and discover whether the middle-aged couple respects the roles they play. In short, while I assist with the problems centered around the daughter, I also address the obvious experiences and transactions needed by nearly all family members at this developmental phase.

These inquiries should be done, in most cases, without alerting the couple to the fact that they may lack skills they desire. For instance, I once presented a couple with a candle and asked that, for the next week, they go out to dinner and burn the candle as they dined. The assignment was to go out repeatedly until all of the candle was burned, then come back and tell me why they thought they were sent to do this (and how it could be of benefit to their daughter). In this way the obvious growth they wanted and needed was therapeutically facilitated without alerting them to the additional problem represented by its absence.

Being Sensitive to Cues

Sometimes therapists place client problems into a "pathology" framework in an effort to "understand" clients and eventually help them feel and cope better. This maneuver puts therapists in the "illusory" position of thinking they know what the "cause" of the problem is and engenders an unfortunate process of "converting" clients to the framework held by therapists. As such, it is a certain way to elicit resistance in those clients who want their uniqueness respected.

Gathering information with subtle, indirect, and even metaphoric maneuvers will prevent this type of "casework" from destroying therapeutic rapport and responsiveness. Therapists who can be alert to nonverbal information indicating the client's feelings and attitudes may not need to resort to perhaps insulting questions like: "How did you feel when your wife left you?" "How did that make you feel when you broke your back?" "What was going through your head when your husband had an affair?" "What did you decide when you dropped out of high school?'

Certainly it is important to get answers to such questions, but the answers are given repeatedly in nonverbal signals from clients. Good therapy is being sensitive to those cues or asking questions that will reveal those cues but not alert the conscious minds of clients to feeling they are guinea pigs or objects of study for our pet theories.

Setting Specific Goals

We have already mentioned contracts, but now I wish to discuss specific goals for each therapy session. If a contract is set to help parents deal with the misconduct of their teenager, our session-by-session contracts ought to deal with specific subsets of this larger goal. For instance, can each parent experience joy at having a child? Can each show his/her joy, sorrow, and pride? Can they ask for help? Can they state their demands coherently and congruently? Can they be comfortable disaffiliating when discipline is called for? Would they like to learn to use any of the above problem-solving behaviors? These are among the many subsets of family experience and behavior necessary for creatively and effectively parenting a teenager.

When we ask ourselves these questions, we must then translate them into goals for each subsequent session. Setting specific goals and going one step at a time is the only way in which complex behavior can be learned. This is perfectly analogous to learning to play a musical instrument such as piano. Whether the goal is to play classical or rock music, students must learn to sit, orient toward the keyboard, strike the keys, hold their fingers on the chords, use the pedals, play syntonic notes, change the chords in progressions, and so on. Learning to do this is a relatively methodical process of increasingly difficult tasks built upon the previous learning. This is how good therapy builds with each session toward the complex tasks necessary to fulfill contracts.

FROM THE CLIENT'S STANDPOINT

So far I have mentioned aspects of good therapy. They are not entirely independent of the theoretical approach taken by other therapists. But I want to add to these ideas from an additional vantage point. I want to ask the question "What makes good therapy?" from the standpoint of the client. I can answer this for me and perhaps the answers will stimulate you to discover ideas that fit for you.

I Want an Enchanting Therapist Who Stimulates Pleasant Mental Excitement

Enchantment is a part of all successful therapy. I don't want a boring therapist. I don't want one who dazzles me either. But I want one who challenges me gently and arouses pleasant mental excitement about the change process.

This can be done if the therapist is confident and poised and introduces ambiguity in the session. Assignments ought to be a bit mysterious. Certain pieces of instructions, questions, and advice ought to be somewhat vague so as to be interesting and allow room for my own personal growth. My therapist should use word ambiguity, puns, and some light-hearted humor. I want to know that the therapist is equal to me and worthy of my respect.

I Want a Therapist Who Is Relevant to My Reality

I don't want a therapist who helps me dig around in memories and fantasies of the past. It is the present and the future I struggle with. The good therapist must let me know that he or she is interested in the reality of my life now and in the near future.

I Want a Therapist Who Will Not Label Me

I suppose it goes without saying that I want to be a person and not a category. Also, I want to terminate therapy when I wish to do it and not be intimidated into continuing therapy because I might fail to live up to some external criteria, especially criteria that are unstated and apparently hidden from my understanding.

I Want a Therapist with Humanity and Humor

Even though my life is serious to me, I want a therapist who can see the humor in living. I want a therapist who treats me as an equal, intelligent, and important person. I don't want one who is aloof or superior. I don't want one who morosely tries to "analyze" what I say. I actually don't mind if everything I do is analyzed, but I don't want it done with a distancing and condescending quality. The therapist who can help me change while helping me feel fully human is doing good therapy.

THE PARADOXICAL PROBLEM OF DOING GOOD THERAPY

When I began this chapter more than one year ago, I had been thinking about how each therapy school wants therapists to adhere to the right and proper tenets of its approach. Therapists of different approaches are criticized for not being family oriented, for not dealing with the deeper problems, for not being elegant, for not attending to the relationship, for intellectualism or the lack of it, and so forth. At the time I was invited to address the Brief Therapy Congress, I thought, "Perhaps I should just make the point that we should just do good therapy."

But now, having made these points, I realize I too have done what I wished not to do. I have made it necessary that you do these "right things" in order to be correct. Paradoxically, I have done what I hoped to encourage therapists to avoid. In an effort to say, "Don't conform to someone else's rules; just do good therapy," I find that I have generated a set of rules. I'm sure that they could be followed to the letter and in such a way the spirit would be totally lost. Perhaps, in summary, what I can best conclude is that each of us ought to understand our own criteria for doing good therapy and follow our own rules — using our own well-developed model and not the model of others.

References

Bandura, A. (1969). *Principles of behavior modification.* New York: Holt, Rinehart & Winston.

Berne, E. (1966). *Principles of group treatment.* New York: Grove Press.

Ellis, A. (1971). *Growth through reason.* North Hollywood, CA: Wilshire.

Erickson, M. (1976). Personal communication. Phoenix, AZ.

Goulding, M. & Goulding, R. (1979). *Changing lives through redecision therapy.* New York: Brunner/Mazel.

Lankton, S. (1980). *Practical magic: A translation of basic neuro-linguistic programming into clinical psychotherapy.* Cupertino, CA: Meta Publications.

Lazarus, A. (1976). *Multimodal behavior therapy*. New York: Springer.

Lowen, A. (1975). *Bioenergetics*. New York: Corward, McCann & Geoghegan.

Madanes, C. (1987). *Behind the one-way mirror: Advances in the practice of strategic therapy*. San Francisco, CA: Jossey-Bass.

Meichenbaum, D. (1977). *Cognitive-behavior modification: An integrative approach*. New York: Plenum Press.

Moreno, J. (1972). *Psychodrama: First volume* (4th ed. with Introductory Notes). New York: Beacon House.

Perls, F. (1947). *Ego hunger and aggression*. New York: Vintage Books division of Random House.

Perls, F. (1973). *The gestalt approach and eye witness to therapy*. Palo Alto, CA: Science and Behavior Books.

Wolpe, J. (1948). *Psychotherapy by reciprocal inhibition*. Palo Alto, CA: Stanford University Press.

Wolpe, J. (1982). *The practice of behavior therapy* (3rd ed.). New York: Pergamon Press.

Zeig, J. (Ed.). (1987). *The evolution of psychotherapy*. New York: Brunner/Mazel.

9

The Occurrence and
Use of Trance Phenomena
in Nonhypnotic Therapies[1]

Milton Erickson bridged the gap between classically understood hypnosis and "nonhypnotic" psychotherapies. Erickson showed us there are more similarities than differences among psychotherapies. Indeed, Erickson defined hypnosis as a state in which "the client concentrates on his own thoughts, memories, values, and beliefs about life."[2] Because trance phenomena like catalepsy, amnesia, age regression, and hallucination are the spontaneous result of prolonged or accentuated involvement in internal processing, they occur not only in hypnosis, but in other psychotherapies as well.

Hypnosis and nonhypnotic therapy have similarities that are rooted in three principles of Erickson's work. First, communication in both therapy and hypnosis elicits an unconscious search process in the client. Second, the client may develop a sense of recognition or understanding that will activate recognizable ideomotor responses. Third, this search process facilitates common trance phenomena. Trance phenomena and the search responses that accompany them are therapeutic choice points in nonhypnotic therapies.

---

[1] Lankton, S. (1982). The occurrence and use of trance phenomena in nonhypnotic therapies. In Jeffrey K. Zeig (Ed.), *Ericksonian approaches to hypnosis and psychotherapy* (pp. 132–143). New York: Brunner/Mazel. Reprinted with permission.

[2] Erickson, M. H. Personal communication, Phoenix, Arizona, August, 1975.

Diverse labels have been attached to trance phenomena, so that age regression may variously be called "unfinished business," a "child ego state," or a "neurotic affect and transference reaction," depending on the therapist's background.

To systematically analyze how these phenomena are utilized by hypnotic and nonhypnotic therapies alike, one must examine communication processes that therapeutically stimulate a client to search for memories, values, and beliefs about life. Therefore, discrete communication operations will be discussed within four analytic schemes, namely, process operations, content operations, linguistic operations, and input operations. Within this framework, trance phenomena are discussed and examples of their occurrence are presented.

PROCESS OPERATIONS

In process operations, three patterns are identified by which verbal and/or nonverbal communication is expressed. These are matching, reversal, and disruption.

Matching involves mirroring the client's communication channel, reflecting the particular mode of the moment. To match movement, gesture, breathing, or tone to that of another requires careful attention to the rhythm of change. In hypnotic therapy, the hypnotist may match the rhythm of his speech to the rhythm of the client's respiration; Erickson used this technique to build rapport with the client. In a similar vein, Erickson might speak the same type of verbal gibberish (word-salad) as a client (Erickson, 1967, p. 500). Matching can be used simultaneously, with other patterns of both a verbal and nonverbal nature.

Reversal involves an opposite response, that of deliberately projecting the reverse of what the client is doing. For example, Erickson might speak slowly to a resistant client who is speaking rapidly, while making a paradoxical statement such as, "You can't go into a trance."

Disruption is a technique for interrupting the ongoing process and related associations. It may be accomplished in a number of ways, including distraction, humor, making an irrelevant comment, and so forth. It is particularly useful when hypnotists issue a direct command that they do not want challenged. For instance, in the "Monde" film (produced by Herbert Lustig, M.D.), when Erickson tells Monde to use her learnings in a directed fashion and then immediately asks her, "You're not cold, are you?" a seemingly irrelevant comment about temperature disrupted conscious consideration of his instruction (Lustig, 1975).

Just as several channels of verbal and nonverbal communication may exist at the same time, two or more of these operations can occur simultaneously. Thus, the hypnotist might match voice tone, tempo, volume, and body posture while reversing the client's verbal content.

CONTENT OPERATIONS

In content operations, one utilizes various patterns to influence the client's verbal responses: specifying response questions, detailing communications, and meta-comments.

A *specifying response question* is designed to elicit more complete background information for assessment purposes. Questions might include: "Who, where, and how specifically . . .?" as well as "What prevents you?" and "What would happen if you did?"

A *detailing communication* specifies desired behavioral responses. For example, Erickson might instruct a client to "sit down, lean back, uncross your legs like this, and listen to my words."[3] Here Erickson detailed four responses he expected from the client.

A *meta-comment* is a comment about a communication. Meta-comment refers to both the simple labeling of an event and an ongoing explanation of some experience or communication. These are abundant in all forms of psychotherapy. In hypnotherapy, meta-comments allow the hypnotist to subtly shift the meaning an experience or symptom has for the client, as when the hypnotist says, "Your unconscious mind wants one thing while your conscious mind wants something else." Jay Haley (1963) speculated that Erickson employed such content operations to achieve therapeutic control.

Both process and content channels can be used singly or in combination. For example, the hypnotist could match body posture, voice tone, and breathing of the client, while meta-commenting, "I'm going to tell you the real reason why you came to see me today," then follow this with the detailing communication, ". . . so sit down in that chair, relax, close your eyes and listen to my words." The very next moment, the hypnotist might employ a process reversal like, "Not that fast, I don't want you to go into a trance this soon," thus achieving response inhibition or fractionation that would serve to deepen the trance.

---

[3] Erickson, M. H. Personal communication, Phoenix, Arizona, November, 1977.

LANGUAGE OPERATIONS

The grammatical syntax of the verbal communication used by the hypnotist can also be divided into three distinctive categories. These are search language, induction language, and metaphor.

Search language initiates an internal search process within the client. This technique utilizes unspecified, vague, and general language forms to stimulate the client to search for personal meaning. Erickson frequently used deliberately vague phrasing like "You're going to recall *some* forgotten experience," "*Everybody* has had the experience of forgetting," or "Your *unconscious* contains a vast storehouse of *learnings*."

Induction language employs embedded commands, indirect suggestion, and presuppositions of consciousness, time, and number to suggest options to the client. Statements like "You will *begin to wonder.* . . ," "You really can, Joe, *feel relaxed* . . .," and "Can you *uncross your legs* and just relax *once again*," illustrate this technique.

Metaphor refers to a noncausal linking of facts that involves matching content and processes in the client's situation, or to an illustrative anecdote or explanation used that incorporates symbolism. Metaphor develops a theme using search language and induction language. Erickson's metaphors often began with a simple lead-in line like "I had a client one time from the Midwest who . . .".

Following a brief discussion of input operations, the way in which these language operations initiate unconscious search processes and the role of the search process in the development of hypnotic phenomena in nonhypnotic therapy will be presented.

INPUT OPERATIONS

Input operations (Grinder, DeLozier, & Bandler, 1977) involve the differing effects upon client visual, kinesthetic and auditory experiences, due to the verbal and nonverbal communications of the hypnotist or therapist. These include packaging, directing, and associating input.

Packaging input consists of the communicator's determining a client's perception of reality, then incorporating these subjective needs into his response patterns through the verbal matching of language processing words. For example, if the client specifies that he doesn't *see* how he is going to overcome his difficulty, Erickson "packages" his verbal communication with visually oriented verbs and nouns like "clear," "picture," "focus," or "bright." If the client says there is no *harmony* in his marriage, Erickson utilizes auditory packaging phrases such as "tune-in," "hear," "listen," "two hoots and a holler," or "amplify." Kinesthetically based words include: touch, relax, comfort, sit, hold, grasp, feel, embrace, solid, and grip. Obviously, many words and phrases lend themselves to this type of feedback. Most important, then, is judicious packaging by the therapist for each client's individual framework.

Directing assists the client in selecting the most useful sensory processing mode. This can be done by congruent changes in gestures, directed eye movement, tone shifts, and so forth. When Erickson wanted a client to consciously think with pictures, he might point or glance upward, influencing the client to break eye contact. Moving his eyes upward, he would initiate the related visualization process. Once eye closure had been established, Erickson would systematically direct the client to the desired sensory mode via stories, illustration, and analogy.

Associating and anchoring, pairing a particular stimulus with a specific client experience, may be induced consciously or unconsciously, using any of the sensory input channels or verbal labeling. Cueing is used as a re-induction signal in hypnotherapy. A signal (a simple word, sound, or touch) successfully associated with a trance state, when subsequently presented, will cue and initiate that same trance state again. Often, re-induction signals are learned in a single trial association. On a more subtle level, the hypnotist can be reasonably certain the client will associate to comfort when he says "comfort."

SEARCH BEHAVIOR AND RESPONSE

The client's ability to make sense of communications received reflects the sensory channel the client uses for input, his perception and his previous learning. Perception and previous learnings are mediated by ego images, which consist of auditory, visual, or kinesthetic impulses with varying degrees of cathexis (Fenichel, 1945). During the momentary search process, the person unconsciously, and at times consciously, attempts to locate previous representations that give meaning to present input. If the hypnotist says, "You have had comfort, have you not?," he has used search language consisting of the complex noun "comfort" and deletions (comfortable where, when, with whom, etc?). The "have you not" is a verbal reversal that will maximize the probability of getting a "yes" response, even from an incongruent client.

The first portion of the statement, "You have had comfort, have you not?," influences the client to sort through internal representations from his/her past and fill in the deletions in the most relevant manner. He will select his most common imagery, and then respond in the manner most typical for him, when presented with deleted complex nouns and deleted noun phrases. Following the search process, the client's ideomotor responses inform the hypnotist of the images and habit patterns developed by the client. These responses allow the hypnotist to modify communication, depending upon the desired goal in the session.

The internal search process is identifiable in any ongoing communication. The best indicators include flattened cheeks, lowered center of respiration, slowed respiration, slowed blink and swallow reflexes, decreased gross motor movement, eye scanning patterns, and increased pallor. These indicators also signify hypnogogic or light trance states. Hypnotists train themselves to notice these responses, whereas nonhypnotic therapists usually do not.

When a person is spoken to, he makes meaning of words, tone, and facial expressions through subjective associations. The client is internally assembling and examining previous pictures, words and feelings. The more ambiguous the therapist communication, the greater the likelihood a person will apply the communication personally. In everyday communication, lack of specificity can create a discrepancy between intended communication and message received. In hypnosis, however, vague phrasing can be helpful.

Classical hypnosis and the various psychotherapies appear to differ most in the way elicited responses are utilized. Typically, hypnotherapists think about eye closure and similar "classical" induction ideas. This orientation alerts the hypnotist to words which retrieve certain valuable memories from the client's history, as the following induction example will illustrate.

Transcript 1

HYPNOTIST: Please be seated like this and notice, really notice, how you can easily learn. (*pause*)

CLIENT: Sits and places hands on thighs and places feet on floor. Head tilts; left ear orients to hypnotist. Face becomes immobile and respiration slows.

HYPNOTIST: You can at least learn that you already know more than you think you know.

CLIENT: Looks down and right quickly, then stares ahead and defocuses.

HYPNOTIST: And your experience becomes like that in a dream now, but you couldn't say how.

CLIENT: Exhales deeply, blink slows, face and stare are immobile.
HYPNOTIST: You can remember better when you close your eyes.
CLIENT: Closes eyes and swallows.

The hypnotist begins by matching the client's behavior to facilitate rapid rapport. This is accompanied by subtle meta-commenting with the word "please," setting a nonauthoritarian tone. As the client searches through memories related to nonauthoritarian relationships, he will likely find images associated with relaxed musculature. Also, search language used by the hypnotist (deletions and unspecified verbs) invites the client to recall associated experiences (such as associations to the word "easily").

Next the hypnotist uses induction language (presuppositions: "at least," "more than"), search language (deletion and unspecified verbs: "think" and "know") and continues to match posture and voice tempo to client respiration. The client continues the search response. Eye movements suggest he has begun the remembered feeling of "easily" (eyes down and right). The defocused stare suggests he is thinking in pictures (probably about previous learning experiences). Continued relaxation responses indicate that relaxation and learning memories have been successfully associated.

Then, the previous structure is emphasized and search language (complex noun "experience," and unspecified verb "becomes") introduces associations to the word "dream." Similar associations are then related to not speaking. The client's response suggests ideomotor behavior associated to dreaming with medium trance depth.

Finally, the hypnotist uses search language to build the final association needed for eye closure. The client complies easily because he is now operating from that portion of his memory where he is experiencing nonauthoritarian, relaxed and dream-like states.

The structure of the hypnotic communication process and client responses can be made explicit in several ways. Two relevant applications are: 1) comparison of nonhypnotic therapeutic communications, and 2) demystification of both hypnotic and nonhypnotic therapy (Stevens, 1975, p. 247 ff.).

Hypnotists are alert to the development of certain search phenomena in their clients. These include: relaxation, catalepsy, eye closure, and dissociation of feeling state from visual imagery. The hypnotist fosters search behavior in the client until the therapeutic associations are built and these interventions alter the customary search-response pattern.

The notion of ideomotor behavior is used to explain how musculature and reflex activity are affected by remembered or constructed images. If the client recalls images associated to pleasant experiences, a smile and increased muscle tonus will be noted. Undesirable images produce muscle distortions. Lacking a well-formed response, the client will begin search phenomena, or hypnotic response. Erickson pointed out that any change in internal imagery (auditory, visual, kinesthetic) results in a noticeable change in the client's expression or behavior (cf. Assagioli, 1965). The classical hypnotic phenomena mentioned below may spontaneously occur as the search process continues.

Nonhypnotic therapies, even family interactions, involve these patterns of communication (cf. Berne, 1972; Laing, 1967; O'Connell, 1970) and similarly elicit the hypnotic responses that will be detailed below. The pattern is as follows: unspecified speech — search — naming or otherwise referring to a desired experience — retrieving the desired experience — using the groups of retrieved experiences in therapeutic patterns.

AN ILLUSTRATION

The following transcript is provided so that the reader can get an idea of how hypnotic responses show up in "nonhypnotic" therapies. Examples are presented of how some of the above-mentioned communication operations are utilized in practice.

Hypermnesia is that phenomenon that occurs in deep trance, when a person can recall events from the past in much greater detail than is possible within a "normal" waking state. The person may not remember events "accurately," but since a therapist is working to alter a "map" rather than a "territory," this distinction is largely irrelevant. The client recreates whatever was real for him or her at that time, and during hypermnesia these realities can become especially vivid and detailed, as the following Gestalt therapy transcript illustrates. The client, Violet, is very depressed, anorexic, and withdrawn. She frequently sits with her feet in the chair and her arms wrapped around her legs, as if to hide. She is not actively suicidal, but did speak of taking her life just prior to the referral. This transcript is her eleventh therapy session.

Transcript 2[4]

1) LANKTON: (Finishing with another client) Now, Violet, what are you experiencing (actually turning and sitting like Violet is sitting; legs crossed, palms up on lap, head erect, and lips together without a smile)?

2) VIOLET: (Jerks back as she notices him) I didn't know it was my turn to work (sarcastic tone of voice).

3) LANKTON: (With sarcastic voice, like hers) You never know what you will experience, until you make yourself available for new experiences.

4) VIOLET: (Pupils dilate, face muscles flatten, blink slows, respiration slows. She nods her head slowly, as if to show agreement.)

5) LANKTON: (Waits, still matching her behavior.)

6) VIOLET: I feel crowded!

7) LANKTON: And how is it for you to feel crowded? Give yourself room to experience being crowded (pauses) and put words to it.

8) VIOLET: (Defocuses her eyes and stares, changes posture as she pulls her legs to her chin and entwines her arms around her legs.)

9) LANKTON: Stay there — with yourself and come to know where you are crowded. (Leans forward but does not further match her specific behavior.)

10) VIOLET: (Closes her eyes) I'm crowded in, closed in.

11) LANKTON: What do you experience enclosing you?

12) VIOLET: I'm in a box. Now I feel like I was (voice gets more faint) just too little. (Begins to cry as her face muscles lose all tonus and pallor increases.)

13) LANKTON: (Changes voice to a softer, melodic tone) Say that in the present tense — "I am just too little."

14) VIOLET: (Haltingly at first) I ... I'm just too little ... I can't push it ... I can't push the ... (changes to original voice tone) I don't know what I'm talking about.

15) LANKTON: (Changes to original tone of voice) You have some unfinished business back there. You will know where after you experience it. Perhaps the safety in this room releases you to find out what you need to finish elsewhere. Go there and reexperience what you will find.

---

[4] Lankton, S. *Violet.* A videotape of private group therapy practice, Ann Arbor, MI, 1979.

16) VIOLET: I don't know ... (pauses, moves her eyes up to the left and then she begins to stare ahead) ... I'm too big to fit in here. I can pull my legs up like this. This refrigerator is big, bigger than those boxes. It opens really hard, makes a funny noise. I like it. (It) feels smooth inside. There is not as much room in here as I thought there was. (pauses) I could go to sleep in here. The door is closed and it's dark, really dark. I don't think I want to be in here any more. The door won't open — I can't get out, I can't get out . . .

17) LANKTON: Make noise!

18) VIOLET: Ahh, Mommy, I can't get out, can't get out, let me . . . HELLLLLPP (cries and leaps from chair)!

19) LANKTON: You're out! (holding her) Can you finish this situation by being here and being free?

20) VIOLET: I'm scared. I'm right here, hanging on tight (to therapist's hand).

21) LANKTON: How are you scaring yourself? There is nothing scary here.

22) VIOLET: (Standing and speaking to the group with a growing smile) I made noise when I was scared. I got out of there. I moved. I thought. I thought about what I needed even when I was scared. That was a good decision. Guess that was what I did (sits down and begins recovering from the unexpected incident).

This transcript was chosen for analysis for three reasons: 1) because it is representative of Gestalt therapy; 2) because amnesia preceded therapy; and 3) because the client relieved an early, repressed, incident. Violet had no conscious memory of having been locked in a refrigerator. Following this therapy session, her mother confirmed that she had, at age two, become locked in a refrigerator. She had fainted and was near death upon being discovered. The family had kept this a secret. Following this incident, Violet had become a quiet, passive youngster. Therapy was directed toward building the kinds of need identification and expressive responses Violet lacked in areas of eating, feeling, and social intercourse.

Vivid recall during regression is typical of hypermnesia. It frequently assists therapists to clarify details or to make explicit influential dialogues from their clients' early years. Therapy goals and theoretical persuasion determine how details gathered during hypermnesia will be utilized by different therapists. Possible uses include gathering diagnostic information, creating therapeutic change (i.e., believing, thinking, or feeling differently in the face of an old memory), verifying recollections received from "normal waking state," and changing portions of problematic imagery that intrude into consciousness.

Analysis of this session reveals the same communication operations found in hypnosis. In lines one through five, I incorporate search language ("experience," "make available") and behavioral matching (posture, tone, tempo). Induction language is used to suggest that she will have the experience. The client demonstrates search phenomena in line four and finally locates the original experience linked to current feelings of being crowded.

The rest of her memory consists of visual images as shown in lines eight through 16. In lines seven through 10, I continue matching, search language and induction language as Violet reconstructs this experience, which was outside conscious remembrance. In line 11, I ask a specifying question about the experience to enhance her reliving the experience and to prevent dissociation. Line eight illustrates her total immersion as her internal imagery stimulates increasingly more congruent ideomotor behavior.

I continue to match changes demonstrated in lines nine, 13, and 15. In line 15, I again use search language ("business," "back there," "know," "experience") and induction language (presuppositions: "you will," "after," "you will find"; and deletions producing embedded commands: "experience it," "find out," "go there," "reexperience"). A new operation is purposefully used when I remind Violet that there is "safety" available. Following this use of association, Violet's retrieval of the experience begins.

In line 16, Violet finds her legs in the chair as she acts from visual/kinesthetic maps. As she becomes more fully engaged in the process, she displays deep trance phenomena. She positively hallucinates the old incident and this entails negative hallucination for events in the room. She age regresses to a powerful degree and experiences, hypermnesia. In lines 17, 18, and 19, I guide her with detailing responses. My directive, "make noise," leads her to access a past learning. Previously unable to formulate the age-appropriate response to express her needs, she had been operating as a two-year-old, until she made this new therapeutic association.

Lines 20 and 22 illustrate how a client can quickly move out of total age regression and use an age-appropriate meta-comment. This indicates how valuable this regression has been in the service of the ego, as she demonstrates synthesis and integration. She can now consciously think of the trauma without withdrawing, or being hostile or quiet, her previous reaction when these images were only preconscious and unconscious.

SIMILARITIES BETWEEN
HYPNOSIS AND WAKING STATE

Hypnotic phenomena occur as the result of communication and concentrated internal attention, not from some physical difference between the normal waking state and trance states. Biofeedback studies of EEG and oxygen consumption during meditation, sleep, hypnotic trance, and waking reveal that the hypnotic state is most similar to the waking state. "The patterns during hypnosis have no relation to those of the meditative state; in a hypnotized subject the brain wave activity takes the form characteristic of the mental state that has been suggested to the subject" (Ornstein, 1973, p. 266). In other words, the physiological phenomena produced by communication and internal search process are most like those of the normal waking state.

It follows that communication in psychotherapy and other waking states produces and uses trance phenomena under various guises. This hypothesis has encouraged me to define the structure of the language and nonverbal communication that produces or initiates these search and association processes, to demystify and improve the quality of both hypnosis and psychotherapy.

Successful communication enables another person to perceive or to conceive portions of experience common to the speaker (Laing, 1972, p. 79). Communication commonly has properties or elements of hypnotic suggestion, frequently in the same semantic order and for the same duration as purposeful hypnotic communication. Therefore, normal communication and nonhypnotic psychotherapies comprise a series of inductions. Therapeutically, these vary in style and skill, reflecting the therapist's or communicator's past training.

Psychology and sociology have much to gain from the study of Ericksonian clinical hypnosis. Practical applications of this approach should provide refinements of communication in such areas as educational settings, clinical psychotherapy, and child rearing.

References

Assagioli, R. (1965). *Psychosynthesis*. New York: Viking.

Berne, E. (1972). *What do you say after you say hello*. New York: Grove.

Erickson, M. H. (1967). Use of symptoms as an integral part of therapy. In J. Haley (Ed.), *Advanced techniques of hypnosis and therapy*. New York: Grune & Stratton.

Erickson, M. H., & Cooper, L. (1959). *Time distortion in hypnosis*. Baltimore: William & Wilkins.

Erickson, M. H., Rossi, E., & Rossi, S. (1976). *Hypnotic realities*. New York: Irvington.

Fenichel, O. (1945). *The psychoanalytic theory of neurosis.* New York: W. W. Norton.

Grinder, J., DeLozier, J., & Bandler, R. (1977). *Patterns of hypnotic techniques of Milton H. Erickson, M.D., vol. II.* Cupertino, CA: Meta Publications.

Haley, J. (1963). *Strategies of psychotherapy.* New York: Grune & Straton.

Laing, R. D. (1967). *The politics of experience.* New York: Ballantine Books.

Laing, R. D. (1972). *The politics of the family.* New York: Vintage Books.

Lankton, S. (1980). *Practical magic: A translation of basic neuro-linguistic programming into clinical psychotherapy.* Cupertino, CA: Meta Publications.

Lustig, H. (producer). (1975). *The artistry of Milton H. Erickson, M.D.* (video). Haverford, PA: Herbert S. Lustig, M.D., Ltd.

O'Connell, V. F. (1970). Crisis psychotherapy. In J. Fagan & I. Shepherd (Eds.), *Gestalt therapy now.* New York: Harper & Row.

Ornstein, R. (1973). *The nature of human consciousness.* San Francisco: W. H. Freeman.

Stevens, J. (1975). Hypnosis, intention, and wake-fullness. In *Gestalt is.* Moab, UT: Real People Press.

Metaphor

10

Multiple Embedded Metaphor and Diagnosis[1]

Autogenic training (AT) is a variation of hypnosis that concentrates on the use of imagery and relaxation (as opposed to the Ericksonian approach, which emphasizes the use of dissociation between conscious and unconscious experience). Autogenic training is designed to teach clients to experience a variety of psychotherapeutic responses, such as heaviness and warmth in the limbs, regulation of heart and respiration activity, abdominal warmth, and cooling of the forehead. In response, the subject is likely to experience slowing of heart rate, reduction of blood pressure and increased cortical discharges in the brainstem (Carruthers, 1981). To the extent that AT does not specify how and when to employ newly learned responses, clients are free to make these determinations according to their unique needs and circumstances. Of course, such freedom will not appeal to certain clients and, as an overall approach to treatment, AT fails to utilize the unique behavior, needs and personality requirements of some clients. Hypnosis combined with related autogenic training, however, has been found useful in migraines, hypertension, cardiovascular disorders (Carruthers, 1981), and gagging (Gerschman, Burrows, & Fitzgerald, 1981).

---

[1] Lankton, S. (1985). Multiple embedded metaphor and diagnosis. In Jeffrey K. Zeig (Ed.), *Ericksonian approaches to psychotherapy, volume 1: Structures* (pp. 171–195). New York: Brunner/Mazel. Reprinted with permission.

The point of this review is that hypnosis as a treatment modality would be more successful if a client were dealt with as more than "a symptom-carrying body." The most beneficial treatment, even when the presenting problem is defined as "only" a symptom, involves addressing the entire personality adjustment. This view is supported by evidence suggesting that purely symptomatic treatment of so-called neurotic clients may not forestall the eventual reemergence of symptoms because such treatment does not adequately take into account particular factors of personality (Eysenck, 1969). Accordingly, this chapter deals with the controlled elaboration of hypnotherapeutic interventions that, because they are developed from a thoughtful diagnostic assessment of the individual personality and family social network, effect long-term relief from and alternatives to a symptomatic means of adjustment. Similarly, thoughtfully subdividing specific goals in sex therapy can reveal improvements in self-confidence, behavior acquisition, symptom removal, and resolutions of "neurotic" conflict (Brown & Chaves, 1980). This chapter traces a logical development from a diagnosis of the personality-in-a-social-continuum, to a treatment plan with therapeutic goals, to the design and delivery of multiple metaphors to reach those goals.

Individuals with symptoms are usually unaware of the conflicts and deficits that combined to create the symptom. Insight therapy assumes that understanding the dynamic cause will help release the inhibited feeling and impulses that led to the tension. Unfortunately, insight into the meaning of the symptom, in itself, does not alter the person's or family's ability to cope effectively with the many roles, expectations, and tasks that represent a variety of parental, familial, and societal demands. To stimulate the experiential resources needed by a client to cope effectively with so many demands, much Ericksonian work is conducted in metaphor. Although metaphoric therapy reduces the opportunity for insight, it does increase unconscious involvement (Lankton & Lankton, 1983), a consequence that is tantamount to pervasive change of a symptom, personality, and a family's developmental course.

DIAGNOSTIC CONSIDERATIONS

Historically, the concepts and terminology of neurosis evolved from psychoanalytic theory. Since Erickson was not known to subscribe to this theory, my use of the term "neurosis" may need some explanation. I use the term to refer to personal difficulties deemed unacceptable by individuals who have a generally well-established sense of reality testing (i.e., ego-dystonic). I do not use the term to categorize these difficulties as situational or transitory, but to indicate that (a) functioning may be more or less grossly impaired, (b) awareness that the difficulty ought to be remedied tends to create a situation where the individual is a relatively willing partner in the therapeutic process, and c) the family, if aware of the problem, usually expresses a consensus that the problem exists.

As relatively willing partners in the therapy, clients (and possibly their immediate families) are most likely to display few communication difficulties with their therapists and little conscious resistance to therapeutic aid. Under these circumstances, hypnosis can be used in a straightforward manner. Communication difficulties within the clients' families or social network often are, however, the root of the problem for the neurotic personality, because "mental disease is the breakdown of communication between people" (Erickson, 1980, p. 75). Erickson placed certain requirements on the assessment of clients' difficulties and on the scope of treatment. I will begin my examination of the treatment scope with an analysis of clients and family members' orientation to the problem.

CHARACTER OF THE INDIVIDUAL

People coming to therapy have a symptom that is dystonic to them and their families, and that causes discomfort they seek to alleviate. Although clients are able to express this desire relatively clearly, each will have an idiosyncratic manner of expression and will manifest personal adjustments that may be viewed as a characteristic interpersonal stance. The first assessment involves determining how to communicate with each person.

Erickson was respected for his ability to relate to the entire person and create a remarkable sense of understanding or rapport. He genuinely related to people on their own ground. Many who experienced Erickson personally contend that he seemed to "look into them" in a manner that they had not previously experienced. I personally find that being still, and briefly ceasing my usual conscious activity by going into a trance, facilitates noticing nuances in the client's ideomotor behavior. This state of observation helps me gain a deeper understanding and respect for the person. Ultimately, speaking to the person's real condition as sincerely as possible and doing so with realistic concern provides me with a guide to achieve some of the empathy conveyed by Erickson.

Assessing a client's characteristic interpersonal stance depends, to a significant degree, upon the personal depth and experience of the therapist. However, some useful guidelines for refining this ability can be shared. Assessment is based on two dimensions: interpersonal dominance and interpersonal affiliation. Individuals make a unique adjustment to their families and the world that becomes their practiced method of coping in interpersonal situations. Their interpersonal stance determines their public posture ("in control," "one up," "helpful," "needy," etc.). I have found it most helpful to organize diagnostically interpersonal behavior on a continuum from relatively dominant-to-submissive and from relatively friendly-to-hostile (Leary, 1957). People who frequently or regularly present a "needy" persona, then, characteristically would be friendly-submissive. As such, their behavior is predictable and I can assume that the person provokes complementary roles and associates with those who are characteristically friendly-dominant. This person will be most comfortable if the therapist takes the complementary role. Similarly, a person characterized as "one up," "smug," or "aloof" will present a relatively hostile-dominant posture. Such behavior typically provokes self-doubt or rebellion (hostile-submission) from others and the therapist should be aware of the rapport that can be achieved when, depending on the degree of either dominance or hostility displayed, the therapist is self-doubting or challenging.

Carrying this initial assessment further, clients who appear "in control" and "sociable" will display a customary interpersonal posture of friendly-dominance. In these cases the therapist will put the client most at ease when appeals are made to the client's leadership or responsible behavior. This is done by being flexible enough as a therapist to display friendly-submissive behavior. Finally, the fourth logical category is for clients who appear rebellious or full of self-doubt: the hostile-submissive stance. This orientation tends to provoke relatively hostile-dominant behavior in others, in the form of either narcissistic and competitive behavior or overtly aggressive behavior. The therapist ought to consider initially joining the client with behavior that will be felt as familiar by being confident, directive, and even somewhat distant.

From this initial assessment, several important factors related to the symptom may be revealed. For instance, the person with certain somatic complaints (hypertension, for example) will often display relatively high friendly-dominant behavior. The preceding discussion suggests that the therapist will put the client most at ease by relative friendly-submission: asking questions, admiring, provoking leadership qualities, etc. One may extrapolate that, in addition to the obvious need for learning to relax, several interpersonal aspects of coping will be essential for the person to learn. For example, can the person induce leadership rather than merely be a leader? Can the person play a complementary role of friendly-submission when a leader is present? In a more psychodynamic vein, can the person identify and express dependency needs, tenderness, and erotic feelings (all a part of friendly-submission)? Also, if the person is firmly entrenched in friendly-dominant behavior, what attitudes and self-image barriers are presented that might prevent use of existing friendly-submissive behaviors and perceptions also acquired? All of the information from this assessment can be formulated into a treatment plan in accord with the acknowledged therapeutic contract.

Further, how can the family structure be altered to accommodate the use of new behaviors? If the spouse of this client has been cast into the complementary role of follower, does he or she know the necessary behaviors, feelings, etc., to play the friendly-dominant role from time to time? How can this enhance the family? What circumstances will encourage this reorganizing?

It can be seen, then, that the initial assessment of the client will reveal: (a) guidelines for immediate interpersonal management; (b) potential goals; and (c) interventions designed with each member's whole personality or family development in mind. The interpersonal style of the client is a significant clue to the behavior that the client customarily uses to cope with demands, and to the deficits in behavior that need to be faced and developed so the client can cope more effectively with these demands.

A complete assessment of personality, then, justifiably includes information of intra- and interpersonal, and social-historical dynamics: the family stage of development, family structure, and the developmental or psychological age of all family members who become clients.

To determine the stage of development of the family, the pressures on the family must be discovered. Since each family is unique, the range of possible difficulties is broad. Factors such as economic and sociometric variables determine, in large part, the expectations and needs of the family. In addition, the impact of each member's personal history and even such frequently overlooked aspects as local weather, chemical pollutants, chemical dependencies, and historically current trends will shape the unique character of each family. With the increasing diversity of lifestyles, such as nonmarriage, single-parent families, homosexual couples, group marriages, reconstituted families, remarriages, and divorces, reconsideration of "normal" trends in family development ought to be undertaken. However important, such a task is beyond the current scope.

It is possible to estimate some of the logical steps of family development and to create a list that can be lengthy, depending upon the degree of detail in which one wishes to engage. It is, in fact, the inclusion of considerable detail that facilitates the list's usefulness in evaluating a particular family. For the sake of discussion, I have a typical list of the changes involved in various stages of family development. Consider, for example, the following series of changes as points of departure for examining any particular client-systems: educational decisions, courtship, initial employment decisions, commitment, marriage decisions (in the heterosexual person), child-bearing decisions, adjustment to the years of marriage stabilization or childrearing, adjustments to children leaving home for school, possible adjustments to relocation and change in employment, coping with possible separation and divorce or child custody concerns, possible domestic violence, alcoholism and other drug abuse, acceptance of life planning consequence, adjustment to children's becoming parents and creating families of their own, retirement, use of leisure, adjustment to community involvement, religious life, eventually coping with the death of loved ones, wills, allocation of property, and finally, adjustment to the imminence of one's own death.

An assessment of the client's stage of family development provides information that is critical in constructing interventions, especially metaphors, which address current as well as future sources of stress. That is, the immediate future stage of development is as important as the present stage. Helping the client move successfully into courtship will be enhanced by teaching aspects of the final stages of courtship that lead, ultimately, to commitment and marriage. When the goals of the treatment are translated into actual metaphors designed to help the client create a reassociation of experience, a portion of those metaphors should deal with the behaviors, feelings, perceptions, etc. that influence abilities the client needs to cope with the sanctions and pressures of current as well as imminent development.

To accomplish this, the therapist must, as methodically as possible, consider the skills, perceptions, and the variety of resources that the client will need to adjust creatively to role demands at the current and the next logical stage of the family's development. In a similar fashion, the resources necessary to adjust and respond to an appropriate family structure must be elaborated. The variety of dynamics that constitute family structure can be discussed in logical segments and, indeed, therapy can address each element systematically, just as most learnings can be reduced to their component elements.

Some of the factors to consider in assessing family structure include: who talks to whom; what do they talk about; what is avoided; what is the typical affect; what is the usual role assumed; does anyone play a complementary role; is the complementary role supportive and healthy; how is the role parallel to the family of origin; does it represent scapegoating or protective loyalties; and does it embody myths or disagreements regarding values, identities, or actions? These factors are included in the diagnostic parameters that follow.

DIAGNOSTIC PARAMETERS

Marital Status . . .
Chronological Age . . .
Number and Ages of Children . . .

The marital status, chronological age, number and ages of children are self-evident sources of diagnostic information. These areas are important guideposts to a thorough assessment of the predictable pressures that influence crisis and adjustment. Chronological age, for example, gives a rough indicator of the client's life experiences. One would expect a person of 20 to know how to maintain a balanced checking account but this would not be readily expected of a child of 11. Likewise, marital status and age roughly indicate the expectations being placed on the individual by others (both current external and past internal expectations of others).

Cultural Background or Identification . . .
Stage of Family Development . . .
Next Logical Stage of Development . . .

Cultural background tempers our understanding of pressures with which a person contends. A gypsy may not need to know how to read but a middle-income Caucasian child is expected to read. Concerning family development, Haley attempted to clarify Erickson's thinking around logical stages of family development (Haley, 1973). In so doing, he explicated important factors of diagnostic assessment. But the requirements and pressures of family development are elusive. It is difficult to categorize comprehensively the stages of "normal" family development.

Needs of courtship differ from the needs of commitment and marriage. In courtship one needs to recognize a variety of abilities, including a sense of self-worth and an understanding that one enhances the life of another. The individual needs to be able to engage in "small talk," to be verbally vague, to say "no," to laugh, to smile, to dance, etc. During courtship, a person needs to

173

relax while in the proximity of the preferred sex, to be able to fantasize, to have a cognitive framework that explains mild social rejection and *faux pas* as natural and necessary occurrences, etc. The subtleties are staggering when they are articulated. But as clients gain a few related skills, they begin to generate other learnings that are closely related. Many clients learn to learn with an ever-increasing efficiency in the present developmental context.

The needs of marriage require a modification of the abilities and skills that lead to success in the courtship stage. The modifications are an ability to keep ever more complex commitments, to value the enhancement one provides for another, and to reciprocate the experience of being valued. Simple fantasizing about being together ought to become goal-directed planning and problem-solving. Small talk must become straight talk, and eroticism must become emotional openness and intimacy built upon risk-taking and trust. The immediate gratifications of courtship must be replaced with the delayed gratifications that are part of a successful marriage. The elements of each stage are nearly endless in number when broken down into all of the experiences and transactions that compose them.

The task of isolating and describing all of the experiences and transactions needed at each stage of family development may seem monumental. But in therapy, one needs only to identify the current developmental stage and then assess the experiences and transactions needed for all clients to most effectively evolve to the next stage. This assessment can become the basis for metaphor content and the object of the therapeutic goals developed with metaphor. Other stages of development in marriage include childbearing, child rearing, financial enrichment, etc., as mentioned. To use these stages effectively in diagnosis and therapy, one ought to develop detailed accounts and explanations of the experiences and transactions typically involved in each stage. An assessment of the stage of development and its particular components is necessary if one is to understand how symptomatic behavior occurs and persists during a particular stage in a family system.

Psychological Age

Determining "psychological age" involves assessing the client's developmental orientation of thought and emotion. Psychological age can be judged by style of manipulating the therapist, vocabulary, rate of speech, values, self vs. other orientation, muscle fluidity vs. rigidity, role-played expressions, naivete, etc. For example, a man was seen for obesity and marital difficulties. The therapist was struck by the man's emotional immaturity and infantile behaviors: His fluid face muscle expressions editorialized everything he heard or saw; his vocabulary for the word "no" consisted of the sound "ehhn," and "inh"; he was extremely self-oriented with complaints, excuses, etc.; and his general demeanor seemed to convey a demand that the therapist "do something" to relieve his discomfort. There was little to indicate that he took personal responsibility for his own experience or life course. By judging emotional age the therapist can create metaphors that more likely would appeal to and hold the attention of the ego state that will be listening in therapy.

Family Structure

The structure of the social network is a vital part of the diagnosis. This information reveals which adjustments to current social pressures are occurring, which needed adjustments are not being realized, and how this situation is being maintained. An Ericksonian approach sensitizes clients and families to resources they have, and engages potentials for coping. Such an approach includes relabeling perceptions, retraining perceptions, reframing cognitions, and challenging attitudes held about any number of things (aggression, sexuality, discipline, fate, anxiety, specific behaviors in a spouse, etc.). The following questions are useful in determining the family structure:

(a) Who talks to whom within the system?

(b) Are the topics of interchange rigid and predictable? What are they?

(c) How involved with one another are the members? Is the involvement over- or underinvolvement? Is it a conflictual or overaccepting involvement?

(d) What is avoided in the relationship?

(e) What is the typifying affect in the interchanges? Is there a way to characterize the usual roles taken by the client(s)? What role(s) is the therapist expected to fulfill?

(f) Are family members needed to play compatible roles of support or criticism or does the client take the typical roles despite "reality"?

(g) How is the current social system a copy of the family of origin of the client(s)? What dynamic interplaying is explainable by seeing the complaints as attempts to recast (or avoid recasting) each spouse's family of origin?

(h)   Are there observable transactions that reflect a disagreement on values, identities, or actions of family members?

(i)   Are there loyalties, scapegoating, myths, or other means of overtly shifting the responsibility and deficiencies of one or more members?

(j)   Is there a function of the symptom expressible in terms of how it secures immediate gratification or manufactures an avoidance of some anxiety-producing behavior for all family members? Can the symptom or its consequences be seen as metaphoric to a current coping pattern in the family?

(k)   What are the available and potentially needed resources of the clients? How might the resources be engaged to propel the clients toward their goals? What will be required to get the family to support healthy roles and to reorganize accordingly?

(l)   What does the client present as the problem and what is the treatment contract that has been negotiated?

Following a thoughtful assessment of the client system, therapeutic goals can be logically formulated.

THERAPEUTIC OUTCOMES WITH METAPHORS

Multiple embedded metaphor is a vital tool used to achieve therapeutic goals. The method involves interspersing one metaphor within another, or a number of others, in the course of a single session in order to address certain aspects of three to five therapeutic goals. Goals that can be addressed with dramatic therapeutic metaphors include: family structure or development change, age-appropriate intimacy or task behaviors, affect and emotional flexibility, attitude restructuring, enhancing self-image thinking, and intensifying discipline and enjoyment.

I intend for these categories to represent a comprehensive and mutually exclusive set of therapeutic goals, but because I have stated the goals in general terms, my intention will not be met in a rigorous sense. These six categories do, however, provide a practical method of satisfying the primary aim of several established therapies: e.g., Gestalt (emotional flexibility); family therapy (family structure or development change); cognitive and rational-emotive therapies (attitude restructuring); psychodrama, behavioral therapies, and assertiveness training (behavioral change); supportive and parental therapies (discipline and enjoyment changes); transactional analysis and Gestalt, encounter, and psychoanalysis (age-appropriate intimacy).

A helpful approach for formulating therapeutic goals is to imagine being a therapist of a specific discipline and answering the question, "What would therapy hope to accomplish?" This method results in estimates of the adjustments that could be achieved in successful treatment for each discipline and for each category of therapeutic goals. For example, what about a case of a workaholic lawyer? As an operant behaviorist or as a psychodramatist, what behaviors does the client need to acquire to make more adequate use of the resources in his or her social arena(s)? For instance, does the lawyer need to ask for help, to praise others, to accept advice, to listen calmly, to learn to agree with others? If so, which of these behaviors will become the behavioral goal for which treatment sessions? This line of reasoning can be conducted for each category of therapeutic goals. It must be remembered that outcomes affect one another and are reached best by interventions that affect all levels of family and personal organization.

The same approach, when applied to areas of family structure, feelings, attitudes, behaviors, discipline, enjoyment, and self-image thinking, yields distinct sets of therapeutic goals — goals that will become the heart of therapy sessions. Each session, while dealing with the presented concerns of the client, will provide opportunities to convey one or more goals from several of the categories, and also can lay the foundations for more complex learnings to be conveyed in the next session. For example, in the treatment of a sexual problem, the first session may deal with the client's emotional connection to his or her parents. The second session may develop that foundation into emotions and feelings of likes and dislikes, and a subsequent session may make actual arousal available in the developing foundation of emotional resources. The learning tasks, such as sexual feelings, can begin with mundane but prerequisite experiences to be built upon in subsequent sessions. Likewise, in the first session simple attachment behaviors (relaxation, smiling, touching) can be developed into social skills (eye contact, small talk, direct confrontation, etc.) and eventually into sexual skill (sensate focusing, kissing, fondling, coitus, etc.). Thus the emotional goals and the behavioral goals would be built hand-in-hand during the sessions. Likewise, attitudes and self-image goals would be identified and offered in support of the emotional and behavioral changes that are accomplished at each step of the way.

Two major points concerning the relationship of metaphor to therapeutic goals remain. First, discipline-enjoyment changes involve the use of metaphor to convey some particular focus on where to find pleasure in the course of disciplined personal conduct. This can be encouraged with suggestions regarding the use of personal resources within a thought-provoking story, so that a depressed father of six- and seven-year-old daughters might, for example, be presented with a reframing suggestion to "give up the joys of childhood so you can take pleasure in finding the joys of manhood." The potential to carry out such suggestions can be reinforced by delineating certain manly joys. The discipline-enjoyment metaphor, more than the other five types mentioned, is employed to deliver indirect suggestions in embedded quotes within the story, thus allowing the client to grasp it or reject it without resistance.

The final point concerns the following two-step sequence: First, there is more to be gained through thoughtfully wording the goal in "nonmetaphoric" terms; and, second, proceeding to a metaphoric counterpart. In other words, one ought to avoid the temptation of hearing aspects of the client's difficulty and thinking, "Oh, this is like the story of . . . ." Professionalism requires one to devise goals first, and be able to justify the use of particular interventions. The Ericksonian approach is more cohesive when treatment goals are thought out at the onset, as nonmetaphorically as possible. Once the goals are determined, the therapist can state them in metaphoric terms, for it is the structure of metaphor that stimulates the client's thinking along clinically relevant lines (family changes, etc.). Actual learning is a joint effort between the client's conscious need to frame the learning and the client's unconscious thought process — an interplay that is facilitated by metaphoric communication — in which clients rely on their own identifications, their own interpretations, and their own conclusions. Therefore, manipulation by the therapist is not coercive in any way, at any time. In a metaphoric approach, compliance and resistance are markedly reduced and freedom of choice for the client is maintained.

The following protocols are meant to provide a convenient and dependable structure for designing dramatic metaphors. The protocols are not meant to constrain but rather to guide and add certainty to the therapeutic process. By way of analogy, consider how a diagram of dance steps assists the learner to become familiar with complex movements. In the execution of the dance, however, one's memory of the diagram is only a background aid and a small and intermittent part of the experience of the dance. The learned diagrams are not meant to inhibit creative execution or enjoyment but rather to give license as well as form, to an otherwise limitless variety of opportunities.

The protocols are the result of countless hours of categorizing, analyzing, and re-creating elements of Erickson's therapeutic metaphors. I will present a succinct three-step version of each protocol. From one angle, they can be considered as recipes in a cookbook. From another, they can be viewed as procedures in a manual. Manuals are meant to be references that users become familiar with and then consult from time to time, especially when difficulties or anomalies occur or when errors need correcting. Manuals are most helpful when complex or unfamiliar tasks are being carried out and success is imperative.

I begin with a therapeutic goal that has been restated metaphorically for each category. Only then should the three-step protocols be applied to design procedures or to develop metaphoric detail. Once the steps have become familiar, they can be used quickly, just as the steps involved in speaking a language and selecting words properly have become largely unconscious. For a period of time, I recommend mentally adjusting each selected metaphor to the three steps. This procedure will add to the therapist's confidence as he or she tells the metaphors while conducting therapy. As one becomes more advanced in the use of these protocols, one discovers an occasional, but remarkable, "syncronicity" between the images, symbols, and themes of the metaphor, and aspects of the client's life that previously had not been explicitly revealed. The protocols are simple diagrams of most complex structures. They are meant to allow maximum freedom for creative thought for the client while providing a dependable therapeutic structure and direction for the therapist.

1. Attitude Restructuring: The Metaphor Protocol

1) Examine the behavior(s) in question from the protagonist's perspective.
2) Examine the same behavior(s) from the perspective of significant others.
3) Relate the consequence(s) of the behavior(s) to the perspective held by both the protagonist and the observing others.

To exemplify the use of this protocol in the selection and design of a metaphor to restructure an attitude, consider the case of a young man of 30, whose attitude toward marriage was expressed in the following remarks: "Marriage is a trap," and "If you come from a bad home life you can't have a happy married life." This outlook caused conflict with his live-in woman friend, who increasingly pressed for marriage and children. He hoped that therapy would help him to continue the relationship and to overcome his fear that marriage would spoil the relationship. He had not considered that his attitude was, in fact, a primary mechanism creating a fear that he used to express his long-held beliefs based on only a few reinforcing observations.

The metaphor used to address this aspect of the young man's difficulty concerned the unfortunate life of Brenda (not her real name, of course) from my hometown, and the life of her counterpart, Kathy. The characters' lives present a metaphoric counterexample to the client as illustrated in the following:

1) Examine the world through the eyes of Brenda: fine home, sociable parents with a good marriage, goals of college, family, children ... smooth sailing.

2) Examine the world through the eyes of Kathy: poor marriage between parents, (some) domestic violence, sad for portion of childhood, lived in foster home for a time. She rather naively hoped but doubted that she could have a college education, a good marriage, children, and happiness.

3) In the dramatic story line Brenda (who was, in fact, modeled after a young woman from my high school) was shot and killed by her husband only a week before our ten-year class reunion, but Kathy had a lovely family and was finishing her master's degree in public health. The story hints that Brenda never learned to work for what she wanted, but Kathy, because of her difficult life, learned many ways to approach and to solve problems.

Delivering a metaphor requires a variety of skills (examined in detail in Lankton & Lankton, 1983) that include attention to the client's ideomotor behavior, to the use of pause, inflection, speed of speech, to the use of the interspersal of indirect suggestions and binds, sincerity, and to the use of drama. An important consideration is the matter of dramatic interest. The story began with, "Even knowing how life turns out, it was a surprise that my classmate had been shot and killed by her husband only a week before our class reunion." From this shocking beginning, the story flashed back to the home life and perspectives of both girls when I knew them in high school.

The element of drama is added to gain the interest and attention of my client, and to call upon his ability to judge the outcome of these girls' lives. To do so he must call his attitude into play — but, it is not clear that his attitude is being challenged and he is not defensive or offended. To the client, the metaphor has all the right reasons but it gets the wrong answer. Thinking through the story, he must conclude that his attitude is incorrect. Otherwise, he is left with the options of (a) requisitioning his memory of what he just heard from me, (b) doubting his skill at predicting in this sort of situation (how marriages turn out), or (c) disregarding the entire incident. Actually, he would resort to the third option only after ruling out the other two, but the process of checking his memory and examining his reasoning possibly will be an overload to consciousness especially since the session continues. His attitude, therefore, becomes more confusing than helpful. Information intended to help resolve the confusion will be provided later in the session in another metaphor, but even this metaphor hinted that the ability to solve problems in marriage was due to having problems before marriage, and had been the most important variable in Kathy's successful marriage.

2. Affect and Emotional Flexibility: The Metaphor Protocol

1) Establish a relationship between the protagonist and a person, place, or thing that involves affect (e.g., tenderness, anxiety, confusion, love, longing, etc.).

2) Detail *movement* in the relationship (e.g., moving with, moving toward, moving away, orbiting, etc.).

3) Detail the internal physiological changes that coincide with the building emotion.

The metaphor for affect need have only one goal: to sensitize the client to, or elicit, the therapeutic feeling. There is no need for this metaphor to connect the feeling to a world that is parallel to the client's world. In fact, if the story can elicit the experience without sounding like the client's life, the client will be less defensive and resistance will not be aroused.

The affect metaphor should parallel real life situations that naturally awake emotions. The metaphor should establish and change a relationship, and then comment on the bodily response to the changes. By way of illustration, consider that sadness commonly represents the loss of an important relationship. A metaphor constructed to elicit sadness would sufficiently depict a positive relationship, followed by an account of the protagonists' moving apart, and concluding with an emphasis on their bodily reactions (to incorporate some of the client's actual experience). This could be a story of two friends (or a child and pet, etc.) who, in the course of the story, become separated. The client, properly engaged in the story, will respond unconsciously by generating various component experiences for sadness. The subsequent focus on bodily reactions helps crystalize that unconscious response and brings it out of the background of experience for use in the overall treatment session.

To elicit the feeling of anger, for instance, use of the protocol is quite the same but the direction of movement is modified: for example, the story might detail a relationship with teenage children who persist in throwing garbage over your fence into your yard to be irritating; the movement must involve the protagonists and antagonists moving even closer. The physiology of adrenalin flow in the body ought to be detailed around points of confrontation.

Joy can be elicited by detailing a relationship between two dear friends who are separated except for jovial phone calls. The relationship changes to move the protagonists closer together rapidly when the friends rendezvous at a bus station. Their feelings of longing and mild pleasure naturally turn into joy. The physiology of blood flow to the tender organs of the body, smiles, etc., in the two friends, again, are to be related to whatever minute changes the client exhibits.

Finally, I will give a slightly more complex illustration. Confidence and its physiological component can be facilitated when the relationship includes a series of mild anxiety-producing moments (say, the protagonist's relationship with an undependable auto on cold winter days) and when the change leaves the protagonist with a series of pleasant experiences in place of the anxious ones (his or her first few days with a new automobile that is dependable — heater works, it starts, tires have rubber, windows seal tightly, radio plays, etc.). The protagonist's increased awareness of bodily changes ought to be correlated as much as possible to the client's responses to the story (relaxation of various muscles, sitting more erect, increased ease of perceptions, raised sternum, etc.). Detailing physiological responses, even when they are not apparent in the client, has the effect of perceptual training, and teaches the client to notice aspects of pleasant bodily sensations.

Sometimes several trainings are needed to perform a response well (e.g., confidence, joy, anger, or any other complex learning). In these cases each session may contain an affect metaphor until the client no longer needs it.

3.   *Age-Appropriate Intimacy or Task Behavior: The Metaphor Protocol*

1)   Emphasize goals and not motives while detailing the protagonist's observable behavior related to the desired behavioral role to be acquired by the client.

2)   Detail the protagonist's internal attention and nonobservable behavior used to support the actions he or she displays.

3)   Extend the metaphoric context in order to repeat the explanation of the desired behavior.

With this protocol, the therapist attempts to convey a heightened sense of the actual, observable behaviors that provide relevant feedback to a person who is learning the behaviors, and attempts to instruct the client in appropriate and successful behaviors by means of the metaphor. The client will need to know some internal behaviors as guides for any new learning. Some clients rely on self-talk, others upon the visual image of the goal, etc. A metaphor that poses a protagonist in a situation where analysis or education about behavior is taking place serves nicely. If the therapist wishes to instruct a husband on ways to praise his wife, or to instruct a depressed single person about how to make friends, etc., the metaphor needs only to be about someone learning new behaviors (preferably in a situation different from that facing the client, in order to allow him or her to consider the metaphor without consciously censoring it) *and* without naming or discussing the motive of the protagonist.

For the husband the story might be about *what* I explained to the new business manager about *how* to give praise (what I told him in trance, later what I expected him to do with employees, and finally, what I noticed him doing). The focus is on both the external behaviors (words, gestures, voice tone, breathing, etc.) and on the internal experience that supports such behaviors (self-talk, memories of praise received, etc.). The focus is not about *why* he needs to learn, or how difficult it is to learn, or about how rewarding it is to learn ... just how it is done! For the depressed person to learn social behaviors, the context of a child in a new neighborhood could be employed. The metaphor can give instructions for several greeting behaviors (smiling, giving name, asking names, listening, etc.), and it can repeat several of the learning and some internal supporting experiences, but not the tension or motives. The goal is to sensitize the client to the behaviors and *not* to emphasize the importance of learning the behaviors in order to "get somewhere" or "get something." That connection is exactly what is not wanted; the story ought not be "you need to learn this and here's why." Rather, the learning about the behaviors should be presented as a clue, or an aside. As such, clients get to make the connections for themselves and earn credit in the process.

4.   *Self-Image Thinking Enhancement: The Metaphor Protocol*

1)   Detail the protagonist's appearance to create a central self-image with

visual imagery that emphasizes the appearance of the person *as* he or she experiences a set of desired experiential (emotional, attitudinal, behavioral) resources previously retrieved.

2) Detail rehearsal of the central self-image through successive scenarios involving increasing difficulty or potential anxiety.

3) Culminate with the use of an experience of actually being a part of an image of a successful future that resulted from reliance on the acts rehearsed in the scenarios. Have the client (from the orientation of the future) "think back" through the events (good and bad, etc.) that led to the success.

The protagonist's experience, of course, ought to overlap with the experience of the client to increase the client's involvement in the learning. A metaphor involving mirrorlike reflection is useful with self-image thinking enhancement. For example, the following is a story that I have used often: One of my clients left an evening session to catch an airplane home. His reflection in the plane window that night was his own image altered by the feelings, attitudes, and behaviors gained in the session. The story progresses through different scenarios as the reflection changes and appears to involve other forms and other persons. The reflection must be described in sufficient detail for the client to understand the possibility of looking, feeling, and acting realistically with the new resources. Since self-image thinking requires a good imagination, leaving proper details up to the client is often a poor use of therapy time. If the client could imagine how to better use personal resources to succeed, he or she might not be a client. Self-image building metaphors ought to follow the metaphors that build affect, behavior, and attitude so that the imagining done by the client in the trance facilitates creating models of success. Clients' thinking about any particular new set of conducts will be richer and more fertile than if they are left to unaided speculation. That is, the child abuser can better imagine himself being relaxed and tender about his children after tenderness is evoked (affect protocol) and he is sensitized to tender behaviors (behavior protocol). Even though each metaphor was about some life different from his, the association he will make to tenderness and tender behavior during the self-image metaphor will be more elaborate than if he used his previously unresponsive and unprepared imagination to construct the new roles for himself around his children.

5.   *Family Structure Change: The Metaphor Protocol*

1)   Illustrate how the protagonist's discomfort is related to his or her family structure.

2)   Illustrate how the protagonist changed his or her relationship within that family.

3)   Show how the discomfort was resolved by change in the family.

The general theme of this type of metaphor is that a problem with a symptom disappears when a change occurs in the family. There is no need to make logical the relationship between the symptom and behavior change in the story. All that matters is that the client is invited to wonder about the possibility of affecting the symptom by adjusting the family's structure toward one that is more adaptive. It is advisable for the symptom to be entirely different from the client's. It is often helpful, however, to illustrate a similar behavior in the metaphoric family as the one(s) needed by the client. (These should be changes he or she has not considered.)

6.   *Enjoyment and Discipline in Living and Changing:*
      The Metaphor Protocol

Finally, this protocol employs an isomorphic construction strategy for metaphors. Metaphors so constructed lend themselves quite well to rather thinly disguised embedded "quotes," commands of psychological implication, direct suggestion, or authoritative advice. Once the decision to act briefly "in loco parentis" has been made, supportive or parenting statements can be delivered to the client. The following protocol provides a useful means for doing so.

1)   Create a metaphoric situation that is isomorphic or matches the client's difficulty.

2)   Focus awareness on how pleasure is to be found in the situation.

3)   Deliver instructions, advice, or commands within the metaphor as with embedded quotes while the pleasure is experienced.

This procedure creates a situation where the client hears direct advice only after he or she has been made experientially ready. It is like telling the protagonist in the metaphor to "make up your mind" after focusing on some pleasant experience such as smiling. The result is that a pleasantly smiling client hears, "Use that experience as you make up your mind about what you're going to do." Consequently, the client can learn a way to develop a more enjoyable way of deciding.

MULTIPLE EMBEDDED METAPHOR DELIVERY

The final stage involves constructing a vehicle to deliver metaphors to be used in the session to accomplish the therapeutic goals. Placing one story within another is a practice conducted by Erickson that we call multiple embedded metaphor (Lankton & Lankton, 1983). It can be used to accomplish a number of results, including interview management, trance maintenance, and a structure for the several therapeutic goals.

The general structure is shown below:

a) Induction		Reorientation
b)	Story 1 begins . . .	. . . Story 1 ends.
c)	Story 2 begins . . .	. . . Story 2 ends.
d)	Story 3 complete.	

MULTIPLE EMBEDDED METAPHOR
STORY STRUCTURE

The metaphors in sections b, c, and d, above, do not need to be lengthy for the format to result in the multiple-embedded structure. In fact, normal conversation and numerous literary and motion picture examples have conformed to this structure. "Normal" conversation might consist of a discourse such as this: "I went to the theater this weekend . . . , by the way I sat next to an engineer and he said the same thing we heard on TV . . . , remember, the Mazda 626 is the car of the year and a very good buy, . . . and he worked for years in the field — so he ought to know what he's talking about, . . . anyway, the play at the theater was *Master Harold and the Boys*. Have you seen it?"

This type of digression probably is familiar to the reader. Such a communication can manage and convey lots of information, much of it out of context. That is, the information about the Mazda belonged in a context of discussing "best buys in automobiles" and not in the context of discussing the theater. But the conversation also indicates that the speaker has a deeper and broader relationship to the listener by presupposing several other contexts in addition to the theater. A similar result comes from telling longer therapeutic stories within the framework. The client is not sure what the context of the comments in b, c, and d really was meant to be. The client is free to assume no threat from the possible inference that he or she needs to take the information therein personally. In fact, the information at the vortex (part d) is often lost from consciousness. With the help of confusion or amnesia suggestions bracketing the material at point d, the material delivered there is customarily able to be forgotten by the client's conscious mind. To some degree, amnesia is created by the contextual shifts in the framework, which interrupt conscious associating mechanisms, and by the relief of closure brought about when story 2 (part c) and story 1 (part b) are completed. Moreover, because of the "recency and primacy" effect, there is a tendency to lose conscious access to material that is delivered in the middle of a series.

The crux of the therapy does not take place in any one part of the multiple embedded structure; it takes place throughout. The need to attend sensitively to the client's ideomotor behavior is of utmost importance because there are times when the treatment plan must be abandoned or temporarily postponed so therapy can deal with unique and unpredicted responses that clients can show. When, on the other hand, treatment is progressing according to plan, it is most efficacious to begin with a metaphor (story 1) that most closely approximates the client's conscious concerns and treatment contract (if he or she came with family concerns, the metaphors might begin with the family metaphor protocol, etc.).

The second metaphor position is well-suited for the retrieval of most or all of the resources that will be used in the session. This is the point for using the affect metaphor protocol or for retrieving trance phenomena (age regression, dissociation, etc.) that will be directly called upon later in the session to reassociate experiences and effect therapeutic goals. The use of indirect suggestions, binds, and short anecdotes while telling the metaphors can increase the client's understanding and involvement in the retrieval of resources. Without the proper engagement of the client in the process of resource development, reassociations or relinkings of experience may be weak, constituting less effective learnings.

Material placed in the vortex (part d) is most protected from the client's conscious mind. It is a fine place to deal with that portion of the problem with which the client is likely to be most defensive or threatened. This is the place in the multiple embedded structure to work toward resolving unconscious emotional conflict with reframing, reciprocal inhibition, catharsis, reliving and redecision, or other "techniques." In addition, this is the place where therapists can be the most direct or instructive. For instance, the therapist working with a pain control case might direct the dissociation (elicited in part c) from the client's levitated arm to the exact location of a pain experience, thus instructing the client to directly deal with the symptom. In the case of a volatile child abuser the vortex was used to assist the client to do that which would be too threatening otherwise, namely, to be relaxed and tender around his daughter! The rule of thumb: Use the most embedded portion for the protocol that is likely to deal with material that is most threatening to the client's conscious framework.

Story 2, the metaphor introduced to retrieve resources, may be designed according to the affect protocol in the first half of the session. In the second phase it should end after utilizing the benefits of the embedded framework. The chart below illustrates which protocols may be used in which parts of the multiple embedded structure and still maximize the logical effect. The column called "Linking" (includes "behavior," "self-image," and "family" protocols) is the most useful for associating the client's new learnings and resources to appropriate contexts, and for maximizing the thoughts of the entire embedded-metaphor structure.

Two protocols can be used to design a single metaphor. Continuity and coherency in the story line can be achieved simply by retaining the same characters and the same locations. For example, in the beginning of story 2 the protagonist is in a relationship that changes and produces bodily-emotional responses (the affect protocol). This story is suspended, and a different story with another protocol, and therefore a different goal, is completed at the vortex. When story 2 picks up again it may employ the behavior protocol. Thus, we might find the protagonist in the process of learning behaviors that satisfy the treatment plan. The situation in which the protagonist uses the behaviors may be entirely different from that established in the beginning of this story. In this process, the story conforms to one protocol, fulfills that purpose, and then the same story line conforms to another protocol and fulfills that purpose.

This aspect of one metaphor combining two protocols in a single story line can be used twice in the multiple structure. Part b of story 1, for example, can be used to suggest that changes in the client's current development will continue in his or her future development; that is, to associate the gains of the therapy to those occasions when the client will be confronted with new or unexpected life-demands. The child abuser who has learned to be tender to his teenage daughter ought to think a bit about tenderly, proudly, holding his yet unborn grandchild. When his teenage daughter eventually produces his grandchild, the prearranged associations produce a feeling of success, rather than one of failure because of ruling with an iron hand. The self-image thinking and the family-structure change protocols fill this requirement very well.

	Begin Story 1:	Begin Story 2:	Story 3:	End Story 2:	End Story 1:
Protocol	Matching	Retrieving	Directing	Linking	Future
Attitude	X		X		
Affect		X	(X)		
Behavior	X	X		X	
Self-image	X			X	X
Family	X			X	X
Discipline	X		X		
Other interventions:					
Trance Phenomena		X	X		
Catharsis/Reliving			X		
Conflict Resolution			X		

It is important to note that the use of three metaphors and five protocols can be too much to plan and present in a single session (the first session, especially). The structure should be modified when this is the case. For example, the extension of therapeutic gains into the future can be postponed until the next session. Nonetheless, a multiple-metaphor structure containing several metaphors and several protocols can be employed in general clinical practice to accomplish therapeutic goals by addressing family members' entire range of personal experience, rather than merely addressing a symptom. Once learned, this approach adds more certainty than difficulty to the conduct of psychotherapy.

The process of formulating therapeutic goals from the assessment may require very little time to several days, but once conceived, the protocols guide the therapist in creating predictable structures to achieve these goals. Once learned and regarded as aids to thoughtful planning, predictable structures can be created in a matter of a few minutes. Such efficiency is one result of this explicit method of formulating Ericksonian interventions.

189

SUMMARY AND CONCLUSION

What I have outlined is the form of intervention used most frequently in my approach to Ericksonian hypnotherapy. It is not necessarily a single session approach, but an approach that I sometimes extend across several sessions. Although there are instances when I do plan and produce the entire structure in a several-hour session, far more frequently, however, a few sessions spanning two or more months are required. In some cases therapy can continue for more than a year, depending on the client's resources, our ability to communicate, and which adjustments of living are being addressed. Most sessions in which I use multiple embedded metaphor take from one to one and a half hours, depending upon how much discussion and feedback of progress precede or follow the treatment.

The thrust of this chapter has been to illustrate one logical structure that underlies diagnosis and treatment planning. It is a structure designed to have an impact on the total person and his or her total life situation rather than on a symptom (C. Lankton, Chapter 10). Thoughtful treatment planning helps therapists organize their attempts to stimulate clients to use their resources to create a holistic change — a change that complements all aspects of their clients' experiential and interpersonal lives. This ambitious aim is undertaken almost regardless of the apparent simplicity of a client's symptoms or problems. Integrating change into all areas of a client's experience is a matter of clinical efficacy that can reinforce, strengthen, and even accelerate the course of therapy (Brown & Chaves, 1980).

Regardless of the intrigue or the promise that the embedded-metaphor structure can prevail upon a clinician's good intentions, it is the general attitude towards a client, as a unique and whole person, that prevails upon a client's well-being. Little has been done to view the benefits of hypnosis within a larger diagnostic framework as in this explication of an Ericksonian approach. Research on successful hypnotherapeutic treatment aimed only at symptom removal is nearsighted. It is necessary to focus on the larger perspective that Ericksonian methodology provides and the extent of improvement that can be realized by considering the whole person.

References

Balson, P. M., & Dempster, C. (1980). Treatment of war neurosis from Vietnam. *Comprehensive Psychiatry, 21*(2), 167–175.

Benson, H. (1978). Treatment of anxiety: A comparison of the usefulness of self-hypnosis and meditational relaxation technique: An overview. *Psychotherapy and Psychosomatics, 30*(3–4), 229–242.

Brown, J., & Chaves, J. (1980). Hypnosis in the treatment of sexual dysfunction. *Journal of Sex and Marital Therapy, 6*(1), 63–74.

Carruthers, M. (1981). Voluntary nervous system: Comparison of autogenic training and siddha meditation. *Experimental and Clinical Psychiatry, 6,* 171–181.

Erickson, M. H. (1980). Hypnosis: Its renascence as a treatment modality. In E. L. Rossi (Ed.), *Innovative hypnotherapy: The collected papers of Milton H. Erickson on hypnosis* (Vol. 4, pp. 52–75). New York: Irvington.

Eysenck, H. J. (1969). Relapse and symptom substitution after different types of psychotherapy. *Behavior Research and Therapy, 7*(3), 283–287.

Gerschman, J., Burrows, G., & Fitzgerald, P. (1981). Hypnosis in the control of gagging. *Australian Journal of Clinical and Experimental Hypnosis, 9*(2), 53–59.

Greenberg, I. (1977). *Group hypnotherapy and hypnodrama.* Chicago, IL: Nelson-Hall.

Haley, J. (1973). *Uncommon therapy: The psychiatric techniques of Milton H. Erickson.* New York: Norton.

Horowitz, S. L. (1970). Strategies within hypnosis for reducing phobic behavior. *Journal of Abnormal Psychology, 75*(1), 104–112.

Howard, W. L. (1979). The modification of self-concept, anxiety and neuro-muscular performance through rational stage directed hypnotherapy: A cognitive experiential perspective using cognitive restructuring and hypnosis. *Dissertation Abstracts International, 40*(4-A), 1962.

Klug, B. (1980). Hypnosis as a treatment modality in psychiatric practice. *Australian Journal of Clinical and Experimental Hypnosis, 8*(1), 37–40.

Lankton, C. Generative change: Beyond symptom control.

Lankton, S., & Lankton, C. (1983). *The answer within: A clinical framework of Ericksonian hypnotherapy.* New York: Brunner/Mazel.

Lankton, S., & Lankton, C. (1984). Ericksonian styles of paradoxical treatment. In G. Weeks (Ed.), *Promoting change through paradoxical treatment.* New York: Dow Jones-Erwin.

Leary, T. (1957). *Interpersonal diagnosis of personality.* New York: Ronald.

Marks, I. (1971). Phobic disorders four years after treatment: A prospective follow-up. *British Journal of Psychiatry, 118*(547), 683–688.

Van Pelt, S. J. (1975). The role of hypnotic suggestion in the aetiology and treatment of the psychoneurotic. *Journal of the American Institute of Hypnosis, 16*(6), 27–33.

Waxman, D. (1975). Hypnosis in the psychotherapy of neurotic illness. *British Journal of Medical Psychology, 48*(4), 339–348.

11

Using Metaphor with Clients[1]

Therapeutic metaphor belongs to that group of therapeutic interventions re-ferred to as indirection. The definition of metaphor as used in therapy refers to a complex story that holds the user's attention and provides an alternate framework through which clients can entertain novel experience. In using metaphor, the therapist can (1) make or illustrate a point to the client; (2) sug-gest solutions not previously considered by the client; (3) seed ideas to which the therapist can later return; (4) decrease the conscious resistance of the client; (5) reframe or redefine a problem for the client so that the problem is placed in a different context with a different meaning (Zeig, 1980); and (6) retrieve and associate experience such as emotion, thought, perception, and expression.

USES OF METAPHORIC STORIES

As a listener becomes increasingly engaged or absorbed in a story, there is a reduction in defensive mechanisms that customarily constrain the listener to sets of common experience. That is, listening to a story that symbolizes ten-derness can lead a person who normally does not shed tears to weep. The def-inition mentions that clients can entertain novel experiences. The concept of a novel experience may need slight elaboration. It pertains to experiences that

---

[1] Lankton, S. (2002). The use of therapeutic metaphor in social work. In A. Roberts & G. Greene (Eds.), *Social workers' desk reference* (pp. 385–391). New York: Oxford University Press. Reprinted with permission.

are commonly excluded from the experiential set of the listener. While listening to an absorbing story, a client may, with relative ease, temporarily experience one or several specific experiences that, if therapeutically managed, can assist the listener in creating personal change. The assistance in creating personal change comes about as clients reexamine perceptions or cognitions, emotions, or potential behaviors in light of a recognition that these new experiences, perceptions, or cognitions once thought to be alien actually are or can be a part of their own personality and experience. In general, it could be said that the usefulness of metaphor in therapy comes into play at any point in therapy where it is advisable or useful for clients to recognize that experiential resources lie within themselves rather than having to introject them from an outside authority.

Metaphor is especially useful when brief forms of therapy, such as grief therapy, solution-focused therapy, hypnotherapy, or family or couples therapy are the therapeutic modality of choice. However, an additional aspect of the ambiguous nature of metaphor suggests that the use of therapeutic metaphor can have great value in long-term therapies, as well.

THE AMBIGUOUS ASPECT OF METAPHOR

Unlike directive and manipulative therapies that, through implication or connotation, tell clients how to perceive, think, feel, or behave, techniques of indirection allow clients to modify verbal input from the therapist and fit it to their own situation with a greater degree of relevance and with an element of ego-syntonic meaning. If clients are instructed to conduct themselves in a certain manner or say certain sentences to their spouse in directive couples therapy, these things may be ego-dystonic since they come from outside as implied or denoted by the therapist as something clients should or must do. However, when clients have determined for themselves a relevant meaning to a more ambiguous input from a therapist, they are acting on perceptions, behaviors, or feelings that truly belong to them as a part of them. Let's examine this ambiguous element more closely.

The degree of ambiguity in a therapeutic story can be regulated by the teller so that the story is more or less vague to the listener. Regardless of the degree of vagueness, listeners create their own relevant meaning in order to understand the story. This accounts for the ego-syntonic nature of the understanding and the lack of mere compliance by listeners. However, as the degree of vagueness increases, there is an exponential increase in the number of possible meanings that listeners can give to the story. It is assumed that listeners sorting through several possibilities at what has been determined to be 30 items per second (Erickson & Rossi, 1979, p. 18) become increasingly absorbed in weighing the best fit for these possible meanings.

This ongoing process of weighing meaning has a number of therapeutic benefits. First, there is an increase in participation by listeners. Second, a heightened valuation in any meaning is found by listeners as it has been made a deeper part of their own experience. Third, there is a depotentiation of normal, rigid ego controls while seeking a best fit. And finally, there is an increase in the duration of time given to examining possible meanings. This last element, in fact, accounts for a therapeutic effect upon the client long after the therapy session has ended. Indeed, for a highly meaningful and yet extremely vague metaphoric story, listeners may continue to turn it over in their mind for years after the therapy session and do so for events that even years later parallel the original therapeutic learning incident. For this reason, the use of metaphor can be summarized as follows: It increases the relevance of therapy for clients and involves clients more highly in their own change process. It expands the usual limiting experience that has led to a stabilization of the presenting problem or dynamic and brought the person to therapy. It offers an engaging element of ambiguity that may continue to alert listeners to their therapeutic learnings for years after a therapy session. And it offers a wide range of potentially correct responses within the therapeutic limits.

REDUCTION OF RESISTANCE

Since metaphor offers listeners the ability to apply a wide range or spectrum of potential understandings to what the therapist has said, there is a corresponding reduction in listener resistance. Any therapeutic modality that finds clients to be resistive, possibly due to the nature of the modality itself, will be able to take advantage of metaphoric stories, provided those stories are constructed and shared in a manner that employs the necessary components of therapeutic metaphor.

THE NECESSARY COMPONENTS OF
THERAPEUTIC METAPHOR

To be effective, therapeutic metaphor must be perceived and be relevant. It also must engage listeners and retrieve experience. There are a number of ways these requirements can be fostered or hindered in the therapeutic process. There should be a consideration of the relationship of the story to the sensory system primarily used by the listener in order to process data, material that is taken out of sequence to create dramatic engagement or enchantment, and the retrieval and use of experience that is therapeutically relevant.

The Perception and Relevance of the Metaphor

The bottom line regarding the relevance of a metaphor or any experience is that it resonates with either clients' current state or clients' future state. In general, the metaphor should be constructed to hold the attention of clients' conscious minds. While there are important exceptions to this rule, it does apply to the vast majority of metaphors that therapists will construct and use.

Therapists should consider that clients' understandings or representations of problems are likely to be characterized by them in a preferred sensory system. That is, some clients will relate their problem with the majority of their sensory-specific verbs in a preferred representational system: visual, auditory, or kinesthetic (Lankton, 1979). This can be ascertained by listening to clients' presentations of their problems. When such a preference is discovered, it is imperative that therapists attempt to communicate with clients in their preferred manner of thinking and representing. When delivering metaphor the conscious minds of clients will be engaged and consider stories more relevant when this connection is honored. However, certain portions of a metaphoric story may be strategically represented in a lesser used system for certain purposes. For instance, certain experiences may be more easily retrieved by means of lesser used representational systems to refer to them.

Consider a client who thinks with a predominantly visual set of mental tools. Relating a story that encourages him to see a father and son hugging will have a moving effect of sadness on his conscious mind if he did not receive that type of attention. But then hearing the words spoken (his secondarily used sensory system is auditory) by the father in the story saying "Come here and let me hug you, son. I love you and I'm proud of you" may evoke an emotion of tenderness and closeness instead of sadness. The difference is due to the fact that the client's understanding of his life is primarily a visual "story" in his mind that he can easily navigate within. Seeing the images created in the telling of the story, it would be easy for him to quickly compare the ideas with his life and "think" about it. However, thinking with auditory imagery is not as easy for him and the experience attached to the imagery used by the therapist is, in fact, the experience he retrieves. Purposeful regulation of this aspect of a story is a matter of training and experience on the part of the therapist.

There are two major categories of metaphor: those that are parallel to the client's problem and those that are parallel to the anticipated goal. Stories that are parallel to the client's current state or problem are far easier to construct and were the first type of metaphors noticed in the process of modeling the therapeutic work of such experts as Milton Erickson (Gordon, 1978; Lankton, 1979).

The basic idea of the metaphoric stories that are parallel to the problem can be summarized in the understanding of the term *isomorphism*. Metaphors that are isomorphic have the body of their content in a one-to-one correspondence with the experience of the client. A simple way of understanding this is that for every major player and situation in the client's problem, and for every major relationship and activity in the client's problem that connects these players and situations, a corresponding part is created in the story told to the client. Again, the degree of distance or vagueness between the elements in the metaphor and the elements in the client's life will regulate the degree of ambiguity that's introduced.

For example, consider the following variation of isomorphic metaphor that matches the problem. Here the husband seeks affection from a wife who ignores him unless blaming him for a fault. The pattern then unfolds as the husband withdraws into depression and the wife becomes angry with him. Table 11.1 lists the situation's components as related by the client, and the two columns show the elements of a story that can be told with varying degrees of ambiguity.

Table 11.1 Isomorphic Construction

Situation	Less Ambiguous	More Ambiguous
husband	lovebird	electric drill
(husband) asks	chirps	(drill) freezes up
needs affection	needs touching	needs oil
wife	girl	mechanic
(wife) ignores	(girl) locks up	throws down
(wife) blames faults	(girl) shouts at bird	worries it will burn
(wife) defensive	(girl) recalls messes	brags of skill
(husband) withdraws	(bird) chews cage	(drill) overheats
(husband) depression	(bird) gets ill	(drill) emits smoke
(wife) angry	(girl) sells bird	throws it out

It should be obvious that despite the similar isomorphic relationship between parts of the story and the problem, the more ambiguous references may not be an apparent match to the listener for some time (if at all). The solution to the dilemma is not shown in table 11.1, only the match to the problem. However, the sketching of part (or all) of the solution would be the next step for the therapist.

The therapeutic value of an isomorphic metaphor exists in two places. First, it outlines the context or heightens the client's awareness for the problem situation in which the solution will be fitted. Second, isomorphic metaphors need to have resolution that provides some metaphoric solution. It's in this second aspect of isomorphic metaphors that beginning therapists may encounter difficulty. There are a few major ways for isomorphic metaphors to be terminated so that they provide a therapeutic conclusion for the problem they have highlighted. The most elegant manner is that which involves the continued and often creative behavior of the protagonist through whose behavior a solution is illustrated. A second, less practical method is for the therapist to introduce into the story direct instructions that represent words spoken to the protagonist.

This second option fails to meet the criteria of retrieving experience for a client and often fails to meet the ambiguity element that prevents resistance in the client. However, it is very practical for clear guidelines, instructions, or directives to be delivered to a client in a fashion that reduces confrontation.

The third and least elegant method to create a goal in an isomorphic metaphor is to introduce a break in the normal flow of the protagonist's behavior owing to some unexpected element such as the protagonist's going to therapy, having a dream, or having some sudden sort of epiphany. While this device within a story will allow the speaker to jump to a solution set, it does so at the expense of the logical flow of the metaphoric content, although it still provides an opportunity for experiences to be retrieved that will help alter perception, behavior, emotion, or attitude.

The second major category of metaphor includes those constructed to become parallel to the goal rather than parallel to the problem (Lankton & Lankton, 1989). It is essential that a basic protocol be followed for specific goals of cognition, emotion, and behavior, and that experiences be so ordered that the metaphor retrieves a specific goal for the listener. This movement can be maximized to facilitate, if not ensure, the listener's experience as one of cognitive alteration, emotional alteration, or behavioral sensitizing. In order to illustrate this, the three self-explanatory protocols for emotion, attitude, and behavior metaphors will be listed (Lankton & Lankton, 1986; Lankton & Lankton, 1989).

A. Affect and emotion protocol

1. Establish a relationship between the protagonist and a person, place, or thing that involves emotion or affect (e.g., tenderness, anxiety, mastery, confusion, love, longing, etc.).

2. Detail *movement* in the relationship (e.g., moving with, moving toward, moving away, orbiting, etc.).

3. Focus on some of the physiological changes that coincide with the protagonist's emotion (be sure to overlap with the client's facial behavior).

B. Attitude change protocol

1. Describe a protagonist's behavior or perception so that it exemplifies the maladaptive attitude. Bias this belief to appear positive or desirable.

2. Describe another protagonist's behavior or perception so that it exemplifies the *adaptive* attitude (the goal). Bias this belief to appear negative or undesirable.

3. Reveal the *unexpected* outcome achieved by both protagonists that resulted from the beliefs they held and their related actions. Be sure the payoff received by the second protagonist is of value to the client.

C. Behavior change protocol

1. Illustrate the protagonist's observable behavior similar to the desired behavior to be acquired by the client. There is no need to mention motives. List about six specific observable behaviors.

2. Detail the protagonist's internal attention or nonobservable behavior that shows the protagonist to be congruent with his or her observable behavior.

3. Change the setting within the story so as to provide an opportunity for repeating all the behavioral descriptions several (three) times.

Dramatic Aspects of Metaphor

The use of dramatic devices in any oral or rhetoric tradition can be seen as a matter of presenting knowledge or information out of sequence. Information that is in a linear, temporal sequence is simply a documentary. However, when various delivery devices such as tonal inflection are used to stress certain words as if their meaning is deeper than that which is denoted, there is an indication that more than just documentary information is being offered. Furthermore, the hints that are provided by tonal stress in a simple, linear presentation of facts cause the listener to seek that connoted meaning by anticipating *what is to come* in the story or reevaluating what has been heard so far. However, the actual tactics of creating dramatic hold within a story are more dynamic than simply stressing connoted information.

Looking at Table 11.2, it can be seen that, in the course of a story line, there will be information known to the protagonist and information known to the listener. If information known to the protagonist is not known to the listener, mystery arises. For example, in the telling of a story there may be a letter read, a telephone call, or a conversation in a secluded location between protagonists. And the information shared in that exchange can be illustrated as having great importance. However, that information can be withheld from listeners as a secret or private event. While it has great meaning to the characters in the story, listeners won't know how the protagonists' behavior has been affected by the information that was concealed from them. As a result, listeners are in a position to try to deduce by anticipation, think back to the character development, or somehow gain a degree of certainty about how the information may affect the outcome of the story.

Table 11.2 Creating Drama

Type of Drama	Client	Protagonist(s)
Suspense	Knows info	Does not know
Mystery	Does not know	Knows info
Surprise/shock/humor	Does not know	Does not know

The element of mystery seems to create a primarily cognitive hold on the listener. It can happen numerous times in a story and it can also be created by means other than dialogues between the characters in the story. An analysis will reveal that the characters have been shown to be privy to some information not known to the listener. In the case of a therapeutic story the listener is the client.

Table 11.2 further illustrates that information known to the client or listener but not known to the protagonists or characters in the story creates the situation of suspense. The hold of suspense is a much more visceral or emotional hold of attention by comparison to mystery. This is often easily created by the storyteller through foreshadowing. In many well-known works of literature, the author will give a glimpse ahead as to how the story is to be framed. This occurs, for instance, when the story begins with comments about how the story will end. It is the same in cinema. The motion picture *Gandhi* begins with the assassination of the protagonist. Here we see the archetypal footprint of suspense by means of taking information out of sequence and foreshadowing the later ending of the man's life. However, in cinema, there are more dramatic devices that can be used, such as flashing lights or the well-known rhythmical percussion in the movie *Jaws*. In a literary or spoken story, material taken out of sequence that reveals flaws or outcomes about the protagonists to the listener will increase the experience of suspense.

Finally, Table 11.2 shows that when neither the listener/client nor the protagonist/character has information about an upcoming event, the result will be surprise, shock, or humor when the event occurs. So, a sudden death in a story that was not foreshadowed for the listener or expected by the characters will be a surprise. When surprise or shock occurs in a story, listeners will search facts they have already heard in the story to put the outcome in perspective or will examine whether certain information had already existed to predict the surprise. And, too, they will begin to test various anticipated hypotheses to try to predict how the story will turn out.

With any of these dramatic methods the effect is to capture attention and engage listeners in the story by means of encouraging them to make sense of the story. The visceral or cognitive energy used to sort through past and anticipated futures in a story is the result of the use of drama. The drama does not need to be award-winning and especially creative. It simply needs to be present in the story to help listeners become more consciously absorbed as they make room to entertain the novel experience created by the protocols mentioned before.

Enchantment

As mentioned earlier, one of the devices for understanding the effect of metaphor is the aspect of ambiguity. Ambiguity is one of the mechanisms that binds the listener to the story. There are few words available for explaining this phenomenon. Perhaps one of the best terms to refer to it is *enchantment*. Enchantment can be defined as holding spellbound by, or as if by, irresistible force, words, or charms and to pique a pleasant mental excitement. It is this last aspect of creating a pleasant mental excitement that is of greatest interest to the therapist constructing a therapeutic metaphor.

Creating dramatic hold in a relevant story with a certain degree of various meanings available maximizes both the interest and usefulness of the story for the client. It was mentioned earlier that the degree of ambiguity can be regulated by means of increasing or decreasing vagueness about the connection between events in the client's life or experiences that will be goals for the client and the elements in the story. That is, the elements in the story can be increasingly mundane or increasingly symbolic and abstract in their denoted content. A degree of skill and practice is necessary to develop the ability to maximize the therapeutic impact by regulating this ambiguity with clients. It requires that therapists continue to have a high degree of observation of the impact of the story upon the listener. Beyond the regulation of controlled ambiguity within the metaphor, there are other devices that create or regulate the experience of enchantment. These include tonal delivery and word selection that create a degree of pathos and highly charged meaning for the listener.

INDICATIONS AND CONTRAINDICATIONS

Contraindications to using metaphor fall in two major categories. One category has to do with the experience level of the therapist and the other concerns the type and severity of the problem of the client. A therapist who has little skill in the use of indirection techniques and who has little clinical skill must consider using metaphoric stories with a greatly limited range of clients, problem severity, and diagnostic categories. The beginning therapist can only comfortably use metaphoric stories for individuals who would be considered vocal and intellectual; mildly neurotic, anxious, depressed, and with problems that are not urgent. With such clients, there is more ability to assess impact and ethically evaluate the efficacy of the technique.

Therapists with a greater degree of clinical experience and experience with the use of indirection and ambiguous interventions will find that it is possible to successfully and ethically employ metaphoric stories with a far greater range of individuals, problem categories, and diagnostic types.

Contraindication for diagnostic types includes individuals who are actively psychotic and those who are moderately to severely borderline. This also includes any neurotic individuals who have extreme difficulties with boundary-related issues. The reason for this concern about individuals with cognitive disorders and boundary problems lies in the fact that the degree of search mentation initiated by clients will make it possible for the individual to apply several meanings. When the individual client has demonstrated difficulty retaining cognitive meaning in life situations, the use of any technique that exacerbates this is contraindicated. Similarly, the boundary problem finds its difficulty in those individuals who come to believe that the therapist can read their thoughts owing to the fact that they have projected meaning into a metaphoric story and failed to realize that it is *their* projected meaning, instead thinking that it is a previously known meaning that the therapist has somehow been able to divine by an extrasensory means or from an extraordinary rapport with them.

These outcomes do not occur for individuals who do not have boundary or cognitive problems. However, a third category of contraindication includes those individuals who have a great deal of difficulty establishing rapport and trust. For these persons, regardless of their diagnostic category or presenting problem, the credibility of the therapist is continually being questioned and evaluated. Since using metaphoric stories relies upon clients investigating what was said for possible relevant meanings and surrendering a degree of habitual reality testing in order to entertain novel experiences as they become caught up in the relevance, drama, and enchantment of the story, individuals who maintain an analytical distance and do so while continually doubting and questioning the therapist are liable to take the ambiguity of the intervention as a sign that the therapist is to some degree not competent. Again, the clinical experience of the therapist may reduce the number of individuals for whom this type of contraindication is relevant. Therapists with considerable clinical experience are usually skilled at carefully judging the manner in which they need to approach clients in order to engage them in the change process.

Using Metaphors within the
Therapy Process

Using metaphoric stories need not be constrained to individuals in the midst of hypnotic trance or to those clients who are invested in the change process. It is well indicated to use metaphoric stories at any point in the therapeutic process, provided the goal is to retrieve perceptual, attitudinal, emotional, or behavior-focusing goals.

During early stages of engagement with the client and prior to the client's having a contractual agreement for therapy, metaphoric stories can illustrate for individuals a way of thinking about using therapy to change their problems. Even lesser complex goals such as helping clients relax, focusing their thoughts back to the situations that have led them to the office, or articulating their problems can be beneficially addressed through metaphor. All of these goals and more at the early stages of therapeutic contact can not only be accomplished with metaphoric stories but possibly be accomplished more efficiently. The reason for this is that the degree of choice the listener has in making sense of a metaphoric story reduces the resistance that can come from otherwise attempting to be specific with direct communications about how a client is to think, feel, or behave.

During the change process itself, metaphoric stories can enhance any aspect of therapy where increased mental involvement is indicated and where specific experiences brought into the foreground can enhance therapeutic movement. These times are more numerous than can possibly be mentioned and the more experience the therapist has, the more such moments will be apparent.

Summary

Using therapeutic metaphor throughout the therapy process can enhance therapeutic movement. Metaphoric stories need to be constructed in a manner that is relevant to the client, holds his or her attention, and facilitates the retrieval of experience that is helpful to the therapy process. The degree of ambiguity should be carefully regulated by observing the client's responses to the spoken words.

Clients will demonstrate three types of responses to the specific words and experiences in the metaphors. In general, clients will exhibit head shakes, head nods, or ideomotor transforms of identification and internal search phenomena. Head nods almost always indicate that the words spoken by the therapist are acceptable to the client's frame of reference and that they have identified a meaningful and desirable personal experience. Head shakes do not necessarily mean the ideas introduced by the therapist are undesirable. More investigation and unconscious communicating will determine whether the ideas did not find a fit with the client's sense of direction or simply that the information did not fit due to unacceptable wording. Indications of mental searching show that clients sense a fit between what the therapist implied and with their own internal frame of reference.

The aim of observation is for the therapist to recognize the degree of relevance the story has for the listener by gauging the degree of internal absorption and search that the client has. It is also for the therapist to gauge the degree of achievement that clients accomplish in retrieving desired experiences. Finally, the aim of observation is to gather ongoing diagnostic information as it pertains to the manner in which the client responds to various words and actions that are denoted and connoted within the story.

Since the activity of delivering and receiving the metaphor is an individual matter, research on the level of resource retrieval and specific resources that a particular metaphoric story may bring is problematic. Clients will respond in a unique way depending upon their needs, background, and motivation, and also depending upon the therapist's skill in observing and delivering metaphor. Outcomes that are achieved by the use of metaphoric stories are truly co-created. That is, they are a blend of factors of the client's history and motivation and the therapist's ability to provide compelling delivery and meaningful content, as well as therapeutically useful protocol.

Finally, it should be remembered that the listener's achievement of meaning fluctuates with the degree of ambiguity and apparent relevance of the story. Therefore, stories should have some immediate impact upon the listener that is useful within the therapeutic sessions. However, some degree of impact can be expected from certain stories years later due to the client's capability to seek useful meanings and project them into the ambiguity provided by a relevant story.

References

Erickson, M., & Rossi, E. (1979). *Hypnotherapy: An exploratory casebook.* New York: Irvington.

Gordon, D. (1978). *Therapeutic metaphors: Helping others through the looking glass.* Cupertino, CA: Meta Publication.

Lankton, S. (1979). *Practical magic: A translation of basic neuro-linguistic programming into clinical psychotherapy.* Cupertino, CA: Meta Publications.

Lankton, C., & Lankton, S. (1989). *Tales of enchantment: An anthology of goal directed metaphors for adults and children in therapy.* New York: Brunner/Mazel.

Lankton, S., & Lankton, C. (1986). *Enchantment and intervention in family therapy: Training in Ericksonian approaches.* New York: Brunner/Mazel.

Zeig, J. (Ed. with commentary). (1980). *A teaching seminar with Milton H. Erickson.* New York: Brunner/Mazel.

12

Choosing the Right Metaphors
for Particular Clients[1]

Generally speaking, any therapy that uses metaphor as an intervention works strategically from available resources and builds needed resources within the client. This two-part procedure of determining available resources and estimating needed resources involves several factors, including: the *treatment contract* and *goals* derived from the *diagnostic assessment*, the client's *developmental age* and *developmental issues*, and the *client's life experiences*, including the *client's own metaphors*.

The use of metaphor in hypnotherapy presupposes that the therapist operates from a strategic approach. The first consideration, therefore, is *always* the unique family and individuals, the treatment contract, and the therapeutic goal(s). Once goals have been tentatively established, the selection of interventions (particularly metaphors) is guided by all of the above considerations. The client's contract and the therapist's assessment are continually refined during therapy.

Several factors are involved in assessment, which can only be mentioned here: the structure of the family or social system, the stage of development of the client and client system, the psychological ages of all individuals con-

---

[1] Lankton, S. (1986). How can you decide which metaphors are right for a particular client? In Gerald Edelstien, Daniel Araoz, & Bernie Zilbergeld (Eds.), *Questions and answers in the practice of hypnosis* (pp. 261–267). New York: Norton. Reprinted with permission.

cerned, the available and needed resources, the pattern or function of the presenting symptomatic behavior, and the treatment contract.

A metaphor provides a context in which to convey a therapeutic learning. Therefore, the strategic therapist must be guided by the goals that have been set to fulfill the treatment contract. The process of changing concepts and imagery within the metaphor should be built around the expectation that the client will learn something that will challenge a held attitude, evoke an emotion, highlight a behavior, encourage a new self-image, etc. Since the actual change process is initiated within the listener from experience evoked by each particular metaphor, the metaphor should be carefully structured to increase the likelihood of accomplishing the specific outcome (attitude restructuring, emotion, behavior, self-image enhancement, etc.).

Such metaphors result from careful observation and feedback. Strategic therapists plan the process of imagery and concept change within each metaphor to conform to the treatment plan; they do not merely "free associate" ideas that may come to mind in the session (Erickson, 1980, p. 336).

The structures that we use to facilitate various therapeutic goals have been elaborated elsewhere (Lankton & Lankton, 1983; Lankton, 1985). Here I will summarize the major requirements for three of these protocols: attitude restructuring, affect flexibility, and behavior change. Again, in choosing metaphors, the concerns and goals of the particular client(s) must be stated first by the strategic therapist. The *content* of the metaphor can be selected to aid the identification and understanding of the client and subsequently be arranged to follow a *process* of change as outlined below. The following protocols simulate the manner of idea formation occurring in the "real world" and, as such, can be expected to help promote and create attitude, emotional, and behavioral learnings in therapy.

ATTITUDE RESTRUCTURING

1) Create a story that examines the behavior or attitude in question from the protagonist's perspective.

2) Alternate within the story to examine the opposite behavior or attitude from the perspective of at least one other protagonist.

3) Conclude the story by relating the consequence(s) of each protagonist's behavior(s) and/or beliefs to the perceptions each held.

A metaphor of this type was used to challenge the attitude expressed by an unmarried male client. Part of his difficulty was that he was firm in his belief that a person from a broken home could not have a happy marriage. An attitude metaphor told to him concerned two high school girls that I had known. One was killed by her husband, who also took his own life, one week prior to our high school reunion.

The story explained that "Brenda" came from a happy home and viewed her future optimistically. Following this character development, the life of the second protagonist, "Kathy," was elaborated. Sally was from an abusive family and her parents eventually divorced. This portion of the metaphor took several minutes and followed steps one and two above. The client could be expected to project his attitude in an attempt to predict the outcome that Sally was killed. Finally, however, the story ends with the revelation that Georgia, not Sally, was the victim.

In this example the client's attitude was evoked and then, presumably, confused or bewildered by the actual ending of the story. Having projected the incorrect answer to the dramatic end of the story, a client must certainly question where his thinking went wrong. Thus, he temporarily suspends his strongly held belief. Hence, he will be more receptive to new learnings in the therapeutic session.

AFFECT AND EMOTIONAL FLEXIBILITY

1) Create a story that establishes a relationship between the protagonist and a person, place, or thing that involves emotion or affect (e.g., tenderness, anxiety, mastery, confusion, love, longing).

2) Change the story so that it provides detail about the *movement* in the relationship (e.g., moving with, moving toward, moving away, orbiting, chasing).

3) End the story with a focus on details of observable behaviors and internal physiological changes of the main protagonist (and coincidentally of the listener) that result from the building of emotion.

An affect metaphor that helps a client increase or build a sense of sadness might be told to a client who has not grieved a loss. Although several story *contents* would be possible, the following *process* of imagery change (in any story with which the listener is likely to identify) will increase the likelihood of a therapeutic success.

The character development initially paints the protagonist as positive and sketches a positive relationship (warm, friendly, loving, caring, understanding, etc.) between the protagonist and another person, place, or thing. The second step in the process of the story must introduce movement, in this case, movement away from or separating the two. As this separation occurs, a listener will make sense of the changing imagery by experiencing a meaningful personal reaction.

The third step suggests that the story culminate with a focus on the bodily reaction of the protagonist and especially those changes that will be exhibited by the listener. Thus, the listener finds himself or herself experiencing aspects of the complex constellation of sadness built unconsciously and beyond the level of conscious resistance. The conscious awareness and identification with the drama of the story line will serve only to capture attention. The unconscious response is created by the movement of imagery in the story according to the protocol and the subsequent experience it evokes in the listener.

BEHAVIOR CHANGE

1) Create a story that emphasizes the protagonist's goals rather than his/her motives, while detailing the protagonist's observable behavior related to the client's desired behavioral role.

2) Include within the story the details of the protagonist's internal attention and non-observable behavior used to support the actions he or she exhibits.

3) Before ending, extend the context of the story so that it is possible to repeat explanations of the desired behavior.

The metaphors that develop a sensitivity to some behaviors, for instance, the behaviors involved in asking for help, entail sharing a story that does little more than make a few specific behaviors explicit. The story might involve a man asking for help in a service station and again in a hardware store. The protagonist's motives would not be mentioned. His behaviors, however, would be explained in detail. These might include: standing with his palms upward, shifting his weight from one foot to the other, using a softened voice tone, dropping his gaze, using the words, "I need your help with this . . . ," etc. The man's internal experience at the time would also be explored. The story would either describe the same man in other situations or observe others asking for help with similar behaviors. Hence, the listener thinks of performing the behaviors but the metaphoric framework removes him one step from possible threat and reduces defensive resistance that may occur.

In summarizing these three basic metaphor process protocols, let me compare them with common experiences. The attitude metaphor follows the format of many of Aesop's fables, like "the boy who cried wolf" and many New Testament stories, like the prodigal son or the story of the twelve talents. The affect format, found in innumerable stories from cinema, could be illustrated with the simple and well-known tale *Love Story*. In *Love Story* the relationship of the starring couple is first shown to be intensely close and loving; then, unexpectedly, the woman contracts cancer and dies. The viewers are left observing the grieved reaction of the other main character. The behavior protocol follows the format of the common television cooking and home improvement shows. Here there is no motive (such as to impress the folks or outdo the neighbors). Rather, the behaviors needed are displayed methodically and repeatedly.

CONTENT OF THE METAPHOR

The selection of metaphoric content is determined, in part, by the client's life experiences. The therapist would not be inclined to speak about ballet dancing to the physicist who has never danced. Neither would the therapist be likely to use a metaphor about nuclear physics with the high-school-educated dishwasher. One guideline for selecting content is the client's developmental age, as shown by vocabulary, values, gestures, manipulations for infantile gratification, and unresolved psychodynamic issues. The metaphorical content may involve vocabulary and issues that are relevant to the client's developmental successes.

If a client's developmental age is determined to be four to six years, the stories told might be about learning that is understandable to a six-year-old child. Nevertheless, this can be done so that clients are not offended. One method of safeguarding the client is to adjust the overall frame or introduction of the story to the needs of the client's conscious mind.

The conscious impact of a story can change radically when the introduction is varied. For instance, a story about a six-year-old child used to teach trust with a client with latency issues might be introduced in many different ways. One might begin, "You, of course, don't need to be reminded ...," and continue in that spirit with a resistant client. For the client requiring a challenge, the introduction and overall frame might be "I'm not sure you understand the learning conveyed in the story of ...." With a compliant client the therapist again must modify the introduction, saying, perhaps, "I wonder if you can fully appreciate how ...," and continuing in this provocative spirit throughout the session. Introducing the same story in different ways, then, will extend the usefulness of the particular metaphor to a wider range of clients.

Metaphors are open suggestions rather than closed or restrictive suggestions. They orient the listener toward an area of potential change and resources but they do not channel and specify a particular limited response. We must, then, consider how indirect suggestions (such as those represented in the delivery of a metaphor) are heard by a client. This can be noticed both in the lingering and thought-provoking aspect of the metaphor and in the client's here-and-now response to what is occurring in therapy. Using a trial-and-error approach, the strategic therapist attempts to make the material presented in the session as meaningful as possible. It ought to go without saying that the therapist does not know how the client will respond nor what meaning the client will derive from the metaphor until after the fact.

When presented with indirect communication, the listener responds to what is relevant and ignores that which is not. An excellent personal example comes from my last visit with Erickson before Christmas 1979. My former wife and I casually mentioned that we did not see a Christmas tree (and implied that one should be present). During the course of the day that followed Erickson told many case stories, some of which I had heard before. Interestingly, when I left the office, I found that both Carol and I had developed a general amnesia for most of the stories. That evening we drove to a shopping center. It occurred to us that we might be able to get a tree and all the trimmings and take it to Erickson's office. We did so and he seemed pleased ... and we were proud to have done it. Several weeks later we received the audiotapes of these final days and discovered, while listening, that he had told a long story about buying (among other things) a "tree and all the trimmings." He even detailed the particulars of the trimmings. They were the ones we purchased! The real learning is, however, that *we* were the only ones who bought the tree. Twelve others who had also been present did not buy trees. The suggestions were taken by those for whom they were relevant. If not relevant, suggestions are ignored. The client's experience determines what is heard and what response is given.

The thought-stimulating aspect of metaphor yields immediate or short-term responses, as well as lingering or long-term responses to meaningful stories. The immediate responses are noticeable as ideomotor changes in the client. These provide a bit of a barometer during the session against which the therapist can measure the connections being made by the client. Long-term meaning, however, is harder to measure. One personal incident concerns my return to Erickson's office after completing an assignment that involved seeking out and finding a boojum tree growing north of Squaw Peak. I was to find the tree and also "the creeping devils" (a horizontally growing web of cactus) that would be nearby. When I returned to his office the following day I was asked if I had, indeed, found the boojum. I answered yes. Then he asked, "And did you see the creeping devils?" I again answered affirmatively but with some reservation. I was not sure if the cactus I found was what he had meant by the term "creeping devils." "Remember that . . . ," he said expectantly, "There'll always be creeping devils nearby." He abruptly changed the topic . . . but the meaning lingers today, years later. The lingering meaning is, however, like a kaleidoscope. Each year the ambiguity seems to take new shape and deliver more meaning and learning than it did the year before. This type of growing or teleological unfolding is an important component of metaphor and indirect communication. It is the aspect that is most elusive and perhaps has the greatest impact. The most common reward of such communication may be the increased respect with which the client regards the therapy. It is difficult for clients not to notice how indirect techniques leave them free to appreciate the answers they formulate for themselves from within.

The therapist's experience also influences the choice of stories. I tend to discredit the notion that the therapist proceeds upon intuitive leads. Therapy employing metaphor is not a matter of "saying the first thing that comes into your head." Occasionally, one will hear that therapy proceeds throughout by telling a story that is only a result of the therapist's intuitive conception of what would be "good" for the client to hear. I hope it is obvious from this short essay that treatment planning plays the largest role in metaphor selection and design.

There is, however, a role for the therapist's intuition when formulating metaphor. Once the goal has been determined and the metaphor structured, intuition plays a role in the selection of appropriate content. The therapist must find a story that fits the strategic goals and also rests firmly within the therapist's skill and experience. It is a mistake to attempt to talk of auto racing, dog breeding, flower arrangement, etc., if the therapist knows nothing of these subjects. Intellectual knowledge is of very little use; knowledge rooted in sensory observation invariably proves to be the most useful kind for therapeutic metaphors. The most simple observation of nature, human or otherwise, often provides the foundation for a teaching story. In order to tell such a story, however, the therapist must have used his or her skills of observation. It is such a simple but important point: If you don't notice anything, you don't have anything to say about it.

References

Erickson, M. H. (1980). The method employed to formulate a complex story for the induction of an experimental neurosis in a hypnotic subject. In E. Rossi (Ed.). *The collected papers of Milton H. Erickson, M.D., Vol. 3* (pp. 336–355). New York: Irvington.

Lankton, S. (1985). Multiple embedded metaphor. In J. Zeig (Ed.). *Ericksonian psychotherapy, Vol. 1: Structures.* New York: Brunner/Mazel.

Lankton, S., & Lankton, C. (1983). *The answer within: A clinical framework of Ericksonian hypnotherapy.* New York: Brunner/Mazel.

Anxiety and Trauma

13

The Scramble Technique[1]

The Scramble Technique is a method of utilizing a client's natural abilities to inhibit the occurrence of a symptom and replace it with necessary emotional or experiential resources. Through a series of six distinguishable phases, the stages of the symptom are identified, rehearsed in sequence, rehearsed in random (scrambled), and then replaced with a previously retrieved resource. The author's method of conducting this technique is presented with explanation and case transcript. This technique belongs within the framework of a total psychotherapy or family treatment program but is provided here in an isolated context that resulted in the successful treatment of a client experiencing anxiety-related asthma attacks. In this isolated context the phases of the technique are easily highlighted. A discussion of the proper circumstances for the use of this technique is provided.

THE SCRAMBLE TECHNIQUE AS BRIEF INTERVENTION

Traditional approaches to therapy have considered the identified patient (IP) as the problem and tend to classify clients and, therefore, design treatment on the basis of diagnostic categories. In the Ericksonian model of family therapy, psychotherapy, and hypnotherapy, the symptom is most often treated via indirect techniques that focus on evoking inner resources and abilities rather than

---

[1] Lankton, S. (1987). The scramble technique. In S. Lankton (Ed.), *The Ericksonian monographs, number 2: Themes and principles of Ericksonian therapy* (pp. 56–68). New York: Brunner/Mazel. Reprinted with permission.

on removing the symptom (Erickson & Rossi, 1979). I prefer to approach the identified patient as a unique individual and assess the family of the IP as a unique family. I avoid working in the role that is thrust upon me by the family. I avoid the role of taking the symptom from the IP. Often I work to help each family member gain the inner resources needed to move the entire family successfully through his or her current developmental stage. Most often this means that direct attention to symptom removal is not foremost in my plans. I have described such incidents of circuitous intervention in other works (Lankton & Lankton, 1983; Lankton, 1985).

Occasionally, however, I work directly with the presenting symptom to reduce or remove it when 1) it appears to function independently of family organization and learned roles (Lankton & Lankton, 1986; Minuchin, 1974; Madanes, 1984) or when 2) it appears that the family members are not amenable to therapy (Lankton & Lankton, 1983, pp. 291–311; Erickson & Rosen, 1980; Erickson, 1980b). Therapy involving primarily symptom-directed interventions is also the best choice when 3) the symptom has been recently learned in response to trauma (Lankton & Lankton, 1983, pp. 280–291, or when 4) the previous developmental situation that gave rise to the symptom has changed and the symptom has taken on a life of its own (Lankton & Lankton, 1983, pp. 258–291).

In situations involving a compromise of our principles, certain goals and values must be surrendered. If the client-system refuses therapy, we must choose between two unpleasant arrangements and determine which is the lesser of two evils: leave the family with no change at all, or make an attempt (although possibly futile) to remove or reduce the symptom. Usually we choose the latter. In so doing, we suspect and hope that the family will become more willing to seek therapy at a later date due to our limited success with the presenting symptom.

The Scramble Technique consists of six phases during which 1) resources are retrieved; 2) the high and low parameters of the anxiety reaction are identified; 3) the intervening stages of the anxiety reaction are identified; 4) the entire sequence is rehearsed in sequential order; 5) the entire sequence is rehearsed in random order (it is "scrambled"); and 6) the symptom is replaced by the previously retrieved resource. It is important to mention that although the Scramble Technique deals directly with the symptom, it does not necessarily take place as an intervention isolated from more comprehensive treatment.

In the following case, the Scramble intervention appears as an isolated intervention in a single-session, symptom-focused treatment. Because of this isolation, the technique is more clearly illustrated here than it might be in another context within a more comprehensive therapy. This more comprehensive therapy would usually include multiple embedded metaphors, various assignments, and other strategic interventions designed to retrieve resources, build new roles, and foster greater interpersonal adjustment. Within that framework, the Scramble Technique can facilitate a therapeutic confusion about symptom sequence that helps the person "unlearn" the mechanics of a symptom that is no longer interpersonally necessary. The Scramble Technique is a systematic and teachable method of treating symptoms with the Confusion Technique (Erickson, 1980a).

STEPS OF THE SCRAMBLE TECHNIQUE

Retrieve Inner Resources

The first phase in the scramble is the retrieval of inner resources that can be used by the person to replace the anxiety when the scramble is completed. Usually, a pleasant feeling from a past experience is elicited to replace the symptomatic anxiety. In some instances, the criterion of pleasant is not the most therapeutically efficient or desirable to the client; a feeling-related experience of another and a more utilitarian nature (such as determination, effectiveness, competence, etc.) is then elicited to provide the necessary coping skills.

My case illustration involves a 36-year-old married man with two children, four and six years old. He would suffer from the sudden onset of asthma attacks whenever he was asked to perform. In other words, he had anxiety attacks in the form of asthmatic reactions. He is a very control- and leadership-oriented man who had been successful and locally admired and respected for his work as a family therapist. His need to be a leader is intimately tied to his self-esteem and he had difficulty asking for help himself. Both at home and on the job, he took the role of friendly leader and was thought to be both fair and firm with his family. He was not well-suited for taking the role of a client seeking help and for that reason alone he was disinclined to be a good therapy candidate. Neither was he willing to involve the rest of the family in what he considered a behavior he learned in childhood.

Ironically, at this point in his life, he is not in situations where he is called upon to perform any tasks that he cannot do well. The anxiety he experienced was out of proportion to real demands. It was, to him, as if he was still performing under perfectionistic demands and without sufficient support or training. As he did not consciously place such expectations on himself, it seemed as if he had learned an automatic habit that was often triggered below the level of awareness and had diverse physiological components. Therefore, I chose to take this client as an individual and address only the symptom. In making this choice, I lost the opportunity to help elicit and guide this client's development and I must trust that he is resourceful enough to change, fittingly, the other aspects of his family communication and relations, his social role, self-image, and so forth. However, this client gave every appearance of a resourceful and capable man.

The first set of resources I wanted him to retrieve were the feelings of success and of a job well done, which were already well-established in the client. The following metaphorical segment was used to help evoke these feelings after the induction of trance.

> I wonder about your ability to succeed in having levitation of the hand off of the lap. And the index finger moving across the corduroy is very convenient for a conscious mind, because the stripes in the corduroy make it possible to accurately graph the gradual movement of fingers. Your thumb moved one small corduroy, and another cord, and the index finger moved half a cord. And if you grew up on a farm, you'd be thinking you had done a lot of work, already moving two-and-a-half cords! You felt like you had chopped wood all day. Whether or not you levitate that hand, you can recall experiences, even though you never lived on a farm, feeling a job well done.
>
> As a teenager I used to try to avoid mowing the lawn many times. We had a large area of grass — the front yard, back yard, side yard. And my father, out of a streak of diabolical parenting, owned two apartments with yards front and back. And he just knew I'd be glad to mow all the grass. And to make matters worse, my mother decided not to put in a garden one year but grew grass where the garden had been. I had sort of a city full of grass to mow! And so it became a constant job.
>
> The best resolution to the entire matter was to set my mind to the task of mowing the yard. Sometimes I'd try to get ahead of it and save my sanity by beginning on a Thursday evening; and on a Friday evening I would mow another apartment. Then, on Saturday morning I could mow the garden, and front and back and side yard, and be done with it. I always had a great feeling of satisfaction. I'd lie down in the grass on a Saturday afternoon, and my dog would come rolling and

jumping on it with me, just lying there looking up at the clouds. It was the satisfaction of a hard job well done; and that I didn't have to do any more.

Living in Michigan I could always depend on the Gods of Weather to ruin one of my weekends of mowing for me. Then, pretty soon, I'd have a yard twice as deep in grass to mow! I developed a certain discipline about beginning at a certain time during the week and finishing early on Saturdays so that I'd have the rest of the weekend to myself. And I still remember those times when I'd lie down in the freshly mowed lawn, watching the Michigan clouds form overhead, the heat on my body. And I knew that physically my work was pretty much over. I knew that my parents were going to be off my back. I felt proud.

I don't know if that is still a feeling to build upon for future reference, but I know that the conscious mind can appreciate that experience. Your conscious mind may feel the experience of thinking that the job is over and that I've done a good job. Your conscious mind might think that there is some pressure, some place. I don't know whether or not you feel the experience of the job well done, or whether it's just an idea in the mind and your unconscious takes care of the body reaction. Usually, you raise your sternum, relax your shoulders, and walk a little taller. I know consciously you can actually have pride in yourself. Everyone must have some similar experience.

Identifying Parameters of the Anxiety Response

The second phase of this intervention, and the first phase of the actual Scramble Technique, is to have the client identify the stages of the building anxiety. The actual words or symbols the client uses to identify the stages can be created "on the spot" in the office. For the client who has not previously considered the progression of the anxiety, I suggest the following procedure.

Ask the client to label the full-blown occurrence of the anxiety as stage 5, with its weakest correlate being stage 1. Stage 1 may even reflect a state-of-being that precedes conscious recognition of anxiety. Next, ask the client to imagine or create the stages and to use the labels, "stage 1" and "stage 5." One precaution must be mentioned at this point: When stage 5 involves a violent or threatening situation, the use of dissociation is strongly recommended. The client can be asked to experience the worst stage in a dissociated state so that the actual physical symptoms are not triggered by the instruction for this phase. This type of safeguard was employed in this case, as the following transcript will illustrate.

> And once these feelings of pride and success are retrieved, then there is nothing else to do in the way of chores. You are prepared to go ahead and do that job with feelings of success and pride unconsciously in the background as a foundation. And I have a different view of procrastination. Now, we've been procrastinating. And I know that your unconscious is capable of recognizing that first indicator *to you* before it reaches your conscious mind, *that there would be an onset of asthma.* I'd like you to imagine or pretend or hallucinate or remember or recall or produce the very slightest indicator, and only the very slightest indicator, that could be recognized as the beginning of the onset of the asthma you spoke of earlier. And when you're aware unconsciously, perhaps even before you are consciously aware, either give me a nod of the head or raise a finger as an indicator that we can use to efficiently communicate. Call that stage 1. Find out if you can recreate it again and raise your finger and be satisfied with your ability to recognize it as stage 1.
>
> Now I'd like you to pretend or imagine — and you may want to dissociate yourself from the experience so that you have no discomfort in the process. I probably don't need to mention that you could float out of your body and sit beside yourself in the chair. Maybe it would be convenient to sit in the audience and observe the feet on the floor, hands on the thighs midway to the knee, your corduroys, dark belt, white shirt, short sleeves, your square shoulders, broad chest breathing from the stomach, beard down to the breast, glasses on the nose a quarter inch from the eyebrows, eyes closed: your bracelet on the right arm, rings on both hands, white gear on the head, and there he sits.
>
> It would be easy for you to use your own knowledge of dissociation if necessary, but whether it's necessary or not, locate some experience that would be considered by your conscious mind to be a full-blown aspect of the asthma symptom you spoke about. Or perhaps some experience just so close in proximity that it would be sufficient for our purposes to be considered equivalent but at the same time free of debilitating aspects. And when you are able to pretend or recall or produce or hallucinate that experience sufficiently to recognize it again, give me the same finger raise as a signal. Allow me to call it stage 5.

Identifying Sequential Stages

Once the high and low parameters of the anxiety have been identified, the intervening stages can be identified by asking the client to locate an experience that is midway between the highest and lowest points (between stages 5 and 1) and call that point 3. The logic implicit is that this bisection results in an identifiable midpoint by all but the most resistant of clients. Continuing the same line of logic, a midpoint between 3 and 1 will yield stage 2, and similarly that point between 5 and 3 will yield stage 4. This phase of the technique can be explained to the client as follows:

Now, unfortunately, you know that I'm going to ask you to recognize the reasonableness that if there's a beginning stage and an end stage, then there must be something in the middle that you can recognize as the middle stage. So, with your very best detective work, your very best geometry, find a midpoint of the experience. With your very best mathematics, divide it in half. Find the experience halfway in between that which would symbolize and indicate to you that we have that same indication. Call it stage 3. And remember that experience.

It's unfortunate that you know I'm going to ask you to find the midpoint between stage 3 and stage 5. It would be nice if it were a surprise. A draftsman would get his compass, an engineer would get his slide rule or Apple-II, and you're going to have to use your unconscious Apple-II to find the midpoint between stage 3 and stage 5. And give me the same indication that sufficient discriminative stimulus can be notified between the midpoint and the full-blown experience. Call it stage 4.

And you might want to have a moment's pause to review what you know so far. And in these first few moments there is such a delicate memorization of subtle experiences. And before you learn another one, you might want to let your thoughts go their own direction.

Now, some place between the beginning experience that you may or may not consciously be able to detect, and the midpoint, which presumably has some ability to be consciously detected, there lies a midpoint, or something close to a midpoint, or some discrimination place between 1 and 3. I would like you to decide or determine where that is, and give me the same signal again when you're satisfied with your ability to detect the midpoint between 1 and 3. Call that 2.

Rehearse the Sequence

Before scrambling the sequence, it is important to reinforce the labels the client has established for each of its segments. This can be done easily by asking the client to give a head nod, a finger lift, or some other ideomotor signal to indicate that he or she can distinguish the particular stage when it is requested. Rehearsing the stages in their proper order (1 through 5) will help the client cultivate his or her awareness of each stage. This rehearsal should be carried out five or six times, or as many times as is necessary to ensure that each stage is easily distinguishable by the client.

> Now, let's review, giving me your signal again so that I know how fast the stages can be perceived, beginning with stage 1. When you have that, give me the signal. Now go to stage 2. Now, at your own speed, give me the signal there. And now go to stage 3 and give me the signal you've gotten there. And now stage 4; when you've gotten there at your own speed, let me know. And finally to stage 5, let me know when you're there. And now go back to stage 1. [*Repeat the process*]

Randomize the Sequence

After the sequence has been reinforced in a straightforward, linear manner, the actual scrambling can begin. That is, the progression is no longer a linear one from 1 to 2 to 3 to 4 to 5; instead, the sequences are scrambled in a completely random order. (There are five factorial or 120 possible permutations for the 5 stages.) It is important that the client be instructed to move from one stage to another without *passing through* the intermittent stages. For example, when going from stage 2 to stage 5, he is told to do so without passing through stages 3 and 4. This will ensure that the stages are retrieved independently, without following the usual sequence. After passing through a few new sequences, the randomizing will become easier for the client and the therapist ought to find that he or she can proceed more rapidly with each new ordering. Eventually, the sequences can be "piggy-backed" in a more complex manner so that the client is told, "Now, go from 3 to 5 and then to 2, and give me the signal when you have completed that portion of the sequence."

At times, the anxiety accompanying each stage will produce physical alterations in the client that are clearly observable. These alterations will add confirmation to the validity of the ideomotor signals being given by the client.

The entire concept of the actual Scrambling phase might be presented as follows:

And I mentioned that so many countries have been helped by the agricultural knowledge about the ability to get minerals replenished in the soil by rotation of the crops. You don't really have a conscious appreciation of why you have this symptom in your life. I often find it necessary to take those kitchen drawers that have become the repository for a variety of junk and organize them all into little piles in little places, so that I can mess it all up again and redo it! Every time I write a paper I have a lot of good ideas. It served me well to get them out on paper. But other times, I cut and paste the organization of those paragraphs, the sentences of those paragraphs, find a better arrangement of all those parts. And although most people only use one certain posture during the day, every practitioner of yoga realizes that the recombination of muscle tension and relaxation in different postures provides a better balance, a better understanding of the self. So it's for very good reasons that I'm going to suggest we try different combinations of the stages of the symptom. And your conscious mind really can't appreciate what your unconscious really can learn.

In your own version of crop rotation, I am still going to require the signal as we proceed in a different order. I'd like you to start with stage 3 without going through 1 and 2. When you can find that stimulus you identify as stage 3, give me the signal. And proceed directly to stage 1 without dropping to stage 2. Give me the signal again. And as quickly as possible go to stage 5 without passing through your intermittent experiences. And drop to stage 4. And go to stage 2 without passing 3, without collecting 200 dollars.

And now, unknown to you, some new arrangement of understanding is beginning to take place. And it's so subtle, you really should try a different combination. Start with stage 2 and go to stage 1. And now jump to stage 5. Then go to stage 3 and find stage 4. That shouldn't be too hard. Now let's start with stage 2 and go from 2 to 4 without passing 3. And then go to 3; and then go to 5 without passing 4. And now follow to stage 1. And in learning, it may take some time to recognize how to make sense of reexperiencing. Open-ended suggestion has a logic of assuming that there is a changing balance in a person's state; the physiology is altered in some small way so that finding a new balance may take a moment. I hope you are comfortable while you're off balance. Now let's go to stage 4 directly. And go to 5. Drop to 2 and go to 3. Drop to 1.

And I don't know if you realize whether or not it would be the factorial, the five-factorial possible permutations. That's 120. And we have a way to go before we try all these possible combinations. Only somebody who had a math background could understand, but you can understand going directly to stage 2, dropping into stage 1, going into stage 4, dropping back to stage 3. There is something humorous about that, maybe when you go to stage 5. Now we only have 116 to go.

So maybe we should start with 1 and go to 2, go to 5, drop back to 4, go to 3, now go to 1, and go up to 4. Do you know the mathematical combinations that would be necessary going back to 3 — if we'd only make a six-piece procedure instead of a five-piece procedure? Now drop back to 2. It's staggering. And it would be easier to go to 5, and just leave it at the five-step procedure, because we'd only have 113 to do to cover all possible combinations. Have we begun with stage 1 and gone to stage 4? Let's try that. And now drop to stage 2; go to stage 3; and let's just fake out and go to stage 1 before we go to stage 5.

Replacing Symptom with Resource

After directing the client to experience the new Scrambled sequences, the client will either have a great deal of confusion about the purpose of the task, or will become bored with the ease of the task. At this point, the final phase of the Scramble Technique can be initiated. The process of examining new sequences will become a tedious ordeal so that the suggestion to discard it and resolve the difficulty by returning to the previously retrieved resource will be welcomed.

> You are probably waiting for the moment when I'm going to suggest it would be easier to drop the whole thing and just go back to that feeling of success and pride in having completed a job well done; or perhaps the feeling of relaxation or dissociation you accomplished. Your conscious mind can have the feeling of relaxation and your unconscious can maintain the dissociation; or maybe your conscious mind is preparing to have a feeling of success in a job well done while your unconscious has the feeling of pride. It wouldn't be necessary for your

conscious mind to go all the way to a feeling of pride while you have a dissociation and relaxation. And we have a job well done.

I don't know if you realize that we have a job well done unless you have a feeling of pride associated with that relaxation while maintaining a slight dissociation. Perhaps you won't have a feeling of a job well done until you have a feeling of dissociation. And your unconscious can have pride in the relaxation that you accomplished. It makes more sense to have a feeling of pride in the job well done, while your unconscious has relaxation associated with that dissociation. It's hard to determine whether or not it's illogical to suggest that you'd have pride associated with the feeling of dissociation.

Reorientation

During the reorientation stage my goals are to complete the trance and test the success of the work as soon as possible. In this particular case, the client's ability to sustain changes after the trance was linked to the concept of "logical contradictions" and then tested by asking him to discover if he could create a logical contradiction and then resolve it. This was demonstrated by his arm levitation as he came out of trance.

In the transcription that follows I chose the concept of "oxymoron" to bring into his awareness three ideas: 1) it seems like a contradiction to keep his hands in trance and yet ask him to be out of trance; 2) he and I were contradictions in terms of our contrasting physical appearance and grooming; and 3) it was a way to say something thought-provoking about the contradiction of breathing with effort and breathing with ease.

That sounds like an oxymoron. Some people don't know what an oxymoron is. An oxymoron is something that is a logical contradiction, like *jumbo shrimp*, or *pretty bad*, or a *terribly wonderful* time. So to associate a dissociation with pride really is a logical contradiction. So many times a scramble experience is terribly wonderful. I hope breathing easy is not an oxymoron for you. There's no reason to have a logical contradiction about breathing easy.

It's really a lot of fun to watch you smile with your mustache. And I've enjoyed this trance greatly, so I hate to bring it to an end too soon. But there is a logical conclusion to a logical contradiction. Sooner or later, you are going to have to come out of trance.

Sooner or later you will levitate that right arm, even though it has the weight of a bracelet. We could make an oxymoron out of this trance by having you go into trance and levitate while your mind came out of the trance. Now, you really want to know how your hand can levitate up at the same speed that you come out of a trance? [*Hand and arm begins to levitate*] And you can come out of trance as a mind and be in trance as a body?

I'll tell you what I'm wondering. I'm real glad that you succeeded in overcoming something that was a weighty hand. I'm wondering whether or not, when you come out of trance as a mind, if you are going to laugh about the oxymoron we've established. I told you we could go to a party as an oxymoron. You did laugh. How does it feel?

C: [*With arm still levitated*] Incredible.
S: You could tell people you were an oxymoron. Have you ever been out of trance this way?
C: No, I never have.
S: *Never* have? So maybe this moment's not real. It's unreal.
C: In many ways, it is.
S: I noticed that you're not looking at the hand. Does it feel like it's unattached?
C: [*Laughs*] No.
S: How long do you think you can keep it that way?
C: Probably forever.
S: Probably forever. But I don't think you will keep it that way forever. Now, the best way to satisfy the need to get everything congruent is probably to drop back into a trance a little bit, catch up with yourself, and come out of trance properly, at your own speed. And now you won't be a logical contradiction anymore. [*With humorous tone*] There's always sadness with the passing of a logical contradiction.

[*Seriously*] Well, thank you. This is over now.

Follow-up

In a follow-up contact with this client a year later, he reported that his asthma continually improved after the therapy. At the time of the therapy he used an inhaler twelve times a day; now he uses it once a day, if at all. He had

had the asthmatic condition since the age of three. No other intervention was begun at the point when he received the therapy.

DISCUSSION

Several studies have shown that hypnosis combined with behavioral techniques is significantly beneficial in alleviating asthma (Kohen, Olness, Colwell, & Heimel, 1984; Milne, 1982; Moorefield, 1971; Hypnosis for Asthma, 1968). However, this paper is intended to illustrate the Scramble Technique and not considerations of the treatment of asthma. Nevertheless, it introduces the need for an additional precautionary and ethical note about asthma treatment.

Perhaps due to notable chemical differences in victims of status asthmaticus (Kowal, Falowska, & Hanczyc, 1969), pharmacological corticosteroid therapy or artificial ventilation is often the recommended treatment (Hypnosis for Asthma, 1968). A severe, sustained, or sudden asthmatic attack or an attack resulting in hospitalization, such as status asthmaticus, requires special attention and should alter the therapist's application of this technique from the transcript displayed here. The severity of the disorder suggests extreme care when applying an intervention such as the Scramble Technique.

It is imperative that, in those cases, if the Scramble is attempted, a well-developed dissociation must be used and the Scramble Technique applied only after confirmation of the dissociation has been established. Even then, the possibility of asphyxiation due to bronchospasm in asthmaticus or status asthmaticus may be a very real possibility when stage 5 is requested. This suggests that the therapist avoid the Scramble Technique in those cases until more testing is done with such severe asthma cases.

The Scramble Technique has been used with exciting results in various cases involving extreme anxiety symptoms such as panic attacks. One noteworthy case concerned a man who had recurrent, involuntary vomiting due to anxiety. He would vomit to the point of discharging blood. This vomiting of blood occurred at a frequency of approximately three times per week and had continued for three years prior to the intervention.

The intervention was accomplished in a single hour-long session. Although the procedure was essentially similar to the above application, it was particularly interesting because of the visible signs of reverse peristalsis exhibited by the client. At times this reversal was dramatic and moving; it provided the therapist with an unusual experience of witnessing the actual effect of the treatment as it was occurring. The client's progress has been followed for four years and he has had only one partial recurrence in that time period. The one episode was so far-removed from the severity of the earlier occurrences as to be insignificant to him.

Similar reports of success occur in nearly all applications of the technique, provided that 1) the symptom is related to anxiety and 2) an incremental building in severity can be identified. It is likely that anxiety bouts that do not have this building aspect to them — that is, those that come into full intensity in an instant — will not be successfully abated by this technique.

In all treatment situations it should be remembered that choosing to intervene in a particular way at a particular time is based on a complex interaction of variables. Most often it is inappropriate to aim the therapy at the removal of the symptom without first assessing the role that is played by the symptom in the maintenance of family structure. While it is not the purpose of this paper to discuss the role symptoms play in family dynamics, the reader should be warned that an adequate assessment of such dynamics must determine the appropriate timing and choice regarding the application of this (or any) technique for symptom removal. Family members will often need to gain health-supporting mechanisms to replace the loss of a symptom. In some cases, the new mechanisms for maintaining family stability will need to be learned prior to the removal of the symptom; in other cases, the symptom will yield to therapy but will result in the acquisition of alternate mechanisms to stabilize communication and roles between family members. Often these alternate mechanisms may be viewed as various other problems. It is therefore important that therapy include guidance for the development of these substitutions during those cases when symptom removal is undertaken.

References

Erickson, M. H. (1980a). The confusion technique in hypnosis. In E. L. Rossi (Ed.), *The collected papers of Milton H. Erickson on hypnosis: Vol. I. The nature of hypnosis and suggestion* (pp. 258–291). New York: Irvington.

Erickson, M. H. (1980b). Special techniques of brief hypnotherapy. *The collected papers of Milton H. Erickson on hypnosis, Vol. IV: Innovative hypnotherapy* (pp. 149–173). New York: Irvington.

Erickson, M. H., & Rosen, H. (1980). The hypnotic and hypnotherapeutic investigation and determination of symptom-function. *The collected papers of Milton H. Erickson, on hypnosis, Vol. IV: Innovative hypnotherapy* (pp. 103–123). New York: Irvington.

Erickson, M. H., & Rossi, E. L. (1979). *Hypnotherapy: An exploratory casebook.* New York: Irvington.

Hypnosis for asthma: A controlled trial: A report to the research committee of the British Tuberculosis Association. (1968). *British Medical Journal, 1* (5223), 71–76.

Kohen, D., Olness, K., Colwell, S., & Heimel, A. (1984). The use of relaxation: Mental imagery (self-hypnosis) in the management of 505 pediatric behavioral encounters. *Journal of Developmental & Behavioral Pediatrics, 5* (1), 21–25.

Kowal, G., Falowska, A., & Hanczyc, H. (1969). Activity of salivary muramidase in allergic bronchial asthma. *Polish Medical Journal, 8*, 584–588.

Lankton, S. (1985). Multiple embedded metaphor and diagnosis. *Ericksonian psycho-therapy, Vol. 1: Structures* (pp. 171–195). New York: Brunner/Mazel.

Lankton, S., & Lankton, C. (1983). *The answer within: A clinical framework of Ericksonian hypnotherapy.* New York: Brunner/Mazel.

Lankton, S., & Lankton, C. (1986). *Enchantment and intervention in family therapy: A teaching seminar on Ericksonian approaches.* New York: Brunner/Mazel.

Madanes, C. (1984). *Behind the one-way mirror.* San Francisco: Jossey-Bass.

Medicine Today: Drugs in the treatment of asthma. (1968). *British Medical Journal, 2* (5607), 750–751.

Milne, G. (1982). Hypnobehavioural medicine in a university counselling centre. *Australian Journal of Clinical & Experimental Hypnosis, 10* (1), 13–26.

Minuchin, S. (1974). *Families and family therapy.* Cambridge, MA: Harvard University Press.

Moorefield, C. (1971). The use of hypnosis and behavior therapy in asthma. *American Journal of Clinical Hypnosis, 13* (3), 162–168.

14

A Goal–Directed Intervention for Decisive Resolution of Coping Limitations Resulting from Moderate and Severe Trauma[1]

The world of therapy offers abundant approaches to every imaginable human problem. Most of these solutions are explained in terms rooted in jargon that is part of a particular theory. In the case of trauma resolution, writers speak about such vague concepts as "working through" and "redistributing cathexis." But many of these approaches simply reexplain various common problems as seen through the lens of that theory. If my favorite theory explains the mysteries of every ailment from ADD to MPD, and from OCD to obesity, then there are workshops to be given, books to be written, and money to be made in the field of therapy. Unfortunately, certain therapists can be very clever at solving certain problems owing to their unique intuitions, not to their unique education. And most theoretical approaches are the same wine in new bottles.

---

[1] Lankton, S. (2001). Goal-directed interventions for decisive resolution of coping limitations resulting from moderate and severe trauma. In B. Geary & J. Zeig (Eds.), *The handbook of Ericksonian psychotherapy* (pp. 195–211). Phoenix. The Milton H. Erickson Foundation Press.

This chapter focuses on a method to help clients decisively resolve traumatic reactions in very brief, often one-session, therapy. Victims of trauma can suffer in significantly different ways before ever seeking therapy. They can be recent victims who are primarily experiencing a great deal of anxiety and disorientation, as is often the case with victims of automobile and public transportation accidents. Or they may have suffered for years from the effects of earlier life trauma and present themselves in therapy with defense mechanisms that limit their experience in terms of joy, sense of self, intimacy, security, livelihood, and more. These two extremes describe vastly different clients and problems and illustrate that total recovery from the effects of trauma, for many people, will not happen in one session. This chapter is not about solving all of a client's problems that may have resulted from trauma. It is not about resolving the grief from loss. It is not about relearning new habits and perceptions to fill learning deficits, and it is not about the social changes that rehabilitation may require. What it is about is overcoming the major limitation on growth that trauma creates. It is about the most decisive technique for getting on with growth and learning in the case of both mild and severe traumas. In some cases, especially patients with recent traumas that have not become part of a lifestyle, this intervention may make up most of the therapy. In other cases, those of long-standing trauma, it will serve as the groundwork to make the journey to more pervasive growth and change possible.

The techniques listed here derive from a complex association and dissociation paradigm. Because the literature on trauma often suggests that therapists must assist victims in some type of reliving and abreaction, an explication of the similarities and differences between association/dissociation techniques and techniques of reliving/abreaction is offered. But I will begin with a global comparison to clarify the major differences in the approaches.

SUMMARY OF RESEARCH

A traditional view of trauma states that the boundary between ego and the outside world is obstructed. Victims lose some of their ego strength and/or potential development as a result. The therapeutic goal of such treatment is the constructing of ego boundaries (Berghold, 1991). The common approach to accomplish ego strengthening for posttraumatic stress disorder (PTSD) often uses regression, recall, abreaction, and a subsequent "reintegrate." It was shown that this method is correlated with hypnotizability (Evans, 1991). Thus, the use of abreaction following age regression has become a popular approach to treatment (Pickering, 1986). In fact, it is often expected that the same "reliving" of the experience should take place, after hypnosis, in the waking state. In the treatment of war neurosis, it is suggested that there is an absolute need to "revivify and develop a psychodynamic understanding of the precipitation stress in the hypnotic state and repeat this in the conscious state" (Balson, 1980).

The therapy of trauma contains elements related to the treatment of phobia, and we can look to research also related to that condition. Several approaches to the treated phobia have been measured and found to be essentially equal in effectiveness: relaxation, approach fantasy, abreaction, and posthypnotic suggestion (Horowitz, 1970).

The idea that abreaction may not be necessary for successful treatment is an orientation that fits the Ericksonian approach. Other clinical research shows that hypnosis is a valuable tool to replace shame with autonomy relating to factors regarding the cure (Eisen, 1992). These include making meaning of the experience, framing the identity of the abuser, and defining levels of regained autonomy. This may be attributable to the manner in which the hypnotic state can operate to block the feedback system maintaining conscious control (Spivak, 1990) and in some manner protect the conscious mind from pain both during and after hypnosis.

THE USE OF HYPNOSIS

It may be that those individuals who suffer most from traumatic situations are those who are most responsive to hypnosis. A high correlation among stress-disordered victims was found with 313 subjects according to the Stanford Hypnotic Suggestibility Scale (Stutman et al., 1985). This type of correlation makes hypnosis a quite logical tool. Hypnosis is shown to be a good technique for accessing and working through the dissociated trauma memory (Spiegel, 1986, 1990). PTSD may be seen as a defense against memory and experience recalled by the event itself. In order to treat this defensive dissociative reaction, Spiegel (1988) recommends what he calls the "8-Cs": confrontation, condensation, confession, consolation, consciousness, concentration, control, and congruence. Some researchers have found that memory content can be changed to aid in the reduction of traumatic experience (Lamb, 1985).

But the treatment of trauma needs to go hand in hand with therapy focusing on the *process*, not on the content (Kingsbury, 1992). This brings us to elements of association and dissociation created by both traumatic events and therapy. Even the simple pairing or associating of relaxed breathing, relaxing, and distraction by counting can reduce the fears and be used as an effective bridge to uncover trauma (Malon, 1987).

The context of storytelling, sometimes called therapeutic metaphor, has even been shown to aid in the therapeutic process of shifting the variables of association to fear or pain. For example, the use of metaphor with children and associating safety; sharing imagination; introducing reality events; addressing issues of loss, love, and trust; and reducing guilt has been effective for victims of sexual abuse (Rhue, 1991).

The overall scope of treatment in the case of traumas should not be confined to helping a client alter memory or emotional experience. Rather, treatment needs to help victims form relationships, transform the memory into meaningful experience, take action to overcome helplessness (VanderHart et al., 1990b), and deal with the various sequelae of guilt and grief or mourning (VanderHart et al., 1990a).

ERICKSON'S APPROACH

Erickson's clinical cases were often used to illustrate several interventions, but not the entire treatment of a client with regard to grief, stress on the family, and other life readjustments. As a result, there are few examples of trauma cases in his collected papers, and of those included, each deals with the recovery of repressed memories using hypnosis. There are brief references to cases of obsessive personality (Erickson, 1980, III, p. 251), hysterical amnesia (Erickson, 1980, II, p. 277), criminal activity (Erickson, 1980, III, p. 221), blood phobia (Erickson, 1980, II, p. 188), and the two cases discussed below. There are only a few detailed cases where Erickson used hypnosis to help unravel the mysteries of people plagued by previous traumas, and all of these involve institutionalized individuals. One case described a man who had repeated outbursts and Erickson used a complicated series of hypnotically induced dreams. The dreams became increasingly less symbolic so that, over a short time, the man was able consciously to interpret them. In this manner, he progressively informed himself of his trauma of incestuous victimization at the hands of his parents (Erickson, 1980, IV, pp. 58–70).

In another case, a woman was induced to use symbolic writing in trance so that communication to Erickson could take place that she seemed unable to face either consciously or unconsciously (Erickson, 1980, IV, pp. 163–167).

Both of these cases used a complicated method of communication within trance: from an unknowing part of the unconscious, through the conscious mind, and, finally, to the therapist. This type of communication was difficult for Erickson, and possibly even more tedious for other therapists and their clients. To employ the same ideas shown in Erickson's cases, but to make the process amenable to those of us (and our clients) who are less talented, I devised an approach that relies on communication between visual mediators of unconscious resources.

COMPARISON BETWEEN DISSOCIATION AND ABREACTION

Consider that you have come to therapy because of the continued tension and anxiety you have experienced since you were on an Amtrak train that derailed and killed many persons and from which you narrowly escaped with some minor medical problems, all of which have been corrected and are healed. The therapist you visit has two major ideas for your therapy.

Reliving and abreaction require that you mentally, emotionally, and experientially return to the disaster. You will be encouraged to verbalize and release your emotions freely for all aspects of the incident. You will be expected, encouraged, and supported in the expression of fear, anger, shock, confusion, panic, helplessness, sadness, dependency, and so on, as the explication of the scene is relived and verbalized. Perhaps you might also be a candidate to express anger and other types of aggression. The major goal of this emoting is to help you rediscover your true feelings and adaptive response mechanisms, to own the emotions you concealed, and to grow in ego strength gained by acquiring previously denied parts of yourself. Your success in reaching some of these goals depends largely on the skill the therapist provides. There will usually be some major resistance to this approach on your part, the client, primarily a general reluctance to show emotions before the therapist and a reluctance actually to experience the unpleasant incident again.

Abreaction can produce a corrective emotional experience, attitude change, and redistribution of psychic energy, and most likely will result in an increased focus on the past as it encourages regression and reduces the use of denial. There is an unfortunate risk of retraumatizing the client during the reliving. More worrisome, perhaps, is the possibility of increasing reliance on the therapist, and becoming alienated from the family of origin (in the case of family-created trauma) or actually reconstructing a past of false traumas in the process of "therapy."

With association/dissociation techniques, by contrast, you can still experience a corrective emotional experience and attitude change, but the focus is on the present and future of your life. There is no risk of reexperiencing the trauma or of increasing dependency on therapists. You can build additional adaptive defenses, learn to use the parts of yourself lost in the trauma, and increase your self-support and personal resources.

In either case, these interventions are not being suggested as the only interventions necessary for a full and complete recovery. They are being used as the major interventions for regaining the ability to cope, function, be creative in living, and recognize that the trauma is behind you and you are improving radically. This association/dissociation model is being offered as an effective, viable, and preferable alternative to abreaction methods. (See Table 14.1.)

Table 14.1
Continua of the Trance Phenomena

	Association/Dissociation	Abreaction
Be a corrective emotional experience	Can	Can
Foster attitude change(s)	Yes	Can
Focus on past		Yes
Focus on present/future	Yes	
Redistribute energy	Can	Can
Encourage regression		Yes
Reduce denial	Can	Yes
Risk pain of re-trauma		Yes
Build additional defense	Yes	
Learn to accept part of self	Can	Can
Learn to use part of self	Yes	
Intrapsychic		Yes
Intersocial	Yes	
Risk distancing family of origin	Can	Yes
Risk distancing self	Can	
Increase stress on current system		Can
More likely to be resisted		Yes

Build self-support	Yes	
Risk increased reliance on therapist		Yes
Construct the reality of the past	Can	Can
Connect with personal resources	Yes	Yes

THREE CATEGORIES OF TRAUMA IMPACT

Results of trauma are divided here into three discrete categories. These are intuitively logical groups that are all-inclusive and, for the most part, mutually exclusive. These three categories dictate three types of increasingly complex interventions. The categories are "type 1 — simple," "type 2 — complex," and "type 3 — state-bound" traumatic reactions. Discussing clients who have psychological and sometimes physical results of trauma requires that we differentiate levels of severity or hurt that might have come from events of the past. A continuum from "type 1 — simple reaction" to "type 2 — complex reaction" to "type 3 — state-specific reaction" facilitates this process. Two of the approaches are discussed in the following scenario and the complex association/dissociation "type 2" is illustrated with a case. Although the personal impact of traumatic events obviously is unique in every situation, the general limiting effects of trauma have some recognizable similarities. Some attempts have been made to assess PTSD in several areas: alterations in sense memory, repetitive behavior, trauma-specific fears, and changed attitudes. Indeed, the range of events from memory, to experience, to relationship change needs to be addressed for effective treatment. It needs to help victims form relationships, transform the memory into meaningful experience, and take action to overcome helplessness (VanderHart et al., 1990b).

Type 1 Trauma

"Simple trauma" refers to the unavailability of resources in certain needed situations. In simple trauma, an individual has been inhibited from learning certain experiences. Consider that the aim of a healthy person is to be able to associate to needed experiences and resources in each unique life situation. However, in the course of suffering a trauma in growth, the victim cannot organize or associate to or retrieve experiences needed in particular situations. For instance, experiences commonly called confidence are needed (or at least are very useful) in public speaking. A simple trauma has occurred when a specific event prevents experiences of confidence from being vividly remembered (or experienced) in the context of public speaking *and* the person is still able to operate in some other area of his or her life with confidence, and even sometimes amble through events that call for public speaking. Public speaking is not impossible for victims of this simplest kind of trauma, but the act of public speaking would result in considerable distress if it could not be avoided. There is not a significant loss of muscle flexibility, there are no significant attitudinal alterations about the world, and the person is likely to be resourceful enough to be quite successful in almost all areas of his or her life.

Type 2 Trauma

"Complex trauma" refers to outcomes that constitute developmental learning problems. In these situations, the effect of the traumatic situation was sufficiently severe to render the person impaired over a *specific developmental area of coping* that would seem otherwise to be within the person's behavioral repertoire. The client with this type of trauma will usually show fairly severe use of denial, have many attitudinal and perceptual changes related to avoiding, and have much tension, which is used to prevent the breakdown of such defenses as reaction formation and denial. There may be frequent outbursts, child abuse, or anxiety attacks as efforts fail to maintain defense mechanisms. For example, a person may be unable to be in a position of speaking to the public and would arrange things so that this situation would never happen. Not merely uncomfortable, public speaking would be such a threat that even the thought of it would cause severe panic attacks. More usually, the events to be avoided are such things as sexual experiences, use of machinery, travel, love, and other major commitments and responsibilities.

Coping skills may be diminished, defensive attitudinal disposition may become a major problem that results in the person's moving away from choices in life, intrusive memories break into consciousness, and the person may experience a major loss of certain muscle groups (such as sexual organs). The panic that can be felt is often handled by alcoholism, avoidance of family members, occasional collapse, institutionalization, and so on.

Type 3 Trauma

"State learning" refers to situations in which the troubling mind-set is very persistent. Being immersed in a state from which one can't recover is often referred to as state-specific, and this is consistent for severely traumatized individuals. A person who experiences this type of reaction to trauma is severely limited by compartmentalized ego states. There are problems for these individuals in *nearly all areas of development* that follow the traumatic event(s). They may show excessive fear, may have amnesia for large areas of their past, and usually feel helpless, not just in the area related to the trauma, but in life in general. They often use the defense of identification with the aggressor that may result in self-harming long after the traumatic events are over. Musculature, perception, attitude, emotional growth, and social skills are all impaired. Severe war traumas and severe child-abuse trauma, including seeing siblings murdered, for instance, may give rise to this reaction.

SOLVING THE EFFECTS OF TRAUMA

The goal of brief therapy is to promote increased and sufficient functioning as soon as possible. To accomplish this, clients need to look at present and future goals, become involved with loved ones and other support, and replace doubt and worry with permission to feel positive. Therapy needs to associate current resources to future tasks, reframe perceived failures, provide posthypnotic suggestions for future success, and train clients in self-image thinking to reassess their skills and strengths.

Successful therapy identifies strengths and stimulates attitude change. In addition, it will increase self-nurturing by retrieving safety, comfort, rehearsal, self-talk, and self-acceptance by helping the often disowned self cast off shame. Finally, there will be an ego-strengthening that comes from grieving, building new boundaries, and developing feedback loops to become self-sustaining in many ways. Other dynamic problems and social problems might also be solved, especially when it can be seen that personal or social situations have been limited by the historical impact of the trauma, or that clients, originally troubled in these areas, were in some ways predisposed to the traumatic effects that they suffered. In most cases, it is effective to involve other family members to help clients cope with helplessness (Moore, 1981).

"COMPLEX ASSOCIATION/DISSOCIATION" PARADIGM FOR TYPE 1 AND TYPE 2 TRAUMA

The rationale for this paradigm is that the conscious mind is capable of noticing representations of internal communications and changes that can remain mostly out of awareness. Therapists merely need a way in which this communication and those representations can be set up. Most people will immediately accept a metaphorical framework of "talking" to other, usually younger, parts of the self, owing to the commonality we all have of family, community, and the ability to use that metaphor to sort experiences in terms of age and size. Once established, this metaphor of dissociative review makes it possible to associate to other needed resources of cognitive, perceptual, attitudinal, and emotional experience. Therefore, by accepting the metaphor of the older self talking to the younger self, clients' needed resources will become available in their experience as they think about and remember bits of traumatic memories. That is, they will have experiences that had been eliminated in the context of recalling bits of their traumas. The detailed outline for establishing and conducting this intervention follows.

STEPS IN THE "COMPLEX ASSOCIATION/DISSOCIATION" PARADIGM

1. Complex association/dissociation: if clients cannot recall the known trauma or resource or if it is an extremely "volatile" memory:
   A. Establish a safe environment.
   B. Retrieve necessary resources.
   C. Ask the client to imagine a "grown self" in the room.
      i. This self is usually a representation of the current aware and resourceful self.
      ii. This self is usually the same age and has the same characteristics. In some cases, this representation will be of a self from the future, when the problem has been solved. The future self may be presupposed to be years or only hours into the future.
      iii. This self is conscious and knows what the conscious mind knows.
         a. Presuppose a position of observation toward the conscious mind.
         b. This conscious mind of the client will communicate with this part of the client.
         c. Client imagines communication taking place between these parts in an unspecified manner (by feeling, words, etc.).
         d. Ideomotor signaling is established for the therapist to con-

tinue with more intricacy. This is usually a head nod from the client indicating that agreement has occurred between the self and this resourceful part.

D. Ask client to ask the projected part to further dissociate.

    i. The projected part (part 1) is asked to see another part (part 2), which is younger.

    ii. This second part (part 2) is often not seen by the client.

    iii. Part 2 represents the more unconscious self and can communicate via the ties with part 1. This part is also usually chosen from all possible younger selves because of some special strengths or resourcefulness.

    iv. Part 1 and part 2, therefore, become buffers between any memories created by part 2 and the real client.

E. Have the client ask part 1 to ask part 2 to review the traumatic events from a comfortable distance. Part 2 would see the trauma happen to a third part, part 3.

    i. Suggest that only by means of dialogue or signaling (such as seeing the "head nods") from the imaginary part 2 to part 1, and then from part 1 to the client, can the client know what is occurring to part 3 in the mind or memory of part 2.

    ii. Conduct a careful elaboration of part 2, reviewing the scenes about part 3 and sharing with part 1 only that which it is safe to share. Have part 2 communicate the review to part 1 by ideomotor signals so that part 1 can report the communication to the client and, likewise, the client can report to the therapy (all by ideomotor signals, such as head nods).

    iii. This presupposes that the memory of the trauma to part 3 exists and is known to some part of the self (at least to part 2).

    iv. The client's conscious report of "not knowing" is expected. In this way, even poorly recalled traumas (to part 3) can be reviewed by the dissociated part 2. In fact, forgotten traumas presumably can be reviewed and overcome in this manner.

F. Repeatedly review and communicate with self from past.

    i. Continually request and guide the client to instruct part 1 to ask part 2 (only) to review the trauma that occurred to the younger part 3 with words and pictures only. Thus, part 2 continues to be at a distance from the trauma that is being seen as it happens to the younger part 3.

ii. Help the client instruct part 1 to instruct part 2 to accomplish (essentially) a simple association/dissociation with part 3. Part 2 should watch the events, see them take place in speeded-up time, watch them unfold in chronological sequence, even watch them unfold in reverse order — all the while verifying that part 1 and part 2 and the client are safe and secure during the process.

G. Remove the intermediate parts gradually and integrate the learning and resources.

i. It is possible for parts 2 and 1 to be gradually removed after the client accepts the presupposition of the safety and security and other desired resources occurring as the traumatic memory is reviewed.

ii. The client must repeat the above steps until it is presupposed that he or she can handle the awareness and have the resources — and possibly even use the bits of memories as signals that desired resources are available and can be experienced and used.

iii. As each part collapses into the neighboring part, one at a time, the client eventually creates the situation of the client in a simple association/dissociation.

iv. Finally, there can be a merging of the secure part with the youngest traumatized part. In doing this, the secure client can be directed to reassure and nurture that younger part. This constitutes a reframing of the role the client has played to the role of self care-giver, nonvictim, resourceful, and empowered. The client, in this way, learns a role that generates strength and maturity any time the traumatized self is remembered in this way. It should also be said that the chances of the client's taking this empowered role in the future are quite high because there has been no other adaptive role mapped out for the client since the trauma. Therefore, this intervention will represent a decisive turning point for the client's growth.

H. Provide posthypnotic associations for the client to find and use these learnings and resources in the future.

It will be especially important to help the client think through possible future times that might have resembled the traumatic event or might have been avoided due to the old traumatized self-image.

Figure 13.1

After this intervention is used (usually a full one- or two-session event), therapy can proceed to deal with any other issues that have arisen for the client. These might include changes in family life, recreation, self-care, grieving, intimacy, sexual functioning, educational or occupational goals, or learned awareness of physical pain. Each client will have unique needs in these areas. It is most likely that clients for whom the trauma was recent will have few maladjustments to correct and clients for whom the trauma has been long-standing will have far more difficulties that have arisen during the years of avoidance, excuses, lower self-esteem, and so on.

The following case illustrates the actual wording for setting up this intervention. This case was a single-session intervention and is useful as an example in that it demonstrates this intervention in isolation and since it shows how to follow the outline while still modifying it slightly in some creative ways to accommodate the client's unique situation. Specifically, this client reported that no part of herself was without fear and anxiety. Therefore, the representation of the self (part 1) was constructed as a presupposed self from the future who was expected to be free of the anxiety. Part 2 was a teenage self who existed before the trauma. Of course, the most distant self (part 3) was the client's self from the disaster. Her head nods indicated the recognition of the relation of part 3 to part 2, if not of her (real self), and an agreement with various swapping of resources and attitudinal self-nurturing comments recommended by the therapist from the real and future self to part 3.

CASE EXAMPLE OF
COMPLEX ASSOCIATION/DISSOCIATION

The "Mobile Amtrak Disaster" refers to an accident in the latter half of the 1990s in which an Amtrak train bridge collapsed and resulted in the death of several passengers trapped in a submerged Amtrak car. This client, "Mary," came to my office within a week after the disaster and was unable to speak about the incident in any way without collapsing into heavy tears and fear. Since the accident had happened only a week earlier, it did not make sense to ask Mary to place an image of two remembered selves in between her traumatic memory *that she had gained since the trauma.* Instead, I asked her to recall an earlier self that was surprisingly strong and a future self that had totally recovered from the effects of the incident. These then were used as imagined mediators in the intervention.

She was asked to have the future self (51 years old) communicate with another, mediating image (that of a 17-year-old), who, in turn, communicated with the Mary who was in the disaster. In this manner of imagining, Mary (48 years old) was asked to review the events of the disaster from the distance of these two imagined intermediaries. The following excerpt comes from 20 minutes into the session and illustrates some of the more difficult communication that typified the heart of the session.

Ask Mary, who is 51 years old, to pass along to that adolescent Mary that she is from the future, that she lived through and overcame the fears and helplessness of the train disaster. Then, have the 51-year-old tell the teen that she is going to help her review the incident of last week — in words and pictures only — when the 48-year-old experienced the train crash. And add that each of you — the 48-, 51-, and 17-year-old — will hold on to the secure and resourceful experiences you each have now.

I want you, the 48-year-old, to tell the 51-year-old to tell the teen that the four of us will figure out how we are going to use the next few minutes cooperatively to overcome fears that have occurred. Ask the 51-year-old to help you by telling the teen that you want very little of her. Ask the 51-year-old to tell the teen that you just want her to stay in communication, if she would, and nod her head when she complies. Ask the 51-year-old Mary to ask the teen to nod her head as a signal that she understands and is willing to participate in that way. And when the 51-year-old sees the head nod, have her nod her head to you. In turn, when you see the 51-year-old nod her head to you, nod yours to me as a signal that we can proceed. And remember, you, the 48-year-old, don't need to watch for or see the teen or the incident she will soon review. Yes, let the 51-year-old see the teen, and when she does, have her nod her head to you.

Usually, it is possible to see smaller nods that seem to represent the client's experience of the series of communications between all the "selves" represented in imagination. I wait for the more exaggerated head nod from the client, which is intended for me. After receiving the affirmative signal of the nod, I continue this rather laborious and careful manner of speaking as I proceed with the steps outlined above. It is important to remember and to remind clients that they do not need to see and hear the trauma, but rather just see and hear that the other "part of themselves" is seeing and hearing it in review. They only need to see the mediating part or parts signal the beginning and ending of the review done by the most remote part of the self. In this regard then, some clients will report that they did not see and hear the review and some will report that they did. In a few cases, clients have even completed this process without ever consciously knowing what was reviewed and what the content of the trauma actually was. Nevertheless, such measures as the reduction of avoidance behavior suggest that the procedure has been successful in dissociating negative emotional limitations and associating to necessary and desired experiences. Thus, the similarities to Erickson's progressive symbolic dreaming and cryptic automatic writing (cited above) are obvious. This procedure appears to offer a method for parts of the unconscious to communicate to other parts of the unconscious, and ultimately to the conscious mind in progressive steps. However, the procedure is far easier for both clients and therapists than in the examples offered by Erickson.

A client has to be quite focused on internal representations to complete the review. Because the representations are symbols of resources the client has not been able to associate to as a result of the trauma, an ego-strengthening occurs. In terms of classical conditioning, we might say that the client has associated desirable experiences to the cognitive images of the trauma. Thus, the memories of the trauma no longer leave clients feeling helpless and without coping skills.

In cases where one of the representations is of a person from the future, as we saw here, the client creates a presupposition of successfully being cured of the traumatic reaction. The power of this presupposition is not trivial and deserves serious research. It appears that the creation of a positive presupposition of success directs people to seek and find desired resources over time. The more that people find their desired resources in contexts in which they need them, the less they report being troubled, having problems, and needing help or therapy.

CONCLUSION

This intervention was absolutely pivotal in the change process as it supplied the means for the client, Mary, to keep her desired experiences in the foreground so she could begin to function immediately in the real world. It also allows clients the increased capability to become more creative and responsible for themselves in the remainder of therapy work. Most notable in this case is that Mary, when she came into the office, had been completely unable to talk about the traumatic incident *at all* without crying, sometimes uncontrollably. However, only one week following the single session of intervention described here, she was interviewed on a national television "talk" show. The hostess made sure to ask all the touchy questions possible during the televised interview. She even played the panicked voices on the audio recording of the 911 emergency call from that fateful night. However, Mary was able to describe and explain the entire incident and answer all questions in detail. Not once did she collapse into tears during the program.

After this single-treatment intervention has been used, most clients describe more energy, greater availability of resources, good reality orientation, more self-support, an integration with earlier emotional strengths, and adaptive, creative behavior. The process is not resisted and defensive mechanisms are replaced by adaptive mechanisms. This procedure works well for traumas that are type 2 or type 1 reactions. In fact, type 1 traumas can succeed with fewer intermediaries in the imagination chain. Type 3 traumas, however, are not likely to be suitable for this procedure and therapists are recommended to refrain from the use of this tool for such persons. A process that involves a greater stabilization of normal waking state, conscious focus, and secure experiences is recommended for type 3 trauma victims.

Total therapy for Mary, or for any client reacting to a trauma, should be expected to require several sessions. Future sessions concentrate on social, occupational, self-image, and other issues, in older traumas, where learned limitation had taken a toll over time. Finally, dealing with grief and self-forgiveness is sometimes essential for a full recovery.

PRACTIAL IDEAS

- Divide trauma clients on the basis of severity and sequelae.
- Identify representations of past experiences that contain strong resources.
- Help clients make visual representations of the past "selves."
- Arrange the imaginations of past "selves" so that clients rely on signals from each.
- Verbalize to clients in such a way as to stimulate a review by a distant "self" in words and pictures only.
- Continue to suggest that a series of selves communicate about and conduct the review of the trauma so that the client does not need to review it directly.

References

Balson, P. (1980). Treatment of war neurosis from Vietnam. *Comprehensive Psychiatry, 21* (2), 167–175.

Berghold, J. (1991). The social trance. *Journal of Psychohistory, 19* (2), 221–243.

Eisen, M. (1992). The victim's burden. *Imagination, Cognition & Personality, 12* (1), 65–68.

Evans, B. (1991). Hypnotizability in posttraumatic stress disorder: Implications for hypnotic interventions in treatment. *Australian Journal of Clinical & Experimental Hypnosis, 19* (1), 49–58.

Erickson, M. H. (1980). The clinical and therapeutic applications of time distortion. In E. Rossi (Ed), *The collected papers of Milton H. Erickson, M.D., on hypnosis, Vol. II: Hypnotic alteration of sensory, perceptual and psychosocial processes* (pp. 266–290). New York: Irvington.

Erickson, M. H. (1980). Negation or reversal of legal testimony. In E. Rossi (Ed), *The collected papers of Milton H. Erickson, M.D., on hypnosis, Vol. III: Hypnotic investigation of psychodynamic processes* (pp. 221–230). New York: Irvington.

Erickson, M. H. (1980). The permanent relief of an obsessional phobia by means of communications with an unsuspected dual personality. In E. Rossi (Ed), *The collected papers of Milton H. Erickson, M.D., on hypnosis, Vol. III: Hypnotic investigation of psychodynamic processes* (pp. 231–260). New York: Irvington.

Erickson, M. H. (1980a). Hypnosis: Its renascence as a treatment modality. In

E. Rossi (Ed), *The collected papers of Milton H. Erickson, M.D., on hypnosis, Vol. IV: Innovative hypnotherapy* (pp. 52–75). New York: Irvington.

Erickson, M. H. (1980b). Special techniques of brief hypnotherapy. In E. Rossi (Ed), *The collected papers of Milton H. Erickson, M.D., on hypnosis, Vol. IV: Innovative hypnotherapy* (pp. 149–173). New York: Irvington.

Horowitz, S. (1970). Strategies within hypnosis for reducing phobic behavior. *Journal of Abnormal Psychology, 75* (1), 104–112.

Kingsbury, S. (1992). Strategic psychotherapy for trauma. *Journal of Traumatic Stress, 5* (1), 85–95.

Lamb, S. (1985). Hypnotically induced deconditions: Reconstruction of memories in treatment of phobia. *American Journal of Clinical Hypnosis, 28* (2), 56–62.

Malon, D. (1987). Hypnosis with self-cutters. *American Journal of Psychotherapy, 41* (4), 531–541.

Moore, C. (1981). Hypnosis: An adjunct to pediatric consultation. *American Journal of Clinical Hypnosis, 23* (3), 211–216.

Pickering, J. (1986). Use of age regression in a case of traumatization during late childhood and adolesence. *Australian Journal of Clinical & Experimental Hypnosis, 14* (2), 169–172.

Rhue, J. (1991). Story telling, hypnosis and treatment of sexually abused children. *International Journal of Clinical & Experimental Hypnosis, 39* (4), 198–214.

Shapiro, M. (1988). Hypno-play therapy with adults: Theory, method, and practice. *American Journal of Clinical Hypnosis, 31* (1), 1–10.

Spivak, L. (1990). Neurophysiological correlates of altered states of consciousness. *Human Physiology, 16* (6), 405–410.

Spiegel, D. (1986). Dissociation damage: Special issue: Dissociation. *American Journal of Clinical Hypnosis, 29* (2), 123–131.

Spiegel, D. (1988). Dissociation and hypnosis of post traumatic stress disorder. *Journal of Traumatic Stress, 1* (1), 17–33.

Spiegel, D. (1990). New uses of hypnosis in the treatment of post traumatic stress disorder. *Journal of Clinical Psychiatry, 51* (1), 39–43.

Spiegel, D. (1991). Disintegrated experience. *Journal of Abnormal Psychology, 100* (3), 366–378.

Stutman, R., et al. (1985). Post-traumatic stress disorder, hypnotizability and imagery. *American Journal of Psychiatry, 142* (6), 741–743.

VanderHart, O., et al. (1990a). Hypnotherapy for traumatic grief: Janetian and modern approaches integrated. *American Journal of Clinical Hypnosis, 32* (4), 263–271.

VanderHart, O., et al. (1990b). Pierre Janet's treatment of post traumatic stress disorder. *Journal of Traumatic Stress, 2* (4), 379–395.

Recommended Further Reading

Dolan, Y. (1985). *A path with a heart: Ericksonian utilization with resistant and chronic patients.* New York: Brunner/Mazel.

Dolan, Y. (1991). *Resolving sexual abuse: Solution-focused therapy and Ericksonian hypnosis for adult survivors.* New York: Norton.

Lankton, S. (1988). *A children's book to overcome fears: The blammo–surprise book!* New York: Brunner/Mazel.

Lankton, C., & Lankton, S. (1989). *Tales of enchantment: Goal-oriented metaphors for adults and children in therapy.* New York: Brunner/Mazel.

Lankton, S., & Lankton, C. (1983). *The answer within: A clinical framework of Ericksonian hypnotherapy.* New York: Brunner/Mazel.

Lankton, S., Lankton, C., & Matthews, W. (1991). Ericksonian family therapy. In A Gurman & D. Kniskern (Eds.), *The handbook of family therapy, volume 2.* New York: Brunner/Mazel.

Mills, J., Crowley, R., & Ryan, M. (1986). *Therapeutic metaphors for children and the child within.* New York: Brunner/Mazel.

15

Motivating Action with Hypnotherapy
for a Client with a History
of Early Family Violence[1]

My demonstration today is a rather open-ended one. It's Motivating Action with Hypnotherapy, which I thought was a broad-enough topic for us to be able to grasp it. I interviewed my potential client yesterday, and she will be my client today.

We talked a bit about the possibility of doing this and the usefulness of doing this, but not specifically about what we would really want to accomplish. I thought we would save that for the discussion now. I can't tell you ahead of time what is going to happen, so I guess we just better do it and find out. I'll tell you afterwards what happened if there are any questions.

LANKTON: Would you be willing to tell us your age?

LINDA: Sure; 42.

LANKTON: When I discussed it with you, you had something in mind. It had a bit to do with self-effacing comments and your general motivation of yourself being inhibited by that. Could you say a little about it?

---

[1] Lankton, S. (1990). Using hypnosis to motivate clients with a history of early family violence. And Commentary. In S. Lankton & J. Zeig (Eds.), *The Ericksonian monographs, number 6: Ericksonian therapy verbatim* (pp. 43–60). New York: Brunner/Mazel.

LINDA: That I have a real strong desire to not be self-effacing. But somehow or other I have a lot of words and sentences that are strong that keep that kind of behavior coming professionally and personally.

LANKTON: And even while you begin to talk about it, your reflection on it makes you sort of sad about this state of affairs or something. And you wish it wasn't that way. Am I reading into your sentences saying that you are unhappy about that?

LINDA: I am unhappy about that. That's right. I'd like to change that.

LANKTON: I would like to change it, if it were me. I'm not quite sure what your motivation is for changing it. Why do you want to? Woody Allen does fine with it.

LINDA: I've thought of going into pictures. *(laughs)*

LANKTON: You've thought of going into pictures? *(laughs)* So, keeping it might not be a bad idea if you could do that, but you don't have any contracts right at the moment. *(laughs)*

LINDA: No. *(laughs)*

LANKTON: And that's why we're doing this, then.

LINDA: It is really unhelpful for me! *(laughs)*

LANKTON: This is a tape screening. This is your screening for the movies. Is that . . .

LINDA: *(laughs)*

LANKTON: But what is your motivation for getting rid of this self-effacement? How do you imagine your life would be improved somehow if you did?

LINDA: I wouldn't be, um, I would be able to be less afraid about being in groups and more able to receive credit when people try to give it to me. I would be able to teach easier without its being traumatic. I mean, those are the things I am doing.

LANKTON: And your tears that you have here, you don't have those usually? It's just when somebody talks to you about it?

LINDA: Or just when I talk about it. *(clears throat)*

LANKTON: I guess you don't do it that much then, because then you would be crying.

LINDA: No, not that much.

LANKTON: I am going to present a paper that suggests that you ask somebody questions like this, and in a way I am hesitant a little bit here to do it because when a person is self-critical and you start asking comments like "How or why in the world do you think you could change that?" it is so easy for you to take the posture of, "Well, maybe he is right, he's implying that I can't, and that's what I thought all along." So I don't know just how to ask you the question: Do you think you can change that?

LINDA: Well, I've been working hard at it. I don't know.

LANKTON: How are you doing? Are you succeeding?

LINDA: Not very well. (*laughs*) No. I mean I was producing different behavior, but . . .

LANKTON: But you have only two options. If you said anything other than "absolutely perfectly" you'd be . . . and if that is the case, then you wouldn't be here.

LINDA: That's right.

LANKTON: So evaluating your progress is something you better not do?

LINDA: It's hard. That's right.

LANKTON: Well, what do you suppose is the central element that . . . I imagine I am the way I am, you are the way you are, because of our . . . way that we remember the past, at least. We blame the past for the ways we are doing this stuff, or we credit the past for the ways we are doing it. What do you blame or credit for how come you are self-effacing?

In some ways I reckon it's a real strength that helped: kept you somehow from getting more punishment than you expect you might have gotten. And by keeping yourself self-critical, you've anticipated punishment and maybe removed some of the actual punishment that you would have gotten; so in a way it's been real handy, and it's sort of a survival strength. But why in the hell did you do it in the first place?

LINDA: You mean as a child?

LANKTON: I guess, yeah.

LINDA: Well, I don't think I would have seen it as self-critical as a child. I grew up in a real difficult home. Um. I learned to watch.

LANKTON: There may be some things you don't want to say about that, in fact. Is that true?

LINDA: Well . . .

LANKTON: There may be difficulties in the home, may be more than you want to talk about here.

LINDA: Lots of violence, and the things that go with it. So . . .

LANKTON: And why self-critical? How come that got in there? Why not like just a constant dialogue like "Jesus, I survived another day!" instead of self-critical? How do you suppose that part got in?

LINDA: I don't know. I am one of seven siblings, and nobody's got that piece.

LANKTON: Are you the oldest? So I suspect you took some responsibility for the others?

LINDA: Yes, quite a lot.

LANKTON: Ya. Well, I'm only asking that to get kind of a feel and to help other people get a feel, too, for um ...

I would like to use the hypnosis, which is our demonstration. We might/could talk for two hours and really get something useful just by talking. I wonder what we could accomplish that would be useful in trance. That's what I would like to attempt to do. And I know that you will seek further help and so on afterwards, to the extent you need it, and you are capable of doing that.

So, with that sense of it in the background, I'd like to sort of arbitrarily move to the trance. It's not exactly the moment I'd do it in my office. I think I'd find out a few more things that you might want to tell me. Is there something that you *do* want to say?

LINDA: No.

LANKTON: Is there something that you'd like to not say?

LINDA: (*laughs*) Yes.

LANKTON: Why don't you start at the bottom of the list where it's the least threatening?

LINDA: Ohhhh. (*laugh*) Nooo.

LANKTON: Is there anything you think I should know that you don't want to say — that if I knew it, I would be more helpful, but you don't want to say?

LINDA: That um ...

LANKTON: Well, you don't have to. I just mean is there something that ...

LINDA: No.

LANKTON: So you kind of think that I am going to be able to be helpful even not knowing all that stuff.

LINDA: I think so.

LANKTON: Oh great. (*audience laughs*) Well, if I am helpful, it'll be helpful in the sense that it will be a springboard for you to do something for yourself, of course. And I know you have been ignoring the group somewhat; so why don't you ignore them a little more by closing your eyes. It's a good idea. Are your feet comfortable?

LINDA: Yes.

LANKTON: And our volume's okay?

AUDIENCE: No, speak louder.

LINDA: Do you want my mike? My mike is probably better.

LANKTON (*to audience*): Thanks for saying so.

LANKTON: You go into a trance in your own way, of course, and in your own time into the depth that is appropriate for you. And, although you may have your eyes open in the trance, you may begin by closing them. Sooner or later the sense of concentrating your attention and becoming comfortable, by letting your conscious mind focus "in" on certain thoughts that are least distressing for you, so that your unconscious can have some freedom to play with other thoughts, entertain other ideas, investigate experiences. You can lean back in the chair all right, or is that a problem?

LINDA: (*leans back in chair*)

LANKTON: One of the things that I sometimes ask people to do in a trance is to dissociate their experience in trance from everything else — to never have the generalization of the successful experience in the trance — not to anticipate having it, not to worry about having it. Just let this experience be all by itself, life standing on the observation deck of the Eiffel Tower. Thinking about all that history, and you're not a part of it.

Like walking through the Louvre and thinking, "I'm glad I didn't have to paint all those emperors." You can stand in front of Michelangelo's works, and it makes you proud to be a human being. And you know you couldn't do it, maybe no one ever again could do it. And it doesn't diminish it for one moment. And it doesn't diminish you for a moment.

And often the more relaxed a person becomes, the more they go into trance. I like to think about those situations where I was all alone, hiding under a card table, pretending I was the Lone Ranger, or running through the mud behind my house, pretending I had landed on the moon.

One person that I know had the fantasy of sending an android to school. He kept all controls in the attic, and when it was time to go to school, he slipped into the attic and sent the android out in his place. And from the safety of that distance, he had moments to think about what to say, consult books, and talk into the microphone, and the android would say the right words. (*long pause*)

I had many hours in a sensory deprivation tank once, when I lived in Jackson, Michigan. And for a year and a half or so, I'd slip into the man's house every night, and he left it in his basement and gave me a key. And I learned to float in the water clock (*long pause*) and think of myself as totally disconnected from everything else. I could review the events of the day and turn on and turn off different sensorium, and my body was just there floating. It's like skin diving, scuba diving. There's a great deal of visual attention that has very little to do with what you're doing. And your body is just floating there. And for me trance is like all of those things. I've been very sleepy at the back of the movie theater. And I don't know why all the other people bothered to come. And so your conscious mind may think of various images like that in order to aid your unconscious mind. And my job is a person who can help by stimulating your conscious and unconscious thoughts in ways that could be of use to you.

Someone asked me about confusion and its role in therapy. I really doubt that you could fail to misunderstand confusion any more than he does at those moments that he is certain of something. And I hope that you'll be very certain only of the fact that you are there in the chair and you are alone there and somehow you're not. Your cheek muscles are relaxed, there's a half-smile on your mouth, your rapid eye movement has decreased, your swallow reflex has slowed, you're breathing deeply from your stomach.

And to the extent that you begin to think about things that are relevant to you, there's no reason to move. I began by pointing out that I would like someone in trance to have the experience that what happened to them here is simply for now and for no other time. And I would like you to go into trance deep enough, if it would be all right with you, to have an experience that you can have isolated from all other parts of your learning and thinking. Maybe you can think of a poem, and you will never remember it again. Or, you can have an experience that you don't particularly need to give yourself credit for or hold it against yourself ever again. This trance is a vacation from real life.

When I did a demonstration in Phoenix in 1983, there was a woman who had had back pain for 40-some years, and during the trance it was entirely gone. And I asked her to make sure that it would come back again after the trance was over so that, while she could remember that it had been gone, it didn't need to influence her real life in any way, unless she wanted it to.

There's another problem in telling metaphors to people in trance, and that is: Who will the person identify with? I think it would be perfectly legitimate for you to identify with everybody I talk about in the metaphor. I might talk about my daughter and my conduct with my daughter. I'd like you to identify with me. I'd like you to identify with my daughter. After all you can't really understand the situation that occurs to the people in the metaphor unless you have projected into it. It is reasonable to assume that you would project into both parts of it. I don't know if you have ever though about holding yourself as a little girl. Everyone sooner or later has the idea. Your conscious mind may have flirted with the idea and allowed your unconscious to have the experience a little bit. Maybe your conscious mind has had the experience a little bit and allowed your unconscious to flirt with the idea.

Sometimes Alicia will come into the office when I'm working, and I'm typing at the keyboard. She crawls up underneath my elbows and gets right in the middle of things. She says, "Hold me, Daddy." And what does a parent do? I say, "OK." And then I tell her what I was typing about and she listens and, after a while, stroking her hair, she crawls away.

I remember on day at a workshop, she came and and she got up on my lap and she said she wanted to go, and I said, "We'll go in a minute. Go play." And then a couple of minutes had passed, and she came back and she said, "Daddy, you said we would go in a minute and it's been a minute." And I said, "All right, I have to go now. I have to keep my word." And I wonder how it makes a child feel, where you'd feel it on your face. What would happen with regard to your heart rate, your breathing rate, your feeling of your musculature, your sense of self? You learn it, it becomes a part of you. You bring it with you the next time you walk into the living room, and crawl over on the couch, and sneak up on my lap, and crawl up on my neck, and say, "I just want to sit here for a while, Dad." And sometimes she says, "Daddy Honey," and then she *knows* that I am going to let her sit there. When she falls asleep in my arms, I put her in bed sometimes, trying so carefully not to wake her up.

One day the other week, she came out of the bedroom and said, "Mommy, you said you were going to lie down with me." Carol was so happy to be able to finally watch some television show, but she jumped up and said, "I will darling," and lay down with her. It only took a few moments before she had fallen asleep, and Carol did get to watch the show. And then sometimes I am up in the middle of the night. I always go past and make sure that she is covered and not cold.

There are a lot of ways that we can have feelings. Children learn to feel brave by pretending — pretending that they are Superman. And I remember the phrase, "You can pretend anything and master it." All those children learn to play guitar; they pretend they are already a rock star; they pretend they are already able to play piano concertos. And not only is there no harm in pretending, it is very good rehearsal to make a space somewhere inside for that new feeling to develop. And how about dressing up like you're older when you're just a child? And pretending you can ride your bicycle "zoom" down the highway. And you are only riding a little cart around the living room floor.

Then you can think about my daughter and you can have those experiences. What is memory anyway except imagination? So go into trance to a depth necessary to allow you to have the imagination of the memory. Feeling that degree of safety and comfort, with the agreement that if you have it now, it's disconnected from everything. It's a trial period. It has no meaning. There's no threat that it will generalize into the rest of your life. Just like an ant digging a little bitty tunnel down into the sand and making a great big hole in which he can live, or a little rabbit that makes a little burrow, down a little thin hole up to the earth. But inside the burrow, who knows what that little rabbit is doing? Maybe just storing jars of honey before that Pooh Bear comes to visit.

And let the feeling of safety be something that you feel more now than you ever felt before. Know what it's like for your little finger to feel it, for your ankle. Feel the skin temperature changes with it. And know that your conscious mind needn't even remember it, but that you have made an agreement that you are going to the depth of trance necessary to have the experience now more than you have ever had it. And let it radiate to the tips of your fingers. Let it radiate out of your fingers and toes. Ooze safety, security, belonging, in a way you most imagined that my daughter probably does. And then I want you to keep it constant for the next five minutes, with the agreement that if there is any difficulty for you having that experience, you can be fully assured that you won't have it again after the trance is over. It's just a little experiment.

You can say to your conscious mind or your unconscious mind, "Oops, it was just a mistake, like the X-ray" — like the discovery of the transistor. But, rather than pull it out of the wastebasket, you can leave it in there. And now memorize and hold onto it. Does it feel good?

LINDA: (*slight head nod and big smile*)

LANKTON: I want you to do three things with it. I want you to open your eyes for a moment, and hold onto it. And close them and know that you were able to open your eyes and hold onto it. Is that correct?

Now, I want you to do the second thing and look at the group while you hold onto the feeling. All those shadowy figures out there from Jung's unconscious. Almost in the darkness. Makes it perfect to project onto them and see what you project onto them, while you feel that feeling. Can you say? What do you see?

LINDA: That they ... they look friendly.

LANKTON: They look friendly? Accepting? They are happy that you are having feelings?

LINDA: I think so.

LANKTON: Now close your eyes again and memorize that, knowing that you can forget all about it after the trance if you like.

And now the third thing I would like you to do is to open your eyes and recover that precious feeling, knowledge, memory, awareness, projecting what you see onto the faces, knowing what that means, holding onto that feeling of safety, comfort. And now I want you to try really, really hard to have any self-effacing thoughts that you can have. Try to hallucinate on top of this scene that you see detrimental aspects and memories from your family-of-origin while holding onto this feeling and watching the group. Let your own hallucinations intermingle. Try to have that memory, find out if you can really make it interfere or not with the experience you are having while you are looking at those people and using them as a way to remember your feelings. And don't listen to me for a moment, just go ahead and do that.

I want to mention to the group a rationale. This is reciprocal inhibition occurring. This is interesting, kind of flooding in vivo. But it is not flooding the anxiety-producing experience of the fear, it is flooding the anxiety-producing experience of the security.

Now let me repeat my instructions and make sure you did it the way I envision it. That you are holding onto a feeling of safety and belonging, you are looking at the group and they are reminding you of the experience somewhat, too. And so you know you are here having that feeling. And you are trying very hard to remember fearful, anxiety-producing, self-critical-generating experiences from the past and see that shadowy memory at the same time.

Sometimes I work with people and I mention that they will have an experience in the trance and they'll gain an idea that they just won't be able to shake when the trance is over. Something will seize their mind as a useful concept or an idea and it will stay with them.

What are you experiencing as you do that?

LINDA: That, um, they are not dangerous and, um, I'm not wrong.

LANKTON: Would you mind trying a little harder to remember even worse experiences that made you, compelled you somehow, to think that you were wrong. Keep your eyes focused on them while you keep this feeling and (*pause*). 'Cause there are going to be times when your memories of the past are used to solve problems in the present, and you want to be sure that you've looked through all your memories of the past and that none of them will inhibit you, that they all will be some kind of aid to you in the future. It would be really nice if all those memories that you are thinking about reminded you, at some level, that actually you were trying really hard to feel bad, and failed at it.

So I would like you to try so hard to feel bad while you are holding this feeling and looking at the group that you become aware that you failed at feeling bad. And maybe criticize yourself for that.

LINDA: (*laughs*)

LANKTON: Now, there's a mixture of happiness here and sadness a little bit. But the happiness is stronger, or not? Can you say what you are thinking of, what the memories are?

LINDA: Of, um, with my sister and, um, of not being able to help the kids and of, um, my brother dying, um, and things not getting better, and my not being able to help them, even as an adult, enough, um, of . . .

LANKTON: What are you feeling while you are telling me this and looking out? Are you looking at the people?

LINDA: Uh-huh. I am feeling, um, surprised . . .

LANKTON: About?

LINDA: I don't, I don't think they think I'm bad, or . . .

LANKTON: Is that . . .

LINDA: New!

LANKTON: . . . different or something?

LINDA: Uh-huh!

LANKTON: You would have thought that if you . . .

LINDA: Ya.

LANKTON: then how do you feel besides surprised?

LINDA: Comfortable.

LANKTON: Is there anything else that you would like to feel comfortable about remembering? There's a lot of violence in the world, there's incest, there's self-mutilation, there's irrational violence that has no definition . . . and look at the people as you do, realize that you are here having this experience, and you are really trying to remember something that would make you feel bad. (*long pause*) Is there anything else? Is that all of them? There's always more. But if the ones you thought of are the worst of them, then the others are sort of inconsequential by comparison. Have you thought of the worst ones?

LINDA: Uh-huh, out of the ones you talked about.

LANKTON: So that's the third thing I wanted you to do. Now close your eyes again and *know* what you've done, just for now. You could look at it in a lot of different ways. You've really made contact with people, and in doing that held onto an experience that was pleasant. And it has a lot of different meanings in different ways.

One time in karate class, I accidentally turned around doing a kata and broke some tile with my hand, months before I expected to be able to break tiles with my hand. And I remember riding down the driveway on my bicycle, certain that my parents or my sister was holding the back of the bicycle. Training wheels had been removed. And when I got to the bottom of the drive, I had made it the whole way, and I turned around to say I made it. And there wasn't anybody there. I went the whole way by myself. I don't know how it happened, but I accidently learned to swim one day. I left poor old Joe Kuchar in the shallow end of the pool and joined the others in the deep end. There are so many things that we do by accident that we didn't plan on ever having connect to the rest of our life.

I don't usually tell fantasy stories, but there is this one story that I was thinking about that has to do with this young man named Sheath, who lived in the desert before the age of technology, before animals were known through classification, when the world was quite a mystery. And he had lived kind of in isolation with a wall around him for a long time, in a city with a wall around it. It seemed perfectly reasonable. It was all he knew.

He had very few possessions, and he carried them with him most of the time: a key — didn't open any lock, a feather that he pretended was an eagle feather (which actually just came from a seagull that had gotten lost in the desert), a whistle that he hardly every used because when he blew it, it didn't make any sound, and a crystal. He really liked the crystal. He wore it around his neck, but he was afraid he would lose it, so he kept it in his pouch.

And they weren't worth much to anyone, but they were all the possessions he had — except a towel. "It's a rough world and you have to know

261

where your towel is." Ford Prefect said that in Douglas Adams' *Hitchhikers Guide to the Galaxy*. One of the best tips, I think, and this was applying to Sheath.

He left the town in his youthful exuberance, filled with delusions, one day and wandered out into the desert to see what he could find. And he didn't find anything — except more desert. And after he had been gone several days (he wasn't quite sure of the number), he had his fill of sand and nothingness and he turned around and went back. But when he got back to where he came from, the city was gone.

His home was gone, and the fountain that he used to sit on was gone, and the wall he used to walk on was gone, and the people he talked to. And all of his childhood memories had been attached to these things. And they were all gone. His first thought was that he had surely gone to the wrong place in the desert. But upon further searching and watching the stars, he was sure he was in the right place. Whenever he did come upon another person and asked them, they didn't know anything of the city. So, he figured it was a conspiracy in which either all people who knew of the city had vanished with the city, or he simply hadn't come upon anybody yet who knew of the city.

His only alternative, it seemed, was to journey several days towards the North Star where the Magistrate who ran the large city was said to be a Magi, a wise man of many talents, and maybe he could help him recover his way to his home. And when he finally arrived, the Magistrate gave him audience, heard his story, and said, "Yes, what we have here is a problem of the heart. And this will be a test of your heart." Sheath said, "You have had this kind of thing happen before?" The Magistrate said, "Well, it's always different in each case. And this one, of course, is unique. But one thing that is certain to me is that sometimes it's a matter of courage and sometimes it's a matter of wit, and sometimes it's humor, and sometimes it's love, and other times it's strength, or endurance. And for you it's a matter of the heart. And the tests that you have will be a test of your heart."

And Sheath said that he had no idea of how to pass any test of the heart. What could he possibly do? The Magistrate gave him the advice that he had learned to give many times before in similar situations. Sheath was to go back to the place from which he came, to go into this meditative state, and to "stay put in that situation until four things come to your mind four times. Whatever these objects are, gather them, bring them back here and your tests will be tests that will evaluate your ability to survive and prove or fail the test of the heart." And with that his granted audience was over. Sheath was to leave.

Sheath went back to where he had come from. He sat down and he meditated. But he didn't know many things, and he didn't own many, and he didn't have many. And, unfortunately, the only four things that came to his mind repeatedly were the key, the feather, the whistle, and the crystal. After a day and a half of trying to find his *true essence* he decided that was surely all that was going to come to his mind, and he set out with these four objects back to the Magistrate.

After an afternoon of walking in the desert, he was relieved to see a circus caravan come by and ask him if he would like to ride, and he said, "Yes, it would be wonderful to take a ride." Unfortunately, he had to ride in an empty cage. It was the only place there was any seating left. And he rode in the empty cage, jiggling and joggling along in the desert on wooden wheels. He fell asleep.

When he awoke all was still. And he thought at first, perhaps, that since it was dusk, maybe people were napping, and he was very quiet gathering his things. And then he discovered the door was locked in the cage, and he said, "Hey, guys, there has been a little mistake here." And there wasn't a sound, there weren't even the sounds of the animals, or the tambourines jingling. And he hollered louder, and he peeked, as best as he could. And he came to the conclusion that his cage had become separated from the caravan and he was alone, locked in the cage.

Then he knew it must be malice. These people were surely part of the conspiracy to hide the city. Then he thought maybe he had been robbed, but, no, he had his materials with him. Maybe it was an accident. Maybe they didn't even know. Maybe he was left to his own devices. And somehow in all this thinking, he had grabbed hold of the key. And as people will do, he had fidgeted the key into the lock. And to his surprise he opened the lock on the cage. He jumped out in such a hurry, he didn't realize that he had lodged the key hopelessly in the lock! It wouldn't have come out if he'd thought to pull it out. So he continued walking across the desert, wondering how upset they would be to find that they had lost this cage, and perhaps remember that he had been in it, too.

Darkness and the night, which is usually absent of animals as far as he was concerned, suddenly became filled with animals. And in the darkness of the desert, the sound of growling and the footsteps seemed to be ominously close. He tried to whistle a little tune to pretend he wasn't afraid.

But that didn't work. That just drew more animals closer. So he tried to be perfectly quiet, but he couldn't — his breathing gave him away. Finally, he was so frightened by the animals, he decided that what he'd better do was to call for help. Trying to call for help he found, as some children will do, that a scream just won't come out when your mouth opens up.

And he reached down and grabbed the whistle that never made any sound at all, and he blew it as hard as he could. And it made a loud shrill sound, almost outside of human range! And then everything was quiet except one thing — the sound of the pieces of the whistle hitting the ground. He blew it apart calling for help so loud. But there weren't any animals around. The shrill sound had blasted their sensitive ears. And he walked until morning.

He napped, and he walked further the next day. Finally he reached the gates of the city. Several miles from the Magistrate's office — there was a large city indeed — lying there in front of the gates of the city was a large beast. Fortunately, we don't know whether it was a dragon or a cyclops or just what it was because animals hadn't been codified back in those days. But it was much larger than the kind you would want to wrestle with in a dark alley.

And he was sure that it was an evil beast, and perhaps he would be devoured if he didn't sneak away. But then he wouldn't be able to complete his mission, find his city, recover his homeland, pass the test of the heart — whatever it was going to be. It was the creature that he know was evil and bad, and nasty and mean — carnivorous, no doubt.

Then he thought, "Maybe it's not. Maybe he is just a large hunk of sleeping flesh." And he reached into his pack to see if he had anything that could aid him. He had no tools, no magic, no weapons — he had a feather. And he reached over and tickled it with his feather. And the slumbering beast rolled a little bit. And he knew then if he kept tickling and kept nudging with that feather the beast might eventually — and sure enough it did — roll over, away from the entrance to the city. And so doing it trapped the feather in one of its armpits and pulled the feather from his hand.

Sheath went into the city now, about to have the victorious moment of seeing the Magistrate, and he reached in his pack and it dawned on him that he only had his crystal left. He had lost the key and his whistle and his feather. He looked at that crystal and he saw his reflection as he walked across the desert, he thought how he had been walking for days to pass these tests of the heart, and now he was going to be a failure. He turned the crystal around and saw the different pictures of his face in despair — twelve facets of despair on his face.

Finally, he met the Magistrate. He told him of his failure, and the Magistrate congratulated him on the job well done. He had passed the test! Now, "How could this be?" said Sheath. "I saw my face full of despair in the crystal." And the Magistrate, "Yes, you could have turned away, you could have denied, but you have a heart filled with *truth* and you saw it. And you could have thought that the beast was evil and malicious, but you thought it was humorous, and your heart passed the test of being a *light* heart. And you saw that the cage had come undone, and you could have thought that it was evil and malicious, but you decided that it was an accident, and you have the *capacious and forgiving* heart. And when the animals threatened you, you could have tried to be brave and pretend, but you have the *trusting* heart and you asked for help. And every step of the way you passed your test. Go back to where you came from now, and you will find, I think, free of delusion, that the home you look for is there. And to make a long story short, that's just what he did.

So when you come out of trance in just a moment, I would like to suggest that you keep an amnesia for whatever we have done here if you would like and know that you never have any responsibility to use the experience that you had here today. It was a vacation. You don't need to generalize it into the rest of your life, and change in any way anything that you've done.

And know, too, that the woman that I worked with in 1983 let her back pain come back for a few days, and over the course of the next six months it went away entirely and is still gone five years later. Because you can use those kinds of unconscious accidental experiences that occur to you, in your own way, at your own speed, and let your unconscious discover just how or *if* you'll use what you've done here today. Hi.

LINDA: Hi.

LANKTON: Do you want to realize that the group is back also? How do you feel?

LINDA: Okay *(wiping her right eye with her left hand)*

LANKTON: Is that a tentative one?

LINDA: Ah, no. *(laughs)* I feel fine.

LANKTON: You are looking like perhaps there's some, ah, is there more emotion now, is there some sadness again, I see?

LINDA: No.

LANKTON: Your voice is gone.

LINDA: I know.

LANKTON: Why?

LINDA: I don't know. I was, I wasn't ready to finish.

LANKTON: And you were ready to finish. You know, usually in a trance I mention you can go back to the experience that is unfinished and think about it when you are alone, or when you are in another trance, or when you dream at night, and complete any uncompleted ideas that you began in the trance. And I really should have said that. So I hope you will think to do that ...

LINDA: Yeah.

LANKTON: ... one way or another. Is there anything you want to say?

LINDA: No thanks. It feels fine. *(she looks off to the group, defocuses her eyes, and looks down to her right slightly)*

LANKTON: Well, thank you for participating. I think it might have been a helpful lesson in some ways to some of us, at least. Thank you, I believe we are done now.

COMMENTARY

The client in this tape, Linda, had a history of physical and sexual abuse in her home. She is 42 years of age, lives alone, and was not married at the time of this therapy. She reported avoiding others due to self-imposed criticisms and thoughts that she was not acceptable. I had interviewed this client at length the previous day, and she had taken, at my request, an Interpersonal Checklist (Leary, 1957) self-report, which showed unusually high scores in the area depicting self-effacement. She specifically requested that the therapy be conducted to help her be more able to accept compliments.

The procedure used in this session is a tool that should be used cautiously in the therapy of incest victims and victims of family violence. It is designed to help reduce reliance upon denial as a defense. Therefore, clients need to be sufficiently interviewed and understood; it must be ascertained that potentials for suicide or other types of destructive behaviors do not exist. Furthermore, additional therapy should be arranged to follow the client after an intervention such as this. These considerations were taken and are mentioned in the session.

During the interview, the client revealed that she spent many years of her childhood trying, and as she saw it, failing to protect her younger siblings from

the violence she suffered at the hands of her father. She indicated that she recalled historical events of what she believed to be her failures. She was unable
to talk about herself without crying, and she commonly believed that others
were unaccepting of her.

During the trance session, Linda demonstrated that she had the ability to
project positive experiences onto others even while she remembered the most
difficult of her memories of family violence. Four months after the therapy,
she reported being surprised to find that she sought out and engaged in more
social contact, including allowing others to touch her for the first time. What
is more, the increased social contact occurred simultaneously with a great deal
of criticism from a co-worker who was in disagreement or in competition
with her. She stated that she was more aware of the incidents from her past
and that she was not self-critical as a result of this increased awareness. She reported that she "opened up." As a consequence, she used subsequent therapy
to do additional "difficult and painful" work involving aspects of her past that
she refused to face or share with others before this session.

What I found most interesting about the session were three areas: 1) the
method of dealing with social avoidance and post-traumatic stress; 2) the paradoxical restraint to prevent her from "failing" with any learning from the
trance; and 3) the emphasis, with metaphor, on reevaluating her life as that of
a person with a "good heart."

In the trance I helped her retrieve feelings of security and worth and then
had her use them in small steps, in each of which she verified her success before proceeding. She kept the feeling of self-esteem with her eyes open while
looking at others (who were looking at her), and she saw the others as accepting her. Finally, she continued to see others as accepting her while she "tried
as hard as she could" to remember, in a sort of visual and auditory hallucination, a range of violent events from her past — the type, I assume, that typically intruded into her normal waking state and resulted in her self-criticisms
and parataxic distortions.

I asked her, paradoxically, to make this session a respite from her normal
life and not to feel that she had to learn from it in any way. She was just to let
this be what it was, an interesting experience, separate from her life. I assumed
that she would grasp at all experiences, including this one, that would help her
growth. In this case, her consciously stated goal was accepting compliments.
Unconsciously, of course, this may have had a myriad of meanings for her, but
all must involve a higher evaluation of her self, a sense of safety and worth

267

around others, and a movement toward others. In short, the things accomplished in this session must be part of the ability she sought to develop.

The reason for asking her to refrain from generalizing from the trance or trying to use the comforts and perceptual skills practiced in it was to reduce her anxiety. I did not want her to leave the session with an expectation from me or even from herself (stimulated by me) that she should use the experience in any discernable manner. Her evaluation of herself almost always reveals to her a less than acceptable performance and creates anxiety, subsequent depression, and withdrawal. There is a risk that this would happen no matter how carefully I worded a request for gradual improvement. In fact, if she were to leave with such an expectation, and conclude that she had not used it well "enough," the therapy would have resulted in yet another letdown and source of anxiety.

She would be less likely to have anxiety about using the experience "well enough" if she were asked, repeatedly and with good reason, not to use it at all. While that sounds like a paradoxical directive, the goal is not to have her use it by telling her to not use it. Rather, the goal is to allow her the freedom not to use the therapy experience and, therefore, help allay her anxiety.

If she were to use the experience to help herself feel more comfortable getting compliments, being close to others, and motivating more work in therapy, etc., it would be preferable. But, if she were not to heed my directive and to, therefore, use the experience, it would be more likely due to her creative involvement with it than due to a performance demand or expectation from me. In conclusion, if she felt she had not gained from the trance experience, she would be free from additional anxiety — she was asked not to gain. So, this directive, developed over the course of the trance, sets up a relatively safe win-win position for her regarding freedom from anxiety that might otherwise have been stimulated by the therapy.

Finally, I told her a fanciful story concerning a person who felt he had little of value and who felt cut off from others. In the course of the story, the protagonist is pitted with a series of tests and the entire meaning and importance of his life are at stake. He seems to have failed at several tasks in the story until, in the end, it is seen that the behavior he considered failure at each step is really proof that he has passed a test of the heart. In fact, he is far better than he imagined in each case due to his limited, negative interpretation of his actions. In this story the protagonist is asked to see his life from a broader perspective — one in which he is a worthy and admirable person for his deeds.

I have reviewed this tape several times, and I really don't know what I would have done differently if I were to have a chance. But I conducted the session as hypnosis and therein, perhaps, lies a clue to what I might have done differently. That is, in a session in my office, not designed to simultaneously demonstrate hypnosis, I might not have used hypnosis. This client may have been able to profit from Gestalt awareness and contact exercises. I believe I would have been inclined to use these viable options if I had not been destined to conduct this session as hypnosis. Yet, I am satisfied with the session and the client's reaction to it during the session and several months afterward.

Reference

Leary, T. (1957). *Interpersonal diagnosis of personality*. New York: Norton.

Index

self-image thinking enhancement, 183–184

task behavior, 182–183

Milton H. Erickson Foundation (Phoenix), 4

International Congresses, 14, 150

mind/body, 27, 113

Minuchin, S., 218

Moore, C., 240

Moreno, J., 143

Mosher, D., 15

multiple embedded metaphor, 167–191, 219

delivery, 186

diagnostic considerations, 168–169

diagnostic parameters, 173–176

story structure, 186–189

musculoskeletal, 58, 59

mystery, 11, 18, 199, 200

neurotic, 109, 168–169, 202

affect and transference reaction, 153

conflict, 168

mechanisms, 35

symptoms, 36

Newton, I., 29

Newtonian world, 31

nonpathology-based model, 107

Novum Organum, 28

Nugent, W., 15, 113, 124

objective reality, 4

observation, 26, 27, 28, 29, 31, 39, 61, 72, 73, 108, 110, 139, 169, 179, 201, 204, 207, 241

aim of, 204

self-observation, 64

sensory, 213

Olness, K., 229

ontology, and M. H. Erickson, 25–38

open-ended suggestions, 115, 225

Orne, M., 112

Ornstein, R., 163

packaging, 155–156

pain, 13–14, 109, 113, 127, 129, 137, 144, 234, 235, 237, 244

pain control, 13, 14, 188

paradox, 26, 40, 97–98, 109, 117, 150, 153

paradoxical

assignments, 107

directives, 5, 19, 106, 268

interventions, 11, 14, 98

prescriptions, 2, 9, 10–11, 78, 96–97

restraint, 267

parasympathetic, 59, 61

participation, 13, 27, 28, 32, 93, 106, 108, 114, 194

past-oriented, 27

pattern identification, 27

Pearce, J., 66

perception, 6, 7, 13, 14, 59, 64, 85, 87, 90, 121–124, 137, 139, 143, 156, 171, 172, 182, 198, 207

and communication, 43

of M. H. Erickson, 25, 65, 73

Ericksonian approach, 109, 175

and goal setting, 9

and metaphors, 192, 193, 195, 196

packaging, 155

relabeling, 175

retraining, 175, 233

self-perception, 138

states-of-consciousness, 77